READER'S DIGEST

CONDENSED BOOKS

FIRST EDITION

THE READER'S DIGEST ASSOCIATION LIMITED
25 Berkeley Square, London W1X 6AB

**THE READER'S DIGEST ASSOCIATION
SOUTH AFRICA (PTY) LTD**
Reader's Digest House, 130 Strand Street, Cape Town

Printed in Great Britain by Petty & Sons Ltd, Leeds
Members of the BPCC Group

Original cover design by Jeffery Matthews F.S.I.A.D.

Reader's Digest
CONDENSED BOOKS

OVERLORD
Max Hastings

THE CHILDREN'S GAME
David Wise

A KIND OF MAGIC
Mollie Harris

TIGER, TIGER
Philip Caveney

COLLECTOR'S LIBRARY
EDITION

In this Volume:

OVERLORD
by Max Hastings (p.9)

Spearheaded by the massive D-day landings in Normandy, Operation Overlord marked the turning point of the Second World War. As Allied armies fought to gain a foothold in Europe, Hitler's efficient war machine was preparing to fight to the last man....

Max Hastings's gripping reconstruction of the campaign captures the horror and intensity of this struggle, whilst overturning a host of traditional beliefs. Commemorating the fortieth anniversary of D-day on June 6, *Overlord* presents an impressive portrait of this epic campaign, seen through the eyes of veterans of both sides.

THE CHILDREN'S GAME
by David Wise (p.123)

Suddenly CIA operations are being sabotaged all over the world—an agent is shot in Vienna, a contact vanishes in Tokyo, a covert manoeuvre is blown in Spain. What is happening? The man charged to find out is ex-agent William Danner, pressed back into service by former colleagues in the CIA. Danner sets about his task, but suddenly the game of espionage becomes a nightmare, as two unwitting victims—his young daughter and the beautiful woman he loves—become inextricably caught up in it.

As the game reaches its conclusion, only Danner can prevent disaster.

A KIND of MAGIC

by Mollie Harris (p.265)

In this nostalgic evocation of Oxfordshire village life sixty years ago, Mollie Harris describes both the joys and sorrows of her childhood.

Growing up as one of seven children in a poor, hardworking family was seldom easy—often there was nothing to eat but dumplings and jam. Yet the compensations were many: her grandmother's homemade wine; bathing in the Windrush in summer; cosy bedtime stories by the fire in winter.

As she looks back on her childhood we can share her memories and see that those days were, indeed, touched by "a kind of magic".

TIGER, TIGER

by Philip Caveney (p.339)

Harry Sullivan is sixty-seven, but few would think it. Thin and wiry, he has a reputation as a hunter that is a legend in Malaya. Yet as time passes "Tiger" Sullivan senses that his influence is waning, particularly after his young friend Melissa sides with brash Australian Bob Beresford against him.

And when a local tiger turns man-eater, Beresford seizes the chance to prove his masculine prowess, posing a challenge to Sullivan that the old hunter only reluctantly accepts.

As these proud men stalk the man-eater, their bitter rivalry builds to a dramatic and dangerous climax.

OVERLORD

A CONDENSATION OF THE BOOK BY

Max Hastings

ILLUSTRATED BY GINO D'ACHILLE
PUBLISHED BY MICHAEL JOSEPH

On June 6, 1944 the Allied forces, under the supreme command of General Eisenhower, staged the greatest amphibious landing in history—Operation Overlord.

Forty years on, Max Hastings has made an important new study of the Normandy campaign which overturns a host of traditional beliefs. The postwar generation has grown up to regard this campaign as a triumphant journey across Europe; few have grasped the intensity of the fighting in the early days of the campaign, which in its horror and ferocity rivalled the bloodbath of Flanders thirty years before. Drawing on a wealth of new material, award-winning war correspondent Max Hastings shows how the German army, suffering from terrible shortages of supplies and weaponry still managed to fight one of the fiercest battles of the Second World War.

Pictured above: The Allied commanders of Operation Overlord: (left to right) General Bradley, Admiral Ramsey, Air Chief Marshal Tedder, General Eisenhower, General Montgomery, Air Chief Marshal Leigh-Mallory, General Bedell Smith.

Foreword

The struggle for Normandy was the decisive western battle of the Second World War, the last moment at which the German army might possibly have saved Hitler from catastrophe. The postwar generation grew up with the legend of the Allied campaign of 1944-1945 as a triumphal progress across Europe, somehow unrelated to the terrible but misty struggle that had taken place in the east. Today, we can recognize that the Russians made a decisive contribution to the western war by destroying the best of the German army, killing some two million men, before the first Allied soldier stepped ashore on June 6, 1944. Nevertheless, despite the poor quality of the German troops initially defending the Channel coast, these same men prevented the Allies almost everywhere from gaining their D-day objectives, and on the American Omaha Beach brought them close to defeat, even before the crack units of the SS and the Wehrmacht approached the battlefield.

Few Europeans or Americans of the postwar generation have grasped the intensity of the early OVERLORD battles. In the demands they made upon the foot soldier they came close to matching the horror of the Eastern Front, or of Flanders thirty years earlier. Many British and American infantry units suffered over one-hundred-per-cent casualties in the course of the summer, and most German units did so. The commanding officer of the 6th King's Own Scottish Borderers found when his battalion reached Hamburg in 1945 that an average of only five men per company, and a total of six officers in the unit, were those with whom he had landed in Normandy in June 1944. "I was appalled," he said. "I had no idea that it was going to be like that." He, like the Allies as a whole, had been conditioned to believe that mechanized warfare in the 1940s need never match the human cost of the earlier nightmare in France. Yet for those at the tip of the Allied spearhead, it did so.

This, then, is a portrait of a massive and terrible clash of arms, and I hope that by focusing upon the fortunes of individuals and units at different moments of the campaign, I have been able to give an impression of the experiences and difficulties endured by thousands of others. I have concentrated upon the battle inland, and the personal experiences of men whose stories have never been told before, above all the Germans. The German army's achievement in Normandy was very great, and I have sought out and interviewed many of its survivors. I have tried to write dispassionately about the German soldier's experience without reference to the odiousness of the cause for which he fought.

All this, I have to say, has made me profoundly grateful that my generation has never been called upon to endure anything of the scale and ferocity that encompassed the men who fought in Normandy.

". . . the greatest thing we have ever attempted."

For a year following the fall of France in 1940, Britain had fought on without the prospect of final victory. Only when Hitler invaded Russia in June 1941, surely the most demented of his strategic decisions, did the first gleam of hope at last present itself to the Allies. For the remainder of that year, Britain was preoccupied with the struggle to keep open her Atlantic lifeline, to build up her bomber offensive against Germany, and to keep alive the only theatre of war in which the British army could fight, North Africa and the Middle East. Then, in the dying days of the year, came the miracle of Pearl Harbor. Britain's salvation, the turning point of the war, was confirmed four days later by another remarkable act of German recklessness, Hitler's declaration of war upon the United States.

To the relief of the British, President Roosevelt and his chiefs of staff at once acknowledged that Germany's warmaking power was far more dangerous than that of Japan, whose collapse, nevertheless, would have speedily to follow that of Germany. The war in the Pacific, therefore, became overwhelmingly the concern of the United States navy, while the principal weight of the army was to be directed against Germany and Italy. Even so, had the United States army been less resolute in its commitment to a landing in Normandy, it is most unlikely that this would have taken place before 1945. Until the last weeks before OVERLORD was launched, its future was the subject of bitter debate between the warlords of Britain and America. "I am very uneasy about the whole operation," wrote the Chief of the Imperial General Staff, Sir Alan Brooke, as late as June 5, 1944.

In the beginning, American thinking was dominated by fear of a rapid Russian collapse unless the western Allies mounted at least a powerful diversion on the continent. However, as the American build-up of her forces in Britain fell behind schedule, as the desert campaign dragged on without a decision, and as the tragic Dieppe raid demonstrated some of the hazards of cross-Channel operations, it became as apparent in Washington as in London that there could be no campaign in France in 1943.

Nevertheless, throughout the remainder of that year, while the British argued for extended commitments in the Mediterranean, possible operations in the Balkans, further delays before attempting Hitler's Atlantic Wall, the Americans remained resolute, determined to countenance no further prevarication. The invasion of northwest Europe was thus provisionally set for May 1, 1944. To the dismay of the British, the Americans also pursued forcefully their determination to execute a landing in southern France, at whatever cost in weakening Allied operations in Italy. This proposal was put to Stalin at the Teheran conference in November 1943, and welcomed by him. Thereafter, the Americans argued that any cancellation or postponement would constitute a breach of faith with the Russians.

Throughout the rest of 1943, even as preparations for OVERLORD gathered momentum, the British irked the Americans by behaving as if OVERLORD was still subject to debate. The Americans believed that the British were seeking grounds for further postponement of the invasion because they feared to meet the main strength of the German army in France, with the prospect of huge casualties that the battered Empire could ill afford. In fact it was patently true that Britain's strength was waning, her people growing weary: "At the

11

end of 1943, the population of Britain was . . . nearing the limit of its capacity to support the Allied offensive," wrote the British official strategic historian. By May 1944 the British army would attain the limits of its growth, two and three quarter million men. Meanwhile, the American army would number five and three quarter millions, still far short of its zenith. British production of ammunition had been falling since late 1942, of vehicles since mid-1943, of guns and small arms since late 1943.

Yet the Americans were often unjust in their judgment of the British. For all his moments of irrationality, his sudden flights of fantasy and moments of depression, Churchill's instinct for the reality of war often towers over the judgment of his professional service advisers. At root, he never doubted the eventual necessity for a major campaign in Europe.

Churchill wrote to Roosevelt on October 23, 1943, "I do not doubt our ability in the conditions laid down to get ashore and deploy. I am however deeply concerned with the build-up . . . My dear friend, this is much the greatest thing we have ever attempted . . ." His uncertainties concerned not the need to invade Europe, but the moment to do so. He saw many hazards in haste, and great virtues in delay. The German army had already suffered two million dead in the east, and was being bled more desperately every day by the advancing Russian armies. The air forces believed that strategic bombing was rapidly eroding the ability of Hitler's industries to arm and supply his armies. And finally, four years of war against the Wehrmacht had convinced Britain's commanders that Allied troops should engage their principal enemy only on the most absolutely favourable terms. Again and again in the Second World War, where British or American troops met the Germans in anything like equal strength, the Germans prevailed. Throughout history they had been formidable soldiers. Under Hitler, their army had reached its zenith. Weapon for weapon and tank for tank, its equipment decisively outclassed that of the Allies in every category save artillery and transport.

Yet, carried forward by American determination, the planning and preparation for OVERLORD now gained pace, drawing upon the fruits of aerial reconnaissance and a canvass of Britain for prewar holiday photographs of every yard of the coastline of France. The limiting factors for an invasion site were the radius of air cover— effectively the range of a Spitfire, 150 miles; the limits of beach capacity; the length of the sea crossing; and the strength of the German defences. For the first three the Pas-de-Calais, opposite Dover, offered the most obvious advantages, but was rejected because of the strength of the German defences. Brittany lay beyond the reach of dominant air cover. The Cotentin peninsula in Normandy offered the Germans too simple an opportunity to bottle up the invaders. Thus, very early on, in the spring of 1943, decisive attention focused upon the undulating fields and woods and beaches of Normandy's Calvados coast.

While the planners studied beach gradients and the complexities of the French railway system, Roosevelt and Churchill considered leaders. On December 7, 1943, Roosevelt was met at Tunis airport by General Dwight Eisenhower. As soon as the two men were in the back of a staff car, the president told him simply: "Well, Ike, you are going to command OVERLORD." Eisenhower, a fifty-four-year-old Texan who had risen from colonel to general in three years, who had scarcely heard a shot fired upon a battlefield, was sensitive later to the well-founded charge that he was no battlefield commander: "It wearies me to be thought of as timid, when I've had to do things that were so risky as to be almost crazy." But history has thus far remained confident that whatever his shortcomings as a general in the field, he could not have been matched as a supreme commander. His behaviour at moments of Anglo-American tension, his extraordinary generosity of spirit to his difficult subordinates, proved his greatness. His failures were of omission, seldom of commission. It remains impossible to conceive of any other Allied soldier matching his achievement.

The Americans, however, were irked by the appointment of Englishmen to all three subordinate commands for OVERLORD— General Sir Bernard Montgomery on land, Admiral Sir Bertram Ramsay at sea, Air Chief Marshal Sir Trafford Leigh-Mallory for the air. Yet another Englishman, Air Chief Marshal Sir Arthur Tedder, would serve as deputy supreme commander, in recognition of the critical importance of the air forces to the invasion.

This was the final occasion of the war on which British officers achieved such a measure of authority over Americans, on which Americans bowed to British experience and supposedly greater wisdom—an irony, since the invasion preeminently reflected an American willingness to grapple with the enemy head-on in a collision which Britain's leaders had sought for so long to defer.

MONTGOMERY ARRIVED IN ENGLAND from Italy on January 2, 1944, and immediately began to whip up a whirlwind. Having spent the night at Claridge's, the following morning he attended a briefing at his new headquarters, St. Paul's School in Hammersmith, where once he was a pupil. He heard the staff of Lieutenant General Morgan, Chief of Staff to the Supreme Allied Commander— COSSAC—outline their plan. Forearmed by a discussion with Eisenhower a few days earlier, Montgomery found little difficulty in taking the floor when the briefers had finished, and demolishing their points one by one in a twenty-minute "Monty special". Like Eisenhower, he had been immediately convinced that the suggested front was too narrow, the assault lacking in power and depth. He sent the COSSAC staff back to their offices to consider a far wider assault, perhaps reaching from Dieppe to Brittany. At the second day's session, he accepted the naval arguments against landing west of the Cotentin peninsula, but continued to insist upon a line reaching at least as far north as what became known as Utah Beach. On the third day, he crushed formal protests from senior COSSAC officers who insisted that what he wanted could not be done with the resources. The resources must be found, he declared flatly, or another commander appointed to carry out the invasion.

It was a masterly performance, Montgomery at his very best in clarity of purpose and ruthless simplicity. After months of havering among staff officers fatally hampered by lack of authority, he had sketched the design for a feasible operation of war, and had begun to exercise his immense strength of will to ensure that the resources would be found to land five divisions and secure a beachhead large enough to provide fighting room for the Allied armies. Sadly, however, having made a vital initial contribution to OVERLORD, he later tried to claim that the new plan was entirely his conception. In reality, of course, most of the staff in England had been conscious for months of the need to strengthen the attack, but had lacked the authority to insist upon it. But throughout his military career the austere, awkward little man in the beret would disparage the contribution of his peers. In consequence his staff and subordinates admired him, but few found it possible to like him. "We never lost confidence in him," said one, talking of the Normandy period, "but we would often say, 'Oh God, what's the little bugger doing now?'"

Montgomery's self-esteem, at its most conspicuous in his dealings with Americans, rested upon his faith in himself as a supreme

14

professional, a monkish student of war. In France in 1940, in England until 1942, and in the Mediterranean in the seventeen months that followed, he had proved himself a consummate trainer and motivator of troops, a superb organizer of battles and chooser of subordinates. He commanded immense respect from those who served under him for his willingness to listen to them, his directness and loyalty. Many senior officers in his armies went through the war quite unaware of the dark side of Montgomery's character, the conceit and the indifference to truth where it reflected upon himself. Also, perhaps, even these vices contributed to Montgomery a quality lacking in many brave and famous British generals— the iron will to prevail. Like many successful German commanders in the Second World War, he possessed ruthless clarity of purpose, the absolute will to win.

General Bradley, Commander of the American First Army in northwest Europe, had landed in England to take up his appointment on a bleak autumn morning in September 1943. Like most Americans, he found his spirit unexalted by the renewed encounter with weary, seedy, rationed wartime Britain, at a Scottish airfield: "The waitress, a stocky Scottish girl with a heavy brogue, offered me a choice of two entrées—neither of which I understood. 'Let me have the second,' I replied nonchalantly. She returned with stewed tomatoes. The first choice had been boiled fish. Prestwick taught me to confine my breakfast thereafter to the US army mess." A steady, thoughtful Missourian, Bradley had served as a soldier for thirty-two years before seeing action for the first time, as a corps commander in Tunisia. Now, just eight months later, he was to bear direct responsibility for the American army's greatest operation of the war thus far. He was fifty years old. If he lacked Patton's driving force and flamboyance, he had proved himself a commander of exceptional stability and discretion, whom men liked and immediately trusted. Bradley could "read" a battle.

Eisenhower reached England on January 15, and on January 21 presided over the first meeting of his staff and commanders at Norfolk House in St. James's Square. There Montgomery outlined the new plan which in the weeks that followed would be transformed into the operational orders of the Allied armies. The Americans, on the right, would go for Cherbourg, Brest and the Loire ports. It was logical to land them on the western flank, on the beaches that were to be codenamed Utah and Omaha, because they

15

would thus be conveniently placed to receive men and supplies arriving direct by sea from the United States. The British and Canadians on their left would deal with the enemy's main body approaching from the east and southeast, landing their troops on the three beaches codenamed Gold, Juno and Sword. Eisenhower accepted Montgomery's proposals, and the immense labour began of translating these into operational reality, devising fire plans, air support schemes, naval escort arrangements.

Millions of maps began to be printed in conditions of absolute secrecy, air photographs copied in thousands, artillery ammunition stockpiled in hundreds of thousands of rounds. Every troop formation required camps in Britain, trains to move them, training areas, rest areas, supplies. 6,250 pounds of sweets were distributed, 12,500 pounds of biscuits, 100,000 packets of gum. At Norfolk House, a succession of twelve-day courses were held for Allied supply officers, seventy at a time, to study the huge problems of their branch. Twenty-five square miles of west Devon between Appledore and Woolacombe were evacuated of their entire civilian population to enable the American assault forces to rehearse with live ammunition. In the assembly areas great tented encampments were constructed and equipped with water points, field bakeries, bath facilities, post offices, each one camouflaged to make it unidentifiable from the air. Week by week, transatlantic convoys docked in British ports, unloading cargoes of artillery shells from Illinois, blood plasma from Tennessee, jeeps from Detroit, off-ration cheese from Wisconsin. American troops' accustomed level of supply was huge: each American soldier in Normandy required six and a quarter pounds of rations a day, compared with three and one third pounds for his German enemy. Meanwhile, the German small arms ammunition scale for a rifle company was more than double that of its American equivalent: 56,000 rounds against 21,000.

IT WAS AGREED that gaining a foothold on D-day was a huge organizational task, but presented no intolerable tactical risks, given the weight of Allied resources. Only with forewarning did the Germans possess a real prospect of turning back the invaders on the beaches. The differences of opinion between German commanders about the best methods of defending Normandy were known through ULTRA, the Allied code-breaking device. The behaviour of the Führer himself, together with the success or failure of the Allies' deception plan, FORTITUDE, based upon a fictitious threat to the Pas-de-Calais, would determine whether the Germans deployed their army to the best—and possibly fatal—advantage.

Between January 15 and June 5—the new target date for invasion, after delay became necessary in order to provide sufficient landing craft—there were never, however, illusions among 21st Army Group about the likely quality of resistance: "The Germans will probably base many of their main and rearguard positions on river obstacles . . . . Our formations will be well-trained, but most of them will have little battle experience . . . . The enemy . . . will fight fiercely in all encounters, whether major battles or battles simply to gain time for withdrawal . . . . An all-out pursuit is considered unlikely until the German army is emphatically beaten in battle, and likely to come only once in the campaign. It will herald the end of the German war."

The Invaders

Disagreements, even full-blooded quarrels, between the services were not uncommon either in Britain or America in the Second World War. But none generated more heat and passion, diverted more attention from the struggle to defeat the Germans, than that surrounding the use of the Allies' vast air power in 1944.

As the directors of OVERLORD gathered the reins of command into their hands in the first months of 1944, one of their foremost concerns was to ensure that the full weight of Allied air power was available to provide whatever support they felt need of as the campaign unfolded. Both the British and American bomber chiefs had been proclaiming for months that they considered OVERLORD a vast, gratuitous strategic misjudgment, rendered wholly unnecessary by their own operations. Air Marshal Harris, for example, bombarded the Air Ministry with minutes declaring that "clearly the best and indeed the only efficient support which Bomber Command can give to OVERLORD is the intensification of attacks on suitable industrial centres in Germany . . . ." In January 1944, he declared his conviction that given continued concentration upon his existing policy, Germany could be driven to "a state of devastation in which surrender is inevitable" by April.

It is against the background of opinions such as these that the struggles between the ground and air force commanders in the summer of 1944 must be viewed. After intense argument, however, Eisenhower gained his point. Direction of all the Allied air forces was placed in his hands for as long as the chiefs of staff deemed necessary. After a further dispute, intensified by Churchill's fears about the level of French civilian casualties, the air forces embarked upon a huge programme of transport bombing of French rail junctions and river crossings, along the entire length of the Channel coast lest concentration westwards reveal the focus of Allied intentions.

Furthermore, the coming of the marvellous Mustang P-51 long-range fighter to the skies over Germany, in January 1944, inflicted a staggering defeat upon the Luftwaffe, unquestionably decisive for OVERLORD. German pilots were being killed far more quickly than they could be replaced, so that by June the Luftwaffe no longer possessed sufficient pilots and aircraft to mount more than token resistance to the Allied invasion of France.

It remains an astonishing feature of the invasion that it was launched with the Allied air chiefs still having devoted minimal thought to close ground-support techniques. Forward air control principles, which had been tried and proven in the desert, were not introduced in Normandy until weeks after the landings. On D-day itself, while the Allied tactical air forces made an important contribution, they lacked forward air controllers with the leading troops ashore, who might vastly have eased the problems of the ground battle. It was many weeks before the organization—not the technology or the skill of the pilots—reached the point at which it could render closely coordinated support to the ground troops. It is impossible to avoid the conclusion that in the spring of 1944, the air chiefs gave far too much attention to disputes about their own authority, and not nearly enough to considering how best they could work in harmony with the armies beneath them.

IN THE SPRING OF 1944, all of southern England and much of the rest of the country had beome a vast military encampment. Under trees beside roads, protected by corrugated iron, stood dump after dump of artillery ammunition, mines, and engineering stores. The soldiers themselves were awed by tank and vehicle parks in the fields, where Shermans and jeeps, Dodge trucks and artillery pieces stood in ranks reaching to the horizon. Above all, there were the

THE ALLIED FORCES IN NORMANDY

A BRITISH ARMY PRIVATE. The "Tommy" waded ashore on D-day with a full kit, including 50 rounds of ammunition, a bayonet, emergency rations, groundsheet, entrenching tool, gas mask, water bottle, ration bag and spare clothing. The rifle this man is holding is a bolt-action Lee-Enfield, an adequate weapon, although it was soon learned that on the Normandy battlefield, when men were rarely able to distinguish a target, the weight of machinegun fire was more important.

US PARATROOPER. Airborne troops were stripped to the minimum for battle, and equipped with little more than an entrenching tool, a water bottle, pistol, ammunition pouch, emergency rations and medical supplies. This man is holding an American "grease gun".

THE PIAT. This shoulder-fired anti-tank weapon used a 3lb projectile capable of pene-trating four inches of armour at a range of 50 yards.

THE AMERICAN P-51 MUSTANG.
A fighter which made its greatest
contribution to Allied victory by
winning the battle for air supremacy
before D-day. It outperformed almost
every Luftwaffe opponent, and in
Normandy was employed in interceptor
and ground-attack roles. Normally
armed with six 0.5 machineguns, it
possessed a top speed of 575 mph.

THE AMERICAN SHERMAN.
The Allies' principal tank, was
reliable, fast and
manoeuvrable, but critically
handicapped by thin armour
and the lack of an adequate
gun. It weighed 32 tons and
moved at 24 mph. Note the
white star painted on the turret
side, the identification symbol
for all Allied vehicles in
Europe. A Browning machinegun is mounted on the tank
shown below.

THE BRITISH BREN GUN.
With its 500 rounds per
minute, this had a far lower
rate of fire than the
fabulous 1,200 of the
comparable German MG-42.

THE BRITISH HAWKER TYPHOON. The "Tiffy", as it was known, was a rugged rocket-firing fighter-bomber, which played a major part in the RAF's low-level ground attacks over Normandy. It was the principal destroyer of the retreating German army at Falaise.

THE AMERICAN THUNDERBOLT. One of the largest and heaviest of all fighters with a single piston engine, its toughness and firepower more than made up for deficiencies in range and manoeuvrability.

THE AMERICAN 105MM FIELD GUN. This was outranged by the British 25-pounder by 1,200 yards. Allied artillery was generally good and plentiful, however, and was responsible for a high proportion of the casualties inflicted in the war.

THE BRITISH 25-POUNDER. With a range of 13,400 yards, this was a fine gun and immensely valuable for "keeping heads down". Its drawback was a lack of killing power against defensive positions.

THE CHURCHILL FLAME THROWING TANK. Capable of only 15 mph and weighing five tons more than the Sherman, it carried flame fuel in a trailer and could incinerate infantry at a range of 40-50 yards.

THE AMERICAN BAZOOKA. This was the first light, portable rocket-launcher. It enabled infantrymen to destroy heavy tanks at a range of 400 yards without having to rely on heavy anti-tank guns or artillery.

men—twenty American divisions, fourteen British, three Canadian, one French, one Polish, together with hundreds of thousands of special forces, corps troops and headquarters units.

One of Montgomery's outstanding contributions before D-day was his careful meshing of experienced veterans from Eighth Army with the keen, untried formations that had been training and languishing for so long in England. Yet many of the men from the Mediterranean, above all the old regular soldiers, were bitter that, after fighting so hard for so long, they were now to be called upon once again to bear the brunt of the battle. Lieutenant Colonel Michael Carver of the 7th Armoured Division found some of his senior NCOs appearing before him to protest about their role, and echoing complaints from their wives, who demanded to know why those who had sat in England for four years could not now take over the burden. It was a sentiment shared by the prime minister.

"It is a painful reflection (he wrote to the War Office early in 1944), that probably not one in four or five men who wear the King's uniform ever hear a bullet whistle, or are likely to hear one . . . . It is my unpleasant duty to dwell upon these facts. One set of men are sent back again and again to the front, while the great majority are kept out of all fighting, to their regret."

Repeatedly, however, Montgomery patiently reminded him of the realities of modern war, of the essential need for the vast "tail" behind OVERLORD, and also of the utter exhaustion of Britain's manpower reserves. The British army that landed in Normandy would be a great force. Thereafter, as casualties mounted, its number must remorselessly decline. This reality brought with it the uncomfortable knowledge that the first weeks in Europe would be the last of British parity with the Americans in ground force strength. In July the American armies would begin to outnumber the British, and thereafter their strength would rise month by month until they dwarfed those of their ally. Already many British servicemen were irked by the extraordinary social dominance the Americans had achieved within Britain, with their staff sergeants drawing the pay of British captains, their vast reservoirs of equipment for themselves and candy for British children. Much can be said about differences and jealousies that developed between British and Americans. Such reports and comments should never mask the cooperation between them, a unity between Allies at working level that has seldom, if ever, been matched in war.

IF SEVERAL BRITISH FORMATIONS that went to Normandy were already battle-weary, some of their American counterparts were alarmingly under-prepared and under-led for the task that they were to perform. If the British divisions were drawn from a citizen army, British military tradition and the British class system caused them to become far more deeply imbued with the manners and habits of regular soldiers than their American comrades. From the first day of the war to the last, the US army could never be mistaken for other than what it was—a nation of civilians in uniform.

Perhaps the greatest of all America's organizational achievements in the Second World War was the expansion of her tiny 1939 regular army of 190,000 men into the 8.5-million-strong host of 1945. Yet even at war, America's ground forces—above all, her corps of infantry remained something of a Cinderella, with too little emphasis placed upon manning the infantry regiments at the very tip of the American spear. The air corps and the specialist branches had been allowed to cream off too high a proportion of the best-educated, fittest recruits. Infantry rifle companies would be called upon to fight Hitler's Wehrmacht with men who were, in all too many cases, the least impressive material America had summoned to the colours.

To some extent, this reflected the contrast between the social attitudes of America's best and brightest young men towards military service and that of their counterparts in Europe. In America, to become a soldier has never been an honourable profession in the European manner, outside a few thousand "army families". It is striking to observe that in the Second World War, privileged young Englishmen still gravitated naturally towards rifle and armoured regiments. Their American counterparts by preference sought out exotic postings in the air corps, or managerial roles on army or diplomatic staffs. Although many did so, and fought with gallantry, it never became fashionable for young Ivy League Americans to serve as front-line officers. Even in their final pre-invasion exercises in Devon, Bradley and other commanders were acutely conscious of the shortcomings of some American formations, above all of their commanders. Marshall wrote in March about the embarrassment of having been compelled to relieve a succession of generals, including two corps commanders: ". . . we couldn't relieve any more without a serious loss of prestige. What seemed to be lacking in each case was aggressive qualities . . . ."

The Defenders

"If they attack in the west," said Adolf Hitler in December 1943, "that attack will decide the war." Whatever the shortcomings of the Atlantic Wall, Hitler's proclaimed impatience for the Allied invasion was by no means bluff. His armies in Russia and Italy were being remorselessly pushed back and destroyed. Their total manpower had fallen from over three million in July 1943 to 2.1 million in May 1944. Germany's one remaining chance of escaping catastrophe lay in the destruction of OVERLORD. If the Allies could be thrown back into the sea, it was inconceivable that they should mount a new assault for years, if ever. Almost the entire strength of the German army in northwest Europe, sixty divisions, could then be transferred east for a fight to the finish against the Russians, and within the year secret weapons and jet aircraft should be available in quantity. Thereafter, Hitler reasoned, anything was possible.

In January 1944, Hitler's Chief of Operations, Jodl, toured the Channel coast and reported grimly on the state of its defences. The perpetual bleeding of the west's manpower to feed the Eastern Front had crippled every division. Commanders complained that they were being denied time to carry out essential training because their men were continuously employed on building fortifications.

The hapless von Rundstedt was never consulted, as commander in chief, about what forces he deemed necessary to defeat an invasion—he was merely informed what was to arrive. The bulk of his army was made up of the over-age and medically unfit, and an entirely unreliable rabble of Polish, Russian and Italian defectors. Even the majority of the first-line divisions which began to move into France in the spring of 1944 for the strengthening of the western defences were formations which had been shattered in the east, needing massive reinforcement and re-equipment. However well Hitler recognized the need to defend against invasion, he was the victim of the remorseless imperative that demanded men and tanks to fight against the present menace in the east, rather than against the prospective threat in the west.

Nevertheless, a decisive factor in the German army's ability to defend Normandy was to be the superiority of almost all its weapons in quality, if not in quantity, to those of the Allied ground forces. In 1942, the Minister for Armaments, Albert Speer, and his staff had

24

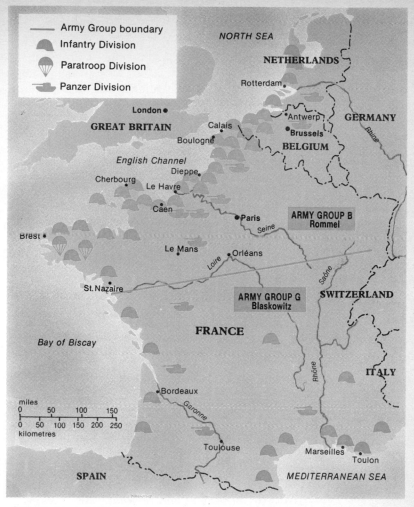

NORTH SEA

NETHERLANDS

Rotterdam

London

GREAT BRITAIN

Calais

Boulogne

English Channel

Dieppe

Cherbourg

Le Havre

Caen

Brest

Le Mans

St. Nazaire

Bay of Biscay

miles
0   50   100   150
0   50   100   150   200   250
kilometres

Bordeaux

Garonne

Toulouse

SPAIN

Antwerp   GERMANY

Brussels

Rhine

BELGIUM

Paris

Seine

ARMY GROUP B
Rommel

Orléans

Loire

Saône

SWITZERLAND

ARMY GROUP G
Blaskowitz

FRANCE

Rhône

ITALY

Marseilles

Toulon

MEDITERRANEAN SEA

Hitler's Army in France

taken the decision that since they could not hope to match the quantitive superiority of the Allies, they would attempt to defeat them by qualitative superiority. Thus, in the first weeks in Normandy, Allied tank units were deeply dismayed by their enemy's weaponry. The Sherman was a superbly reliable piece of machinery, far easier to maintain, and with two other important

25

advantages over its German opponent: a faster speed of turret traverse to engage the enemy, and a higher rate of fire. But it suffered from a critical tendency to catch fire. Also, it was undergunned. A Tiger could knock out a Sherman at a range of 4,000 yards, while the American tank could not penetrate a Tiger's frontal armour at all.

As to infantry weapons, the Americans possessed an excellent rifle in the semi-automatic Garand, and the British an adequate one in the bolt-action Lee-Enfield. But on the European battlefield, commanders learned, men seldom fired their rifles. What mattered was the weight of fire to saturate the battle area. For this the Germans possessed the supreme weapon in their MG34 and 42 machineguns—known amongst the Allies as Spandaus. The MG42's 1,200 rounds a minute, compared with the Bren's 500, proved deeply demoralizing to men advancing against it.

The handle on the German "potato-masher" hand grenade enabled it to be thrown far further than its British or American counterparts. The German Schmeisser was a far superior sub-machine gun to the American "grease gun" or the British Sten. Above all, Allied soldiers detested the *nebelwerfer*, the multi-barrelled projector whose mortar bombs were fitted with a brilliantly conceived siren, causing them to wail as they flew through the air, with an effect on those who heard them which was often more penetrating than their explosive power.

German infantry anti-tank weapons were also markedly superior. British battalions were equipped with a spring-loaded projector named the Piat which threw a two-and-a-half-pound bomb one hundred and fifteen yards. Even in short-range tests in England, the Piat scored only 57-per-cent hits. The American bazooka packed a wholly inadequate projectile for penetrating German tank armour. The Germans, meanwhile, were equipped in Normandy with the excellent *Panzerfaust*, the finest anti-tank weapon of the war.

Nor did the Allies possess any weapon with the physical and moral effect of the German 88mm, the high velocity anti-aircraft gun that was used with dazzling success in Normandy. It was also formidable against infantry, firing high-explosive airburst shells that stopped Allied attacks dead in their tracks again and again. The unforgettable lightning crack of an 88mm remained implanted in the memory of every survivor of the campaign.

In fact, Germany's principal weakness on the Channel coast in the

A WEHRMACHT INFANTRYMAN. This German soldier is seen carrying a Schmeisser sub-machine gun, which was far superior to the comparable American "grease gun" or British Sten. Tucked into his boot is a "potato masher" grenade with its long handle.

AN SS TANK CAPTAIN. Hitler deployed a number of crack SS panzer divisions in the defence of Normandy. These men proved to be the most determined and fanatical opponents facing the Allied armies.

THE MG-42. Known as the Spandau among Allied troops, this was a first-class general-purpose machinegun, with a staggering 1,200 rpm rate of fire. The Spandau barrel could be changed in five seconds during periods of heavy fire.

ME 109. By June 1944 the
Luftwaffe was in a desperate
weakened state as a result of
disastrous losses earlier in th
year. By D-day the Germans r
longer possessed sufficient
pilots and aircraft to mount
more than a token resistance
the Allied invasion. The ME 1(
fighter was one of the
outstanding aircraft of the wa

TIGER TANK. The Panzer VI,
or Tiger, was the most feared
German tank in Normandy,
almost impenetrable by frontal
Allied tank gunfire, and
packing a devasting punch
with its 88mm gun. Its
principal shortcomings were its
clumsiness of movement and
mechanical unreliability.

PANZERFAUST. This was the best hand-held
infantry anti-tank weapon of the war.
It was a one-shot throwaway weapon and,
weighing only 11½ lbs, was exceptionally
useful in close country where its operators
could reach Allied tanks at very short ranges.

PANTHER TANK. The Panzer MKV, or Panther, was the outstanding German tank of the campaign in Normandy, less heavily armed but more mobile and reliable than the Tiger. With a top speed of 34 mph it was considerably faster than its sister tank, and its only serious weaknesses against the Sherman were the poor periscope optics and slow turret traverse.

88MM DUAL PURPOSE GUN. This was the decisive force in the German destruction of many Allied tank attacks in Normandy. It was the best gun produced by any nation in the war, with a formidable killing power much feared by Allied troops.

THE NEBELWERFER MULTI-BARRELLED MORTAR. A formidable weapon, this caused a staggering proportion of the casualties suffered by Allied troops and was nicknamed "moaning minnie".

spring of 1944 was her blindness. The Luftwaffe, lamentably directed for years by Goering, had lost not only its strength but its will. Despite the difficulties posed by Allied command of the air, some measure of air reconnaissance might yet have been possible, given real determination by the German airmen. "That the Luftwaffe did not carry out minimal reconnaissance of the east coast must rank as a miracle of the same dimensions as the destruction of the Armada in 1588," one historian has written. Furthermore, brilliant British counterintelligence operations had deprived Germany of authentic agents in Britain. It was the Germans' utter uncertainty about where the Allies would come that contributed decisively to their débâcle in June.

Rommel's achievement in galvanizing the building of coastal defences in the spring of 1944 was very real. But he shared the High Command's indecision and lack of grip, in allowing resources to be wasted creating fortifications in all manner of places where it was absurd to imagine that an invasion could occur. All along the three thousand miles of Occupied coastline, bunkers were created, positions dug. Admittedly some Allied deception schemes made no impression on the Germans—for instance, the dispatch of an army pay corps lieutenant and former actor to impersonate Montgomery on a tour of the Mediterranean, and the creation of a mythical army in Scotland for the invasion of Norway. But a climate of uncertainty had been masterfully brought into being, which would decisively influence German behaviour until deep into July.

Additionally, Hitler's manic suspicion of his generals, his obsession with dividing authority among them to deny overall power to any one, created a cumbersome command structure in France. In Paris, the dour, unbending von Rundstedt presided as commander in chief. At Army Group B's headquarters at La Roche Guyon, Rommel was to be responsible for directing the battle against the invaders. If the Allies gained a foothold, Rommel's preference was to withdraw to a river line to hold them. Hitler's absolute determination to yield no ground precluded this. Everything would hinge upon the Germans' ability to halt the Allies upon the beaches. Hitler was correct in believing that his field marshal's ability to dominate the battlefield was deeply flawed by doubt that this was possible, so Rommel was denied direct control of the panzer divisions of OKW (German High Command) reserve. All that spring Rommel wavered between outbursts of buoyant confidence and deep depression. "If I were doing the invasion," he said to his staff one morning, "I should be at the Rhine in fourteen days."

His driving energy was undiminished, but he was no longer the Desert Fox, the supremely confident panzer leader of 1941-1942. Too many defeats had intervened.

THE MEN OF THE GERMAN ARMY in France in June 1944 were sustained by a combination of fatalism and blind faith. Above all, perhaps, by a sense of unreality, of a comforting impossibility about the notion that their stretch of windswept dunes, their familiar billets and battery positions, should be chosen above all others by the Allies to become one of the great battlefields of history.

One May morning, Rommel had visited the 1716th Artillery Regiment in their positions around Ouistreham. He told the assembled circle of officers: "If they come, they'll come here." Lieutenant Rudolf Schaaf did not really believe him. Twice wounded in the leg in Russia, Schaaf was one of many men posted to France because they were unfit for further duty in the east—he walked with a pronounced limp. He and most of his comrades were enjoying their time in France, with plenty to eat and drink, all of it cheap. Above all, they were thankful to be out of the east.

There was a wide gulf between the men of the coastal divisions— at best cynical about their role, at worst openly defeatist—and those of the crack units. Lieutenant Walter Kruger, a signals officer with 12th SS Panzer Corps, was an SS man in the classic mould, asserting his "absolute confidence in victory from first to last." The troops of this, the Hitler Youth Division, were to prove the most determined and fanatical opponents facing the Allied armies. They had practised repeatedly the advance from their camps near Evreux to the Normandy coast. "They had received a proper training in the Hitler Youth," said Kruger proudly. "They had a sense of order, discipline. They knew how to sing!"

Much depended upon the performance of this and the other nine armoured divisions in France. General Guderian, Inspector General of Armoured Forces, wrote: "All hopes of successful defence were based upon these." Lieutenant Colonel Kurt Kauffmann, Operations Officer of Panzer Lehr, the finest armoured division in the Wehrmacht, believed that the invasion could be defeated. Despite Panzer Lehr's lack of opportunity to exercise as a formation, 75 per cent of its men were veterans and it was superbly equipped.

Kauffmann's chief worry was about the performance of its commander, General Fritz Bayerlein: "He was a very good soldier, but he was worn out. In Normandy he showed himself nervous and weak."

Throughout those last weeks before June 6, the mobile formations behind the coast exercised with varying degrees of intensity, their movements watched with deep apprehension by Allied intelligence, while the men of the coastal units dutifully laid yet more concrete and field telephone wires, pottered between the minefields carrying their little cans of milk from the local farms, hung their washing to dry on the edge of the bunkers, and cherished their hopes that the Tommies and the Americans might come somewhere else. If high morale means having the motivation to give everything for a cause or an objective, few of them possessed it. Their senior officers were haunted by the knowledge of their units' inadequacy for the task that they might have to face. The highest-hope of most of their men was to survive the war. For few was it to be fulfilled.

To the Far Shore

At St. Paul's School on May 15, Montgomery carried out his final presentation of the OVERLORD plan for the senior officers of the Allied armies, crowded on wooden benches behind a single row of chairs at the front for the King, Prime Minister Churchill, Field Marshal Smuts and Chief of the Imperial General Staff, Sir Alan Brooke. One of the greatest throngs of commanders ever assembled was gathered in the hall, and Montgomery's presentation on that day was acknowledged even by his critics as a brilliant performance: a display of grip, confidence, absolute mastery of the plan.

Now, in fact, during these last weeks before D-day, the principal dissension within the Allied High Command concerned not OVERLORD, but the projected invasion of southern France, Operation ANVIL, to which the Americans were firmly committed but the British bitterly opposed, because it would certainly cripple operations in Italy. Shipping difficulties compelled ANVIL's postponement from a landing simultaneous with OVERLORD to a secondary operation ten weeks later, and the arguments between London and Washington continued until the final days before its launch. This became the first major decision of the war over which the Americans adamantly refused to bow to British pressure, and went their own way. It was an augury of other painful blows to British confidence and pride which lay ahead.

It was a remarkable tribute to the power of the image-builders that even among the Americans, in those last weeks before D-day, nothing did more to boost the confidence of the men of the invasion armies than Montgomery's personal visits. From mid-May until June he devoted his energies almost entirely to inspecting the troops under his command. The mannered walk down the ranks, staring piercingly into men's eyes; the order to break ranks and gather round the general on the back of the jeep; the sharp, brittle address—all were theatrical, yet defy the cynicism of history. "Even Ike, with all his engaging ease, could never stir American troops to the rapture with which Monty was welcomed by his," wrote Bradley. "Among those men, the legend of Montgomery had become an imperishable fact." At Tidworth Camp, in Hampshire, 12,000 men of the US 2nd Armored Division gathered to hear Montgomery on the football field. "Take off your helmets!" he ordered, and off came every helmet except that of Maurice Rose, beside the jeep. "You, too, General," said Montgomery. He paused and gazed slowly, in silence, round the great mass of men. At last he said: "All right, put them back on. Now, next time I see you, I shall know you." It was brilliant stage-management.

There was less enthusiasm from the British government for the speeches Montgomery made to factory workers at the time, for they smacked too much of the national warlord. And when he drew up a two-page outline, complete with hymns and prayers, for a proposed national service of dedication at Westminster Abbey before the invasion, the plan was speedily squashed. Montgomery would sail for France leaving behind many men who admired enormously his skill in bringing OVERLORD to reality. But he would also leave behind a deep reservoir of animosity and bitterness. As long as he remained victorious, he was invulnerable. But scores of senior officers had been discarded—some for good reasons, others suffering merely for the misfortune of being unknown to the new commander in chief and should the campaign falter under Montgomery's direction, he had provided many powerful hostages to fortune.

IN THE LAST DAYS of May and the first of June, the vast columns of men and vehicles began to stream south into the assembly areas where the invaders were briefed and equipped before being loaded aboard the fleet. The men crowded into the tiered bunks in the huge tented camps were loaded with seasickness pills and life jackets and new gas-protective battledress which everybody detested because of its extra weight and smell, and issued with their ammunition. Each soldier was given a leaflet about getting on with French civilians which urged him to say nothing about 1940 and not to buy up everything in sight at extravagant prices. Until the last minute the men worked obsessively upon the waterproofing of their vehicles, conscious of the horror of stalling with a flooded engine, under fire in the surf.

The tannoy systems in the camps were rarely silent by day or night, as groups of men were mustered, loaded into trucks, and driven through meticulously signposted streets to numbered docks where they joined their transports. The concentration and loading operations were among the great achievements of OVER-LORD. For once there was little need to motivate men to concentrate upon their tasks. They understood that their lives depended on it.

The postponement from June 5 to June 6 on account of the adverse weather forecasts much increased the mental strain on the men crowded in the ships. They played cards, chatted quietly, in many cases simply lay silent on their bunks, gazing up at the bulkheads. Some—most—passengers were seasick.

On all the ships, officers and NCOs pored over the maps and photographs of their landing areas that they had at last been ordered to strip from the sealed packages: it remains one of the minor miracles of OVERLORD that although hundreds of men and women had been involved in their making and printing, there was no security leak.

Brigadier General Norman "Dutch" Cota assembled his staff of the advanced headquarters group of 29th Division, of which he was deputy commander, in the aft wardroom of the USS *Carroll*, and addressed his team for the last time: "This is different from any other exercise that you've had so far. The little discrepancies that we tried to correct on Slapton Sands are going to be magnified and are going to give way to incidents that you might at first view as chaotic. The air and naval bombardment are reassuring. But you're going to find confusion. The landing craft aren't going in on schedule, and people are going to be landed in the wrong place. Some won't be landed at all. The enemy will try, and will have some success, to prevent our gaining lodgment. But we must improvise, carry on, not lose our heads."

In the late evening of June 5, when the men of the seaborne assault divisions had already been at sea for many hours, Private Fayette Richardson of the US 82nd Airborne Division was still in camp in England. A short, wiry twenty-year-old from a small town near Buffalo, New York, he stood among the rest of the team joking self-consciously with each other as they struggled to stow a mountain of personal equipment about their bodies. A radar set was strapped below the reserve parachute on his stomach. Fragmentation grenades were hooked onto his harness, gammon bombs and a phosphorus grenade, chocolate rations, fighting knife, water bottle, anti-tank mine, a small syringe of morphia, and an armed forces paperback edition of *Oliver Twist* were stowed about his person.

On top of all the kit, Richardson was supposed to carry a rifle. He decided to leave this and make do with a .45 pistol, strapped to his high paratroop boot where he could reach it. The pressure of the pistol belt, the tightly laced boots and equipment made him feel oddly secure, as if he was wearing armour. When the trucks came for them, the paratroopers tottered forward and were boosted aboard by the cooks and maintenance men who were being left behind.

Soon after darkness fell, they were airborne. The man jammed alongside Richardson, in the belly of the plane, nudged him and pointed down to the moonlight shining on the water. It seemed to the paratrooper to be frozen in smooth, unmoving ripples. Richardson saw a flash of light in the sky outside, and understood after a moment of puzzlement that it was anti-aircraft fire.

By the time "Rich" Richardson jumped over the fields of the Cotentin peninsula, soon after 1:30 am, thousands of other Allied paratroopers were already on the ground ahead of him. Men of the British 6th Airborne Division seized the bridges over the Caen Canal and the Orne at Ranville, on the eastern flank, a few minutes after midnight. A total of 8,000 British and 16,000 American airborne troops were to land by parachute and glider. The drops were marred by the poor performance of many of the Allied Dakota pilots, who by a combination of unsteady navigation and extravagant reaction to German flak, released their parachutists with near-criminal carelessness. The glider pilots, by contrast, performed miracles of determination to land their craft on their objectives.

The airborne operations of D-day emphasized painfully for the Allies the cost and difficulty inseparable from massed drops, even before paratroopers could engage the enemy. Thousands of young Americans found themselves struggling, alone or with little clusters of other lonely figures, to find a path through the hedges and swamps of the Cotentin which drowned hundreds of men before they could escape from their harnesses. It was a remarkable tribute to the US 82nd and 101st that, while thousands of their men found themselves miles from their units and their objectives that night, they engaged the Germans wherever they encountered them. The great achievement of the American airborne forces on June 6 was to bring confusion and uncertainty to the Germans across the breadth of the Cherbourg peninsula.

After a brief moment of euphoria when the men from the first wave of planes over Richardson's landing zone jumped as planned, he was dismayed to see the second wave approach on the same course, then drone on without dropping a man. There was silence in the field again. The silence persisted, for the expected third wave of aircraft never came. Instead of a powerful paratroop unit at the assembly point, there were only a few dozen men.

Richardson's own company was among those which had failed to arrive, so he simply joined the nearest group of men digging slit trenches. When he had made his own foxhole, he dropped into it and fell asleep.

GERMAN SLUGGISHNESS in responding to the first Allied movements of D-day has passed into the legend of the war. The failures of the German navy and airforce were obviously central to the defenders' lack of warning of the invasion. The navy had failed to station patrols in the Channel because of its conviction that the weather was unfit for an invasion; Fifteenth Army's interception of the known BBC codeword for the French Resistance to begin their D-day tasks was ignored; and the Luftwaffe had failed even to observe the concentration of minesweepers operating off the Normandy coast at last light on June 5.

But the absence from headquarters of so many vital senior German commanders was also a misfortune of critical importance. The whereabouts of General Edgar Feuchtinger of 21st Panzer have never been confirmed, but it was widely believed by his own men that he was incommunicado with a female friend. Colonel Kauffmann of Panzer Lehr was on honeymoon near Stuttgart. Most of Seventh Army's senior officers were attending the war games in Rennes. And Rommel had retired to Germany to celebrate his wife's birthday and to importune Hitler for a more realistic attitude to the defence of the Atlantic Wall.

On the night of June 5, exploiting Rommel's absence, his Chief of Staff General Hans Speidel invited several of his fellow anti-Hitler conspirators to join him for drinks at the château at La Roche Guyon. It was here, after they had all dined together, that Speidel was telephoned by Fifteenth Army headquarters at Turcoing and informed of the intercepted BBC message. Fifteenth Army had been placed on alert. A staff officer telephoned von Rundstedt's headquarters in Paris for a decision on whether Seventh Army also should be alerted. It was decided that it should not.

Seventh Army was finally alerted at 1:35 am, in the wake of reported paratroop landings. The confusion was compounded by the Allied drop of thousands of dummies and six uncommonly brave SAS soldiers to divert the defenders inland. At 3:00 am, von Rundstedt's headquarters reported to OKW, Hitler's High Command, in Berlin that large scale air landings were under way. At 4:00 am, General Kraiss of 352nd Division sent a regiment on bicycles in pursuit of paratroopers at a location where, in reality, only dummies had landed. The discovery of these doubled the Germans' uncertainty about a possible bluff. At 6:00 am, von Rundstedt's headquarters told OKW that a major invasion appeared to be taking place, and asked for the release of the armoured reserve, 1st SS Panzer Corps, outside Paris. With Hitler asleep, the request was denied. It was not finally granted until ten hours later. At 6:15 am, Speidel learned of the opening of a massive naval bombardment and air assault on the coastal defences, but it was a tribute to the Allied deception plans that every key German commander greeted the news of operations in Normandy as evidence of *an* invasion, not of *the* invasion; and it was not until after 10:30 am that Rommel himself finally left his home in Herrlingen to drive headlong for his headquarters, over an hour after Allied radio had formally announced the coming of the invasion. It was almost twelve hours before he reached La Roche Guyon.

Admittedly the probability remains that the Allies could have gained their beachhead against any German reaction on D-day. But the early release of the OKW armoured reserves would have made matters incomparably more dangerous for them, and it must be said that the senior staff officers of all the major German formations behaved with a negligence verging upon utter incompetence.

The Landing

Before dawn, the invasion coast was lit by flares and flashes, as British naval guns pounded the defences. A few miles out to sea hundreds of launches and landing craft scuttled amidst the dim silhouettes of the battleships and cruisers, transports and rocket ships, and no man who saw it ever forgot the spectacle of the vast invasion fleet crowding the Channel at first light on the morning of June 6. Seven battleships, twenty-three cruisers, ninety-three destroyers, seventy-one corvettes and sixty-three frigates and destroyer escorts dominated the great assembly of converted liners and merchantmen and tank landing craft now shaking out into their positions a few miles offshore—nearly seven thousand landing ships in all. Alongside the transports, overburdened men clambered down the scrambling nets into the pitching assault craft below. For many, this was among the most alarming experiences of the day.

As the first waves of landing craft headed for the shore, the guns ceased their barrage, according to the time schedule. As a result, with so many landing craft running so many minutes late, the German defences enjoyed a precious pause before the first infantry hit the beaches.

PROBABLY THE FIRST Allied vessel to be destroyed by the shore batteries was an American patrol craft leading landing craft towards Utah Beach. Lieutenant Halsey Barrett was concentrating intently upon the task of holding his course at 5:34 am, when, just fifty-eight minutes before H-hour, they were hit. "There was a crash—not terribly loud—a lunge—a crash of glass, a rumble of gear falling around the decks—an immediate, yes immediate, 50-degree list to starboard—all lights darkened and the dawn's early light coming through the pilot house door which had been blown open. The executive officer immediately said, 'That's it,' with finality and threw down his chart pencil. I felt blood covering my face and a gash over my left eye, around the eyebrow."

While most of the crew took to the life rafts as the craft turned

1. General Sir Bernard Montgomery (right), Commander in Chief of the British 21st Army Group, confers with General George Patton (left) commanding US Third Army, and General Omar Bradley, Senior Commander of the US forces in France.

2. Hitler greets Field Marshal Erwin Rommel, responsible for defending 3,000 miles of coastline. In Hitler's opinion, Rommel was flawed by his lack of confidence in final victory.

1. American troops clamber into their landing craft for the invasion at dawn on June 6.

2. On their way at last: the faces of these US army troops reveal mixed emotions as they await the landings.

3. British soldiers pass the time learning about their target.

4. Ramps down, and the assault troops file onto Omaha Beach. At times the invaders had to battle against 3-4 foot waves, and only dogged determination, helped by timely naval support fire, saved the day. Amazingly by midnight 33,000 men had been put ashore.

5. Waves of follow-up assault troops stream ashore.

turtle, Barrett and a cluster of others clung to the upturned hull, watching the great procession of landing craft driving on past them towards the shore.

"A landing craft with thirty or so men aboard was blown a hundred feet in the air, in pieces. Shore batteries flashed, splashes appeared sporadically around the bay. Planes were flying in reasonable formation over the beach. Aft of us an LCT (Landing Craft Tank) lay belly skyward, no trace of survivors around it. The USS *Nevada* a mile off to the northwest of us was using her 14-inch guns rapidly and with huge gushes of black smoke and flame extending yards and yards from her broadside. . . . There was a beautiful sunrise commencing. . . . A small British motor launch picked up one of our men, shrieking for help while hanging onto a marker buoy. His childish yells for help, despite his life jacket and secure buoy, was the only unmanly incident which I saw. . . ."

Most men, even those who had suffered as savage a shock as the crew of this patrol boat, felt reassured by the sense of the Allied armada's dominance of the sea. Barrett and the other survivors knew that somebody would pick them up as soon as they had time to spare, as indeed they did. For the men of the British and American navies, there was an overwhelming sense of relief that they faced no sudden, devastating attack from the Luftwaffe as some had feared, despite the reassuring intelligence reports. "The Luftwaffe is obviously smashed," wrote a sailor on the corvette *Gentian*.

IN HIS FOXHOLE in the Cotentin, Private Richardson of the US 82nd Airborne was woken by daylight, and the overhead roar of an Allied fighter bomber. Hungry and thirsty, he munched a chocolate bar until word came to move out. Then, among a long file of men unknown to him, he began to march across the fields. They reached a hedge by a road and halted while at the front of the column, two officers pored over a map and discussed which way to go. Suddenly everybody was signalled to lie flat. A car was approaching. Richardson and the others could see the heads of its three German occupants passing the top of the hedge like targets in a shooting gallery. It seemed that no one would move against them, each American expecting another to be the first to act. Then one man stood up and emptied a burst of automatic rifle fire at the car. It swerved off the road into a ditch, where somebody shouted "Finish 'em!" and tossed a grenade. But the Germans were already dead.

Like Richardson, many of the paratroopers had never seen a man killed before, least of all on a peaceful summer morning in the midst of the countryside. They found the experience rather shocking. They left the Germans where they had fallen, and marched on through the meadows and wild flowers, disturbed by nothing more intrusive than the buzzing insects.

Richardson's experience was scarcely universal, because as his group were making their way across country with little interference, many other American paratroopers were engaged in desperate battles around the causeways and villages of eastern Cotentin, and the British 6th Airborne bridgehead northeast of Caen was under fierce German pressure. But the young New Yorker's story catches the dreamlike quality, the curious sense of detachment, that so many men felt in those first hours after being wrenched from the peace of the English summer, and thrust onto an alien battlefield.

AS THEY APPROACHED Sword Beach, one of three designated for British landings, Lieutenant Charles Mundy's men of the 22nd Dragoon Guards did their best to dull their sensations with the rum rations which they had saved and bottled for three months, in anticipation of this moment. They were still over a mile offshore, gazing like eager tourists towards the beach ahead, when a shell smashed through the side of their landing craft and the entire troop were ordered to close down in the tanks. Their Sherman flail tanks, specially mounted with chains on a revolving drum for minesweeping, were to lead the landing on the eastern flank. Mundy, a thirty-one-year-old Londoner, was impressed to see that the shoreline ahead conformed precisely to the photographs that he and his men had studied so earnestly.

Some men reacted theatrically to their parts. A bugler of the East Yorkshire Regiment sounded the general salute as his landing craft passed the British command ship. Commander Angus Mackenzie, aboard the destroyer *Undaunted*, stood in his Highlander's bonnet playing the bagpipes from his bridge as landing craft crammed with crouching infantry ploughed past his ship towards the beach.

ALTHOUGH THE CURRENT at Utah Beach drove the American landing craft to make the assault two thousand yards south of the area designated by the plan, in every other respect the US VII Corps's operations conformed more nearly to the timetable than those of any other Allied formation that day. Twenty-eight of the thirty-two amphibious tanks launched reached the sands. At 6:30 am, the three regimental combat teams (the US equivalent of British brigades) of 4th Division began to come ashore under very light enemy fire. The Germans had thought it most unlikely that Allied troops would land immediately in front of the wide flooded areas beyond the beach. The navigational error caused by the current had brought the men of 4th Division into the most lightly defended sector of the entire Normandy front; besides which, every gun and every bunker had been sited to match Rommel's certainty that the Allies would come with the high tide. In consequence, most troops of the lone defending German regiment surrendered as soon as the Americans came to close quarters with them.

The Americans' difficulties, however, began as soon as they left the beach. When they clambered over its high, sandy bank and started to plunge through the flat, flooded fields behind the dunes, their movement became agonizingly slow.

To Private Lindley Higgins and his companions of the 12th Regiment, struggling under their impossibly heavy loads of weapons and equipment, the swamps seemed endless. Shorter men found themselves stumbling into concealed ditches that almost drowned them, from each of which they had to be painfully extracted. Higgins was carrying an entire carton of Lucky Strikes in his invasion jacket, but by the evening the only smoke he managed to salvage was from the pack in his helmet. All along the line, time was already slipping.

Yet the landing of 23,000 men on Utah, at a cost of only one hundred and ninety-seven casualties, was almost a miracle of good fortune and good judgment. A few miles eastwards that morning, on Omaha Beach, other divisions were enduring ten times their losses, and very many times their fear and confusion.

Here, the Germans were defending the strongest natural positions facing the entire assault—hills and cliffs rising steeply up to two hundred feet from the beach and the seawall above it. The Americans below the bluffs faced by far the greatest concentration of German fire on the entire invasion front.

There is no more demanding task for infantry than to press home an attack across open ground, under heavy fire. The American assault on Omaha Beach on June 6 came as close as the experience of any Allied soldiers in the Second World War to the encounters between flesh and fire that were a dreadful commonplace in the battles of thirty years before.

At least ten landing craft were swamped during the run-in, drowning many of the infantry. The attempt to land artillery from amphibious trucks failed disastrously, and thirty-two amphibious tanks were launched, by a serious error of judgment, 6,000 yards from the beach. Each one, as it dropped off the ramp of the landing craft, plunged like a stone to the bottom of the sea, leaving pitifully few survivors to struggle in the swell.

The infantry were thus called upon to storm the beach without benefit of the vital supporting armour which was intended to shoot the way ashore. Each man was grotesquely heavily loaded with gas mask, grenades, half pound blocks of TNT, pole or satchel charges, two bandoliers of rifle ammunition, rations and water bottle—sixty-eight pounds in all. Now, in an instant, they were compelled to rouse themselves from the cramped, crowded stagnation of the landing craft and stumble forward into the hail of machinegun and mortar fire from the German defences, which killed and wounded many before they even reached dry ground. Others, still groggy with seasickness, desperately sought cover among the Germans' beach obstacles, or lay paralysed amidst the harvest of wreckage that quickly gathered on the shoreline.

Grounded and damaged landing craft clogged the beach early in the assault, some hulks being swept broadside against the German obstacles to create a logjam impassable by the next wave of boats. The plan demanded that two hundred and seventy specially trained demolition men, who followed the lead infantry onto the beach, should immediately begin to blow up these obstacles, clearing the way for the 25,000 more men and 4,000 vehicles that were due on Omaha with the second tide of the day. In reality, only a handful of obstacles were exploded that morning, and of sixteen armoured bulldozers sent ashore, only six arrived, three of which were quickly destroyed. Among the infantry, hundreds lay prone in the shallow water seeking cover, or dragged themselves painfully up the sand with wounds suffered before they were even out of the landing craft, to huddle beneath the seawall at the head of the beach, seizing the only shelter Omaha offered. Hundreds of men were already dying or dead—there would be more than 2,000 casualties on the beach that day.

When Gerard Rotthof's mother heard that her son was to become a radioman, she had said: "Well, at least he won't have to carry a rifle any more." But now Rotthof lay trapped on the beach beneath the weight of his sixty-pound SCR 284 set, wounded by mortar fragments in the face and back. He received the last rites, but somehow survived terrible internal injuries. Only sixty-two men of the 2nd Rangers who were landed on the western flank of Omaha reached the seawall, out of one hundred and thirty launched from the transports before dawn.

Corporal Bill Preston of the 743rd Tank Battalion watched five of his unit's Shermans sink on launching offshore, before the officer commanding, realizing that conditions were impossible, brought their group of landing craft up to within two hundred and fifty yards of the beach. Then they ran in, crawling out of the water amidst huddles of isolated infantrymen and intense small arms fire. Preston could see dead engineers floating beyond the beach obstacles, where so many wounded men also died as the tide came in over them. They later found to their dismay that they had run over a man, for they discovered his clothing jammed in their tracks. Twenty-one of their unit's fifty-one tanks were destroyed on Omaha that morning, and the neighbouring battalion fared even worse.

FROM THE BRIDGE of the cruiser *Augusta*, General Bradley watched the events on the beaches, standing beside the task force commander, Admiral Kirk, peering through his binoculars at the distant smoke shrouding the shore. By midmorning the apparent collapse of the landing plan had plunged V Corps's staff into the deepest dismay. Colonel Benjamin Talley, cruising in an amphibious truck a few hundred yards from the beach, told of landing craft milling around the smoke-shrouded sands "like a stampeding herd of cattle." Bradley "gained the impression that our forces had suffered an irreversible catastrophe."

The reports that reached him from Omaha that morning were not merely gloomy, but at times almost panic-stricken. A monstrous traffic jam had developed off the beach. By a serious flaw in the timetable, soft-skinned vehicles were beginning to arrive to offload, in the midst of the battle. Among naval crews who displayed exemplary courage, there were others whose lack of experience and determination magnified the confusion.

Lieutenant Colonel John Williamson, commanding the 2nd/18th Infantry of the 1st Division, led his men into their landing craft soon after 8:00 am—more than an hour late. The craft began their run-in, not in an orderly wave, line abreast, but in a column, a queue, jostling for position on the sands. "The beach was loaded with men, tanks, amphibious trucks," said Williamson. "I was surprised that nobody had moved off." Major Frank Colacicco of the same regiment stood among his men on the deck of a landing craft offshore, watching the spectacle in utter bewilderment: "It was like a theatre. We could see it all, we knew that something was knocking the tanks out, but we kept asking, 'Why don't they clear the beach? Why aren't our people getting off?' " When at last their own turn came, Colacicco's craft struck an obstacle whose mine blew up as they approached the sands. Some men were hurled into the water by the blast, while others found themselves struggling in the surf as the craft settled. At last someone on the beach got a lifeline out to them, and the soaking men dragged themselves ashore. Slowly they began to work up the hillside, crawling over the immobile figures of men of the 116th Infantry. Colacicco tore a strip off one man he saw firing, apparently recklessly, along the hillside: "Just settle down," said the major. "That's our men over there."

"But sir, they have overcoats on," insisted the soldier. Indeed, they were German riflemen.

ALTHOUGH, ON OMAHA, the defenders possessed the capability to maul, impede and disorganize the American landing, they lacked the power to halt it absolutely. Despite the casualties and the terror inflicted upon thousands of inexperienced troops, a great many men survived to reach the seawall finally to swamp the vastly outnumbered German defenders. General Marcks's reserve, the 915th Regiment, had set off in pursuit of the mythical paratroop force of Allied dummies at 4:00 am on June 6. It was hours before they could be reached by dispatch rider and brought back. The defenders thus lacked any force capable of mounting a coordinated counterattack either against the attackers of Omaha, or against the British threat to Bayeux, further east.

The defenders possessed the strength and determination to fight doggedly from fixed positions. But where the Americans, inch by inch, gained ground, they were able to keep it.

Like a trickling stream slipping between pebbles, a handful of courageous American leaders and their men found their way round the German strongpoints covering the beach exits, and forced a path

47

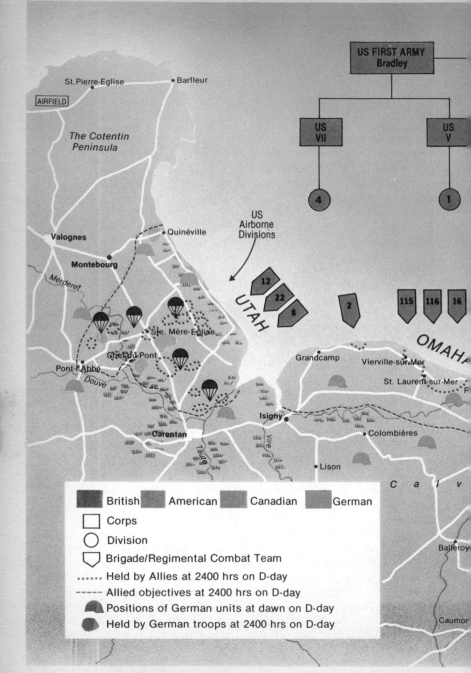

The D-day Landings: The most ambitious amphibious invasion in history

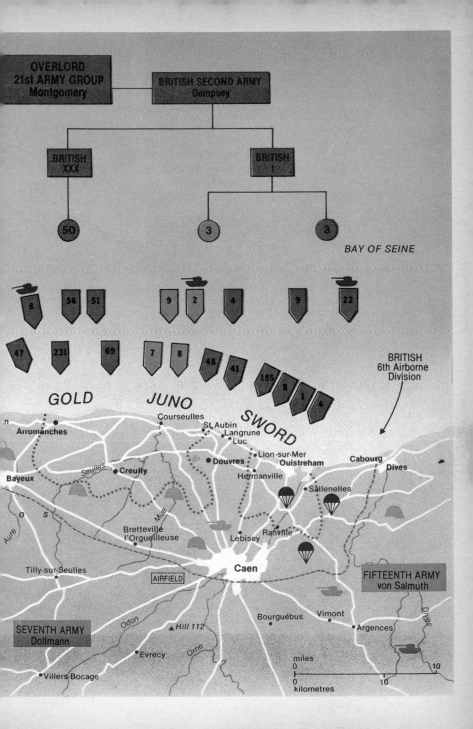

for the American army off Omaha Beach. The overall plan for the attack was a failure, but the men on the hillside, in the midst of their own desperation, found their own means to gain the high ground.

It was individuals, not divisions, which determined the outcome of the day. Staff Sergeant William Courtney and Private William Braher of 2nd Rangers were probably the first Americans to reach the top of the cliff, around 8:30 am. When the rangers gained the summit, they were too few in number to achieve a decisive success, but in the next two hours, a succession of similar small-scale actions took place all along the Omaha front, driving vital wedges into the German defences.

Brigadier General Norman Cota and his 29th Division command group had reached the beach at 7:30 am. The general began to move among the bewildered tangle of infantrymen, rangers, naval beach maintenance parties and gunner forward observers. When he found a group of rangers claiming to be pinned down, Cota himself walked ahead of them across the open ground to demonstrate that a man could move and survive. Many men who attempted to set this sort of example, on June 6 and in the weeks that followed, were killed instantly. But Cota lived, and the rangers moved forward. All that afternoon, the brigadier moved relentlessly up and down the hillside, urging on the men clambering in sluggish files through the minefields.

By 4:30 pm, now up on the high ground, Lieutenant Colonel Williamson and his regiment had advanced to within a mile of their designated D-day objectives. Like every American soldier above Omaha that day, he and his men were cursing the hedges of the *bocage*, the small fields and narrow wooded lanes behind the beach, which provided such perfect cover for snipers, and were already inflicting interminable delays upon advancing units. Men sought cover whenever firing sounded nearby. Crossing a gap, the young soldier in front of Williamson was shot. The colonel put a Browning automatic rifle on top of the hedge and raked the area with fire. They moved onwards a little way without further casualties, then took up position for the night just short of Colville. The Omaha beachhead had been secured.

Although the events of D-day had emphasized the limited ability of high explosives to destroy strong defensive positions, by the night of June 6, the Americans nevertheless controlled a perimeter up to a mile deep beyond Omaha, while the 4th Division on Utah had linked up with General Maxwell Taylor and his men of the 82nd Airborne Division, west of the causeway from the beach. The Americans suffered 4,649 casualties among their seaborne landing force, to put ashore 55,000 men, and even if the American line at midnight on June 6 fell some distance short of its planned objectives, V and VII Corps had achieved their vital strategic purposes merely by establishing themselves ashore.

It was on the British front on D-day, where so much rested upon fast and ruthless progress inland from the beaches, that far more dramatic strategic hopes were at stake.

AT 7:25 AM, AN HOUR after the Americans began landing on Omaha, the minesweeping flail tanks of the 22nd Dragoon Guards touched Sword Beach at the eastern end of the Allied line, precisely on schedule. Lieutenant Charles Mundy in *Leander I* drove ashore into the mortar and machinegun fire with the hatch open as usual because of his haunting fear of his tank catching fire inside and "brewing up", as it was called.

His column of five Churchills took up echelon formation to begin flailing, thrashing the sand with their great probosces of chains, creeping forward astonishingly unscathed to the metalled road, where they switched off their equipment and began engaging the German defences with their 75mm guns. Thirty-four of the forty Sherman amphibious tanks launched also arrived as planned, ahead of the infantry, cleared the beach successfully and became heavily engaged in the dunes beyond.

A few minutes later, the twenty landing craft carrying the first wave of the 1st South Lancashires and the 2nd East Yorkshires dropped their ramps and launched the lead companies, followed twenty minutes later by the second wave. These point battalions suffered less severely crossing the beach than those which followed, and by 9:00 am the South Lancashires were between one and one and a half miles inland, at Hermanville. At the outset, the Sword landing was a remarkable success, but now vehicles and supporting units were pouring ashore, clogging the beaches, successive waves becoming helplessly entangled with each other, creating a great jumble of men, vehicles, landing craft and wreckage on the waterline. Furthermore, the strong onshore winds had caused an unprecedently high tide. Instead of a normal width of thirty yards of sand, that morning the incoming mass of armour and soft-skinned vehicles were attempting to manoeuvre towards the beach exits across a mere thirty feet.

The seizure of the La Breche strongpoint covering the beach took three hours, during which troops coming ashore continued under its fierce fire. The South Lancashires, who bore the brunt of the battle, lost eleven officers and ninety-six other ranks on D-day, the East Yorkshires about the same. Private Len Ainlie was an anti-tank gunner of the King's Regiment. A regular soldier since 1938, he had asked for a transfer to airborne forces, but his colonel had refused to forward the request because Ainlie was a battalion bugler. Now, his landing craft, a hundred yards offshore, was struck amidships on the starboard side by a shell. Ainlie was appalled by the devastation immediately in front of him. A cook's head vanished, the company commander's batman lost his legs. Men began to struggle over the side of the sinking hulk, as a jumble of broken bodies drifted amidst the rush of water pouring through the side. The survivors swam and stumbled through the dead and the wounded to the beach, where they saw the battalion's commanding officer killed a few minutes later. They were all soaking wet, and their battledress and boots and equipment would be stiff with salt for days.

SOME OF THE FIRE falling upon Sword Beach during the morning came from the four 150mm self-propelled light guns of the Germans' 1716th Artillery Regiment, firing from a position at Plumetot, 3,000 yards inland from the coast. After standing by since midnight, at dawn its commander Lieutenant Rudolf Schaaf walked forward a little way until he could see the great invasion fleet stretched out before him off the coast. He found the spectacle impressive rather than frightening—it all seemed somehow detached from himself. "Well," he wondered thoughtfully, "what do we do now?"

Around midmorning, Schaaf was suddenly ordered to take his self-propelled guns immediately north to the coast, and assist an infantry counterattack. It was a pathetic episode. The German infantry were middle-aged men. They were strafed from the air as they advanced in open order down the gentle decline to the sea, and soon found themselves under fierce gun and small arms fire. Schaaf watched British infantrymen scuttling for cover, but lacked heavy weapons or tanks to deal with them. When the Germans at last despaired and began to pull back, only twenty men remained with the guns. A few minutes later, Schaaf was telephoned by the excitable Major Hof, his battalion commander, and ordered to advance immediately to regimental HQ, two miles away on Hill 61, and attempt to extricate them from heavy attack.

ON JUNO BEACH, a few miles west of Sword, the Canadian 3rd Division had also broken through the coastal crust, but at heavier cost. Twenty of the leading twenty-four vessels were lost or damaged, a total of ninety out of three hundred and six employed on Juno that morning. Most of the tanks made it, but arrived behind the leading infantry rather than in time to provide suppressive fire ahead of them. Tanks and infantry moved inland together, becoming entangled in heavy street fighting in Courseulles and St. Aubin. But in accordance with the plan the Canadian follow up units passed through the assault troops, ignored the snipers who continued in action until nightfall, pressed on towards their objectives, and by nightfall had established themselves strongly up to five miles inland.

THE 50TH DIVISION attacking Gold, the most westerly of the three British beaches, ran into their first serious difficulty in front of the fortified German positions at Le Hamel. The British supporting tanks arrived too late to give the infantry immediate support, and the British landed under furious fire from bunkers scarcely scarred by the bombardment.

Major Dick Gosling, an artillery battery commander, who landed with the Hampshires' battalion headquarters, was pleasantly surprised in his first moments ashore to find that the beach "was not the raging inferno some people had feared." Then he saw ripples of sand being pitched up all around him, and heard a noise like a swarm of angry bees over his head, his first encounter with enemy fire in six years of soldiering. A blast close at hand felled a man beside Gosling, and suddenly he found that he could not walk. A mortar fragment had struck him in the leg. Somehow he reached the dunes, and began desperately scraping a hole with an entrenching tool. Most of the Hampshires' wireless sets had been knocked out by a blast in the midst of the headquarters group, and the gunner found his own set so helplessly clogged with ships' Morse and other units' communications that he was unable to send a single radio message that morning to his own guns offshore.

Gosling eventually managed to hobble down to a German pillbox on the beach, where he sat among other casualties waiting for evacuation. The former occupants had clearly been disturbed over breakfast—coffee and sausage lay on the table, a picture of Hitler hung on the wall. Gosling found a letter from a French girl named Madeleine, obviously addressed to one of the garrison, promising to meet him on the evening of June 6.

By then the rest of his division, although short of most of its D-day objectives, was, however, solidly established in the Norman hedgerows with only limited German forces on its front.

ONLY FOR COMMANDERS and historians is it possible to say that a battle proved a great deal easier than expected, and casualties remarkably light. For the men taking part, there were moments of violent intensity and horror on the British beaches as shattering as anything that happened on Omaha. It would have availed them little to know that their experience was much less terrible in scale than that of the Americans, for in kind it was equally deadly.

Yet nothing could damp the exhilaration of those who had survived, sitting as wondering sightseers on ground that over four long years had attained for them the alien sense of mystery of the dark side of the moon. By 10:00 am, the British Second Army had landed fifteen infantry battalions, seven commandos, seven tank regiments, two engineer assault regiments, nine field artillery regiments and scores of supporting units. There had been setbacks, local failures, severe casualties to certain units, poor performance by some specialist equipment. But, overall, the plan had succeeded stunningly well. Almost everywhere along the British line, the German coastal positions had been rolled up. It now remained to press forward to complete the second phase of the D-day operation, ruthlessly to exploit German shock and surprise and to seize the vital ground inland.

Inland

Hitler's appointments for the morning of June 6 were not altered by the news of the Allied landings. He was in Berchtesgaden. At midday that day both he and OKW's Chief of Operations, Jodl, were compelled to drive for an hour to Klessheim Castle, where they were officially receiving a Hungarian state visit. In a room beside the great entrance hall of the castle, Hitler was briefed on the first reports of the invasion. He approached the map of France on the wall, gazed at it for a moment, chuckled, and declared in unusually broad Austrian tones: "So, we're off!" Then he departed to meet the new Hungarian prime minister, and a junior officer was dispatched to von Rundstedt, to emphasize that there must be vigorous local counterattacks against the beachhead.

CORPORAL WERNER KORTENHAUS and the rest of his company of 21st Panzer had begun to move up the Falaise-Caen road at 8:00 am. They were deeply unhappy, for the road ran perfectly straight and open, and they were repeatedly compelled to pull in to the side and scramble beneath their tanks, as Allied aircraft roared low overhead. South of Caen, they spotted two British soldiers standing alone in the corn by the road with their hands up, almost certainly men of 6th Airborne who had been dropped hopelessly wide. The panzers had no time to take prisoners, and hastened on towards the British paratroopers' bridgehead north of Caen, cursing the Luftwaffe as they watched the enemy overfly them with impunity. Where, they asked, were the thousands of German aircraft that they had been promised would be in the sky to support them on "The Day"?

All that morning and well into the afternoon, 21st Panzer's powerful armoured regiments moved northwards amidst checks, delays and changes of orders imposed more by failures of intelligence, and their own command's indecision, than by Allied interference. The panzer battalion with which Kortenhaus was driving was already approaching the British paratroopers' bridgehead when it was halted by orders from General Marcks, who believed this to be a wasteful use of armour. One company only was left to support operations there, while the remainder were diverted to join the counterattack west of Caen. Thus it was already around 4:30 in the afternoon before this, the first major German armoured counterattack of the invasion, was ready to jump off against the British 3rd Division.

Montgomery had demanded dash and determination from his commanders, to carry them to the city of Caen, since the only possibility of dramatic success had lain in a concentrated, racing armoured thrust. However, two thirds of British armour on Sword

1. Lending a helping hand on Omaha Beach.

2. Engineers plan clearways through the wreckage after the initial assault.

3. American troops help comrades whose landing craft have been sunk by enemy action. There were more than 2,000 casualties on Omaha Beach on D-day.

4. British soldiers assemble in their sector.

❶

❸

❷

was too deeply entangled in the fighting on the beaches and immediately inland to be available for the movement south. The brunt therefore fell on 3rd Division's infantry brigades. These comprised only the 8th and 185th for their reserve brigade had come ashore too slowly to join the advance.

By 4:30 the 8th Brigade had been delayed by German strongpoints but the leading battalion of 185th Brigade was fighting a brisk battle for possession of Hill 61, from whence Major Hof had telephoned Lieutenant Schaaf and asked him to bring his self-propelled guns to the aid of regimental HQ. Schaaf duly advanced across the cornfields. He saw heads peering at him over the standing corn, rapidly disappearing again when he opened fire. But by now, a squadron of British Shermans had caught up. When Schaaf spotted these, he determined that for self-propelled guns to engage tanks was beyond the call of duty. He beat a hasty retreat. When next he found a telephone line and tried to contact regimental HQ, an English voice answered the call.

It was here, just three miles short of Caen, that panzergrenadiers or the infantrymen of 21st Panzer Division met the leading battalion of 185th Brigade, and here, late on the evening of June 6, Allied hopes of seizing Caen, one of the most vital objectives of the day, vanished. At 6:00 pm, the leading battalion halted under fierce German fire. "We were not unpleased with ourselves," wrote Captain Rylands, and indeed, at a cost of one hundred and thirteen men killed and wounded, their achievement had been remarkable. But a single infantry battalion with limited tank and artillery support had not the slightest hope of generating sufficient violence to gain a foothold in Caen.

The last important action on the British left on June 6 was the battle against 21st Panzer's armoured thrust. General Marcks told the panzer regiment's commander: "Oppeln, if you don't succeed in throwing the British into the sea, we shall have lost the war." The armoured officer, a former Olympic equestrian champion, saluted, and mounted his vehicle. The tanks raced north across the open ground, driving headlong into the gap between the British and Canadian perimeters, only to recoil westwards on meeting heavy fire. By a dramatic coincidence, only minutes later the fly-in began of two hundred and fifty gliders of 6th Airborne Division, to a landing zone eastwards, near the Orne bridge. This was too much for the Germans. 21st Panzer was a sound enough formation, but lacked the ruthless driving force of an SS armoured division. Arguing that the glider forces threatened them with encirclement, they withdrew up the hill towards Caen. By nightfall, they were strongly emplaced around the city, with the support of their twenty-four 88mm guns. But they had lost seventy of the one hundred and twenty-four tanks with which they had begun the day.

ALONG SIXTY MILES OF FRONT, men lay over their weapons, peering out into the darkness amidst occasional flares and tracer. Some soldiers of the British and American airborne divisions were still probing warily through the darkness miles from their own lines, on the long march from their mis-aimed dropping points. Some thousands lay dead, others wounded in the field dressing stations or positions from which they could not be evacuated. There were already Allied stragglers and deserters who had slipped away from their units, lingering in villages the length of the invasion coast.

In England and America, the newspapers were being printed. *The Times* for June 7 carried the headlines: "The Great Assault going well; Allies several miles inland; Battle for town of Caen; Mass attack by airborne troops."

The Allied command of the air was obviously decisive on June 6. Given the difficulties that the invaders suffered against the Atlantic Wall, it is hard to imagine that they could have pierced it at all had their assault been subject to serious attack from the Luftwaffe. As it was, they were ashore. But they were still gasping to regain breath after the vast strain of getting there.

The British before Caen

In the minds of both German and Allied commanders, there was never any doubt that in the immediate wake of the invasion, the vital strategic ground lay where the British Second Army stood before Caen, waiting to break into open tank country to the southwest, freeing airfield sites and gaining fighting room before the mass of the German army could be committed to battle. But the weeks that followed were to raise serious questions about the fighting power of the British army, and to demonstrate decisively the genius of the German soldier in adversity.

Also, in these first days as much as at any phase of the campaign, the Allies felt their lack of an infantry personnel carrier capable of móving men rapidly on the battlefield alongside the tanks. From first to last, infantry in Normandy marched rather than rode, and too many tired soldiers were asked to march far as well as to fight hard. Furthermore, for the tank crews there was the certain knowledge that a hit from a German Tiger, Panther or 88mm gun would be fatal. The same was not true the other way round.

A British tank officer, newly arrived in France in June 1944, recorded a conversation with his regimental adjutant about the state of the armoured battle: "What do the Germans have most of?"

"Panthers. The Panther can slice through a Churchill like butter from a mile away."

"And how does a Churchill get a Panther?"

"It creeps up on it. When it reaches close quarters the gunner tries to bounce a shot off the underside of the Panther's gun mantlet. If he's lucky, it goes through a piece of thin armour above the driver's head."

"Has anybody ever done it?"

"Yes. Davis in C Squadron. He's back with headquarters now, trying to recover his nerve."

"How does a Churchill get a Tiger?"

"It's supposed to get within two hundred yards and put a shot through the periscope."

"Has anyone ever done it?"

"No."

Between June 6 and the end of the month, Montgomery directed three attempts, first to seize Caen by direct assault, and then to envelop it. All were in vain. Throughout June 7 and 8, the Canadians and the fanatical teenagers of the SS Hitler Youth fought some of the fiercest actions of the campaign, with heavy losses to both sides.

Lieutenant Schaaf was at corps headquarters in a mineshaft outside Caen, when a swaggering colonel from 12th SS Panzer arrived to announce his intention of halting nowhere before the sea. This, of course, was the legendary Kurt "Panzer" Meyer, only thirty-three years old, tall and stiffly handsome, the archetype of the Nazi fanatic. Even as a prisoner, in 1945, he told his interrogator: "You will hear a lot against Adolf Hitler in this camp, but you will never hear it from me. As far as I am concerned he was and still is the greatest thing that ever happened to Germany."

While the Germans coordinated armour, infantry and artillery superbly, the Canadians did not. While 9th Brigade was facing 12th SS Panzer in heavy combat, 8th Brigade spent the day preoccupied with mopping up strongpoints in their rear. The following morning, June 8, 7th Brigade came under heavy attack, with the Royal Winnipeg Rifles' positions being overrun, compelling the Canadian Scottish to mount a major counterattack to recover the lost ground. That night, Panthers of 12th SS Panzer, led personally by Kurt Meyer on his customary motorcycle, hit 7th Brigade yet again. As fires and flares lit up the area, at one stage the Regina Rifles reported twenty-two Panthers around their own battalion headquarters. The Canadians lost contact with all but one of their companies. "It is hard to picture the confusion which existed," said their commanding officer.

The Canadians were unbowed, but shaken. Meyer's panzers had successfully thrown them off balance, caused them to concentrate chiefly upon holding the ground that they possessed, made them cautious about launching any attacks without secure flanks and powerful gun and tank support. They found themselves unable to advance beyond Authie.

On June 7 the British 50th Division, on their right, occupied Bayeux, which the Germans had evacuated on D-day, and pushed forward towards Tilly-sur-Seulles.

By June 8, when Montgomery himself came ashore to establish his tactical headquarters in the grounds of the château at Creully, the prospect of breaking through the line in front of Caen was very small.

"The Germans are doing everything they can do to hold on to Caen," Montgomery wrote to the War Office that day. "I have decided not to have a lot of casualties by butting against the place. So I have ordered Second Army to . . . make its main effort towards Villers-Bocage and Evrecy, and thence southeast towards Falaise."

The fact must be faced, however, that the sluggishness of Allied movements in those first, crucial days before the mass of the German army reached the battlefield, provided the Germans with the vital opportunity to organize a coherent defence and to bring forward the reinforcements to contain the beachhead. The huge tactical advantage of surprise had already been lost.

NEVERTHELESS, FOR THE ENEMY also, the struggle east of the Orne remained an appalling memory. Caked in dust, unwashed and often unfed, amidst the appalling heat and stink of their steel coffins, the tank crews fought through days and nights of attack and counterattack.

"We became very depressed," said Kortenhaus. "We had given up any hope of victory after repeated failures in attack." Yet the Germans had held their ground despite the Allies' overwhelming superiority of fire support.

It was at this stage that Montgomery determined to commit his two veteran divisions of the old Eighth Army, 51st Highland and 7th Armoured, in two major flank attacks around Caen.

On June 10, when the 7th Division moved through British positions west of Caen, its commander, Major General Erskine, could report that he "never felt serious difficulty in beating down enemy resistance . . ." It thus seemed all the more remarkable that the Desert Rats made little progress on June 11. British infantry who penetrated Tilly—whose lyrical name had become a synonym for fear and endless death among men of 50th Division—were unable to secure the town for lack of tank support. But, as opposition stiffened in front of them, the corps commander, Bucknall, perceived a yawning hole in the German line between Caumont and Villers-Bocage, to the right. On June 12, 17th Armoured swung westwards to launch a new attack on this southeasterly axis.

On the morning of June 13, bypassing isolated enemy tanks, the leading regiments of the 7th Armoured advanced up the winding road lined with great chestnut trees and entered Villers-Bocage, to be greeted by enthusiastic local civilians.

Yet already nemesis, in the form of a single Tiger tank commanded by Captain Michael Wittman, was approaching every British hope around Villers. His company had left Beauvais on June 7 and, after suffering severely from an air attack near Versailles, had travelled only in darkness to reach their present position on June 12. Now Wittman stood in his turret studying the halted British column beyond Villers, going peacefully about its business. "They're acting as if they've won the war already," muttered his gunner. Wittman said calmly. "We're going to prove them wrong."

Charging down the stationary line in one of the most devastating single-handed actions of the war, he slammed shell after shell into armour and truck at almost point-blank range, finally ramming aside a last Cromwell tank blocking his path into the narrow high street of Villers-Bocage. Here, he destroyed three tanks of the City of London Yeomanry's HQ group, and was able to demolish a last Cromwell before reversing away. Having devastated the spearhead of 7th Armoured in five minutes of ruthless action, Wittman refuelled and re-armed his tank in time to join four other Tigers and an infantry group falling upon the surviving British forces. This time the British were ready for them, and destroyed his Tiger and three other German tanks, but their crews escaped unscathed because virtually no British infantry remained to support the armour and anti-tank crews.

That night, with German reinforcements still concentrating around the town, the surviving British forces were withdrawn to 7th Armoured's main positions around Tracy-Bocage, two miles west. They had lost twenty-five tanks and some twenty-eight armoured vehicles.

The following day, a new series of British attacks failed to gain ground.

For reasons that will never be known, General Bucknall failed to ask Second Army for infantry reinforcements to provide direct support for the isolated tanks of the 7th Armoured Division. Under cover of darkness on June 14, the British withdrew four miles to positions east of Caumont, their supporting infantry slumbering, exhausted, on the hulls of the Cromwells.

The Germans considered that the day was decided by the new *Panzerfaust*, the superb hand-held infantry anti-tank weapon which they were able to use to formidable effect against Allied tanks advancing in the close country, but by any measure, Villers-Bocage had been a wretched episode for the British, a great opportunity lost as the Germans now closed the gap in their line. As Second Army reviewed the events of the past four days, it was apparent that the 7th Armoured Division had begun its attack led by tanks widely separated from their supporting infantry. Thus, when they encountered snipers and pockets of resistance manned by only handfuls of Germans, the entire advance was blocked for lack of infantry close at hand to deal with them. Yet again and again in Normandy, British tanks outran their infantry, leaving themselves exposed to German anti-tank screens, and the foot soldiers without cover for their own movement under fire.

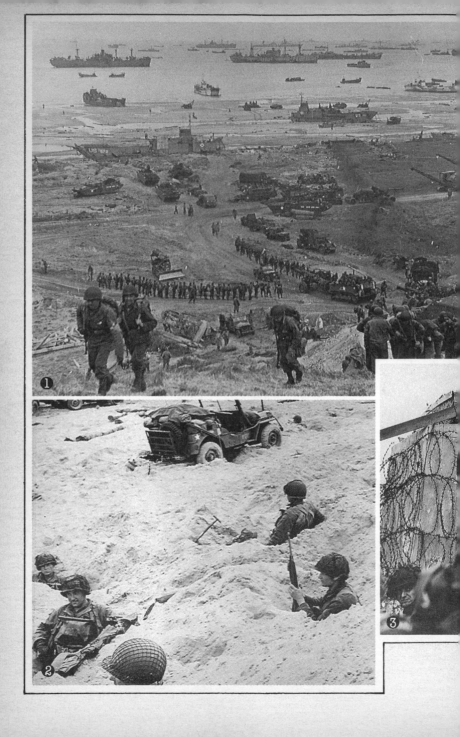

1. The build-up: miles of men and equipment stream inland.

2. Landing parties keep watch from foxholes hastily dug on the beachhead.

3. A quiet stretch of the Atlantic Wall. Canadian troops relax in front of the German machinegun nest they have just captured.

4. A loaded US army "duck" (amphibious truck) accelerates past a Lockheed fighter on a makeshift airstrip on the beachhead.

5. A bird's-eye view of a tank action among the Normandy hedgerows.

Admittedly the Tiger tank was incomparably a more formidable weapon of war than the Cromwell, and the German panzergrenadiers were also equipped with an exceptionally good armoured half-track vehicle to carry them across the battlefield, but the suspicion was also born, hardening rapidly in the weeks which followed, that 7th Armoured Division now seriously lacked the determination which had made it so formidable a formation in the desert. Many of its veterans felt strongly that they had done their share of fighting in the Mediterranean, and had become wary and cunning in the reduction of risk. In fact, although among most of the units which landed in Normandy there was a great initial reservoir of willingness to give of their best, which was exploited to the full in the first days of the campaign, many battalion commanders determined privately, after bloody losses and failures, that they would husband the lives of their men when they were ordered into attack, making private judgments about an operation's value. The war had been in progress for a long time. Now the possibility of surviving it was in distant view. As the campaign progressed therefore, and as the infantry casualty list rose, it became a more and more serious problem for the army commanders to persuade their battalions that the next ridge, tomorrow's map reference, deserved of their utmost.

The débâcle at Villers-Bocage marked, for the British, the end of the scramble for ground that had continued since D-day. The Germans had plugged the last vital hole in their line. Henceforward, for the men who fought in Normandy, the principal memory would be of hard, painful fighting over narrow strips of woodland and meadow, of weeks on end when they contested the same battered grid-squares, the same ruined villages.

In the days following Villers-Bocage, with the remorseless build-up of opposing forces on the Allied perimeter, it was no longer sufficient to consider the commitment of a single division to gain significant ground.

When, on June 26, Second Army began its third attempt to gain Caen by envelopment, Operation EPSOM, the entire VIII Corps was committed to attack on a four-mile front towards the thickly wooded banks of the River Odon. Three of the finest divisions in the British army—15th Scottish, 11th Armoured and 43rd Wessex—were to take part; 60,000 men and more than six hundred tanks supported by over seven hundred guns on land and sea, embarked on the great new offensive.

"The minute hand touched 7:30," wrote a young platoon commander, "concealed guns opened up from fields, hedges and farms in every direction around us, almost as if arranged in tiers. During short pauses between salvos more guns could be heard and, right away, further guns, filling and reverberating the very atmosphere with a sustained, muffled hammering . . . . Little rashes of gooseflesh ran over the skin. One was hot and cold, and very moved. All this stuff in support of us."

In the first hours, VIII Corps achieved penetration on a three-mile frontage. But then, amidst the hedges and hamlets, fierce German resistance developed, and some of the great Scottish regiments of the British army—Gordons, Seaforths, Camerons—began to pour out their best blood for every yard of ground gained.

Nor was the struggle much less painful for the men of the armoured units. A tank wireless operator on the British left flank recorded in his diary on the morning of June 26: "The whole squadron was now in the field, with the tanks scattered around near the hedges. We soon discovered from the wireless that we were in a trap. There appeared to be Tigers and Panthers all round us . . . . then the tank behind us was hit. It was Joe Davis's. I saw a spout of earth shoot up near it as a shot ricocheted through it. Some smoke curled up from the turret, but it didn't actually brew up. We did not know till after that the whole turret crew had been killed . . . ."

On June 28, amidst mud and rain, British tanks at last crossed the bloody stream of the Odon, to gain the heights of Hill 112 the next day. Two panzer divisions, newly arrived from the east, were hurled against them—and driven back. It was a fine fighting achievement by the British divisions and their air support. But, owing to a tragic misreading of the balance of advantage, their withdrawal to the west bank was ordered, and Hill 112 was lost. Montgomery had decided that EPSOM should be closed down. VIII Corps had lost 4,020 men.

One of the most remarkable features of EPSOM, like almost all the Normandy battles, was that its failure provoked no widespread failure of confidence by the troops in their commanders generally, or Montgomery in particular. The men fighting the battles became more cautious in action, but at no time did their faith in the direction of the campaign falter. "We thought the senior officers were marvellous," said Trooper Stephen Dyson. "They had all the responsibility, didn't they?" Lieutenant Andrew Wilson of the Buffs "found it increasingly difficult to see how we should get out of all this—it seemed an absolute deadlock. . . . But when Montgomery passed us one day in his staff car, all my crew stood up in the tank and cheered."

IT IS INTERESTING to turn to German intelligence reports of this period, such as one from Panzer Lehr which declared that "a successful break-in by the enemy was seldom exploited to pursuit. If our own troops were ready near the front for a local counterattack, the ground was immediately regained." A German report from Italy at about this time is also worth quoting, for it reflects similar criticism made by Rommel's officers in Normandy: "The conduct of the battle by the Americans and English was, taken all round, once again very methodical. Local successes were seldom exploited . . . . British attacking formations were split up into large numbers of assault squads commanded by officers. NCOs were rarely in the 'big picture', so that if the officer became a casualty, they were unable to act in accordance with the main plan . . . . The conclusion is: as far as possible *go for the enemy officers*. Then seize the initiative yourself."

Another German report, captured in northwest Europe, was circulated to British senior officers: "The British infantryman," it declared, "is distinguished more by physical endurance than by special bravery. The impetuous attack, executed with dash, is foreign to him."

Battalion and brigade commanders seemed capable of little beyond the conventional set piece assault "by the book". Montgomery made a vain effort to urge British units to show more flexibility in a circular to commanding officers, late in June. He deplored the habit of preparing troops to fight "the normal battle". He wrote: "This tendency is highly dangerous, as there is no such thing as 'the normal battle'. Leaders at all levels must adapt their actions to the particular problems confronting them."

It was of course Montgomery himself who had declared that the British are a martial, not a military, people. There was nothing cowardly about the performance of the British army in Normandy. But it proved too much to ask a citizen army in the fifth year of war, with the certainty of victory in the distance, to display the same sacrificial courage as Hitler's legions, faced with the collapse of everything that, in the perversion of Nazism, they held dear. Individual Allied soldiers proved capable of immense sacrifice and

68

bravery, men who felt that winning the war was their personal responsibility. But the British failure to gain Caen in June 1944 revealed an undeniable weakness of fighting power and tactics within the British army.

The Americans before Cherbourg

Usually a week of intense action suffices to transform most infantrymen from novices into either veterans or casualties. Thus, for the men of Bradley's divisions fighting to expand their beachheads on the Western Front, to secure the Cotentin peninsula, and then to press on to Cherbourg, the first encounters with the enemy amidst the close confinement of the Norman *bocage* proved a testing experience. The huge earthen walls, thick with tree and brush roots, that bordered each field, were impenetrable to tanks, each one a natural line of fortification. In the Cotentin, the difficulties of the ground were compounded by the wide areas of reclaimed marshland impassable to tanks, which were thus restricted to roads.

Following the capture of Isigny and the link-up of the American beaches, the eastern American flank gave the Allied High Command little anxiety in the aftermath of its troubled landings. Instead, all attention was focused northwestwards, upon the struggle of General Collins's VII Corps to secure the Cotentin and press on to Cherbourg.

The German forces in the peninsula might lack the mobility and cohesion to mount a large-scale counterattack against the Utah beachhead, but they could still defend the hedgerows and causeways with bitter tenacity, and launch a succession of local assaults in battalion or regimental strength. June 7 found the airborne divisions still fighting hard to concentrate their scattered companies.

Private Richardson of the 82nd Airborne Division was last described marching through the meadows of the Cotentin on the morning of June 6. By the night of June 7, he was dug into a hedgerow looking out across a field to a wood, amidst the machinegun platoon of his battalion. Moments later, very accurate mortar fire began to fall among them. "Men I had just lain shoulder to shoulder with began screaming in pain, screaming for help, hysterical helpless screams that made my stomach tighten. Because of the apparent protection of the hedgerow and our inexperience, we had not realized the necessity of digging in, and few of us had holes, which would have saved us from all but a direct hit."

That night, the survivors withdrew. The following morning when Richardson returned to the scene of the action with a patrol, he found men dead, others dying; his friend Johnson lying among the medics, wounded in the arm and eye: a farmer who could never farm again. In the days that followed, while the Allied commanders were marking the expansion of the Utah beachhead with perfect equanimity on their maps, among Richardson's little group marooned among the hedges there was a rumour that the invasion had failed. The radar operator wrote to his girlfriend declaring that it was all over with them.

Searching desperately for a German machinegun position in action one morning, Richardson was exasperated to encounter a French farmer who would give him no help or guidance: "He just didn't want to be involved." He began to remember each day and each movement only for the men who died in it: in particular the NCO he most admired, Sergeant Metford. Richardson had told Metford that he was sure that he himself would be killed, but the sergeant had answered that he couldn't afford to think like that: "I can only go on doing this because I just know that I'm going to get home and put my feet under the table and eat a chicken dinner."

One day his platoon came upon a heap of abandoned German bicycles, and in a brief spasm of escape, when they felt as if their whole war was ended, they rode them whooping through a village street like exultant children. Richardson found himself gulping cognac, the first liquor he had tasted in his life. When his unit, and the other survivors of the airborne divisions, were withdrawn from the battle at the beginning of July after thirty-three days in action, his division had suffered forty-six-per-cent casualties.

Private Lindley Higgins of the US 4th Division went into his first attack with his battalion at a tiny village near Ste. Mère-Eglise, three days after the landings. They advanced past the church in their long straggling files, rifles at the port, and rounded a corner to meet a long burst of machinegun fire which seemed to come from their rear. Higgins lay on the ground for a few moments, then scrambled into an archway where he found himself gazing at a large crate of German stick grenades. He was reaching out to pick one up when an NCO knocked his hand away, crying out, "They're booby-trapped!" A big sergeant named Rush suddenly shouted, "Hey, man!" in a moment of utter astonishment, for he found himself hit. Higgins felt unmoved. He had never liked the man. They advanced through the village and into a hedgerowed field, when shellfire began to fall among them—88s, they said, for every new arrival who was shelled in Normandy believed that he was being fired upon by an 88, just as every man who saw a German tank knew at once that it was a Tiger. They lay and prayed for it to end, and their young platoon lieutenant said unhappily, "It doesn't look too good." Late in the afternoon the shelling stopped abruptly and the rest of the regiment moved up behind them. Considerably to their own surprise, they found that they had survived. They had gained a little ground. But it was grindingly slow work.

In the days that followed, the men gradually shed the sense of surprise about all that was happening to them. Major Frank Colacicco of the 18th Infantry Regiment said: "We had been very naive about going into combat. We had felt 'Let's get in there and get it over.' Now we learned, as time went on, that you're not going to win this war in one day." They discovered more about fighting, and about enduring. But they also discovered how pitifully quickly their most energetic officers and NCOs were killed.

The 29th Division's narrative of an action south of Lison on June 11, when two companies of the 175th Infantry advanced across the Vire, perfectly reflects the experience of scores of units in those bitter weeks in the *bocage*, when every yard of ground was gained with such painful slowness.

"It was with difficulty that Major Miller managed to get his heavy machineguns up to a base-of-fire position, to sweep the hedges of the suspected road. The entire command weight of the company at this point rested upon small unit leadership. Could the sergeant make his men do what he wanted? Was the sergeant a leader? Some exemplified all the finer qualities, about one third fell down in this respect. All were handicapped by a general lack of understanding of the situation that confronted them. The enemy never presented himself as a target in this phase, and the fire of the company had, seemingly, little effect on him."

All wars become a matter of small private battles to those who are fighting them. But this was uniquely true of the struggle for Normandy, where it was seldom possible to see more than a hundred yards in any direction, where forward infantry rarely

4

1. For those who fought in the bitter struggle for Caen, the principal memory would be of "hard, painful fighting over narrow strips of wood and meadow, of weeks on end when they contested the same battered grid squares, the same ruined villages." Here British infantry attack from a concealed position near Vimont.

2. After four days with little sleep, Allied troops take a well-earned rest.

3. On patrol to the west of Caen, infantrymen are alert for the first sight or sound of the enemy.

4. An exhausted British doctor pauses between operations at a forward dressing station.

glimpsed their own armour, artillery or higher commanders, where the appalling attrition rate among the rifle companies at the tip of each army's spear was rapidly to become one of the dominant factors of the entire campaign.

Southwards, Carentan fell only on June 12, and it was June 13 before the two American beachheads were at last in firm contact. In the two weeks that followed, although V Corps progressively pushed its perimeter south towards Caumont, American attention still focused upon the drive for Cherbourg, with the critical OVER-LORD objective of gaining the Allies a major port. Already, the American commanders were profoundly conscious that time was slipping away, more German forces were arriving on the battlefield, and the ground was being only slowly gained. Yet the chronic shortage of supplies—above all, of artillery ammunition—was such that First Army could sustain only one major thrust at a time.

Bradley concluded therefore that to strike hard and fast for Cherbourg would be an intolerable risk unless the peninsula was first cut, to isolate the port from German reinforcements. So V Corps launched a drive westwards, completed at the little coastal holiday resort of Barneville on June 18. For many of the Americans, it was an exhilarating dash, infantry clinging to the hulls of the Shermans and tank destroyers as they bucketed across the country-side, meeting only isolated pockets of resistance. German units proved capable of stubborn resistance when defending bunkers against direct assault, but lacked the will or the means to interfere with manoeuvring American units in open country. Also, at that time almost every single German formation of quality was fighting against the British around Caen.

None of this devalues the speed and energy which VII Corps displayed in reaching the port. Their general, Collins, was already revealing himself as the outstanding personality of the campaign. The tenth child of a Louisiana Irish family, he was forty-eight years old, and possessed uncommonly catholic tastes for a soldier. He had travelled widely in Europe and the Far East, was a fine shot and an opera lover. A ruthless driver of men, he sacked unhesitatingly officers of any rank who failed to match his standards. Intolerant of excuses, with a superb eye for opportunity upon the battlefield, he was a commander in a mould from which the American— and British—forces in Normandy could sorely have used more examples.

Just twenty-two hours after gaining Barneville, on June 22, preceded by a massive air bombardment, the Americans opened their attack against the three ridge lines on which the German defence of Cherbourg was centred. Cherbourg's defences had been designed principally to meet an attack from the sea, and the combat efficiency of all the German troops was low. Nevertheless, the enemy's network of strongpoints had to be reduced one by one in dogged fighting, the assaulting infantry scaling the open approaches under withering machinegun fire. Now, in the streets of Cherbourg, they began two days of nerve-racking house-to-house fighting on the road to Fort du Roule.

By the exemplary acts of sacrificial courage which alone enable infantry to seize strongly fortified positions, 9th Division eventually stormed Fort du Roule. When Corporal John Kelly found his platoon pinned down by machinegun fire, he crawled forward to fix a pole charge beneath the German firing slit, but returned to find that it had failed to detonate, and went back with another one. This time, the explosion blew off the protruding gun barrels, enabling the corporal to climb the slope a third time, reach the rear door of the pillbox and grenade it into silence. Kelly was awarded the Congressional Medal of Honor.

Underground in their tunnels and bunkers, thousands of German personnel lay crowded beneath the bombardment: naval ratings, Luftwaffe ground staff—all the ragtag of a huge base, wretchedly conscious of their isolation and demoralized by days amidst the stink of their big generator motors. On a wall map in General von Schlieben's command post, his operations officer Major Forster marked the remorseless progress of the American advance— Collins's men had unknowingly bypassed the Germans' switchboard bunker, leaving their communications intact. On June 26, the unhappy von Schlieben surrendered with eight hundred of his men, when tank destroyers began firing direct into the tunnel entrances above him. But organized resistance in Cherbourg ended only on June 27, and the 9th Division was obliged to fight hard for several days more to reduce the defences of Cap de la Hague, at the northwest tip of the peninsula.

One battalion finally reached the entrance to a huge underground bunker there, seized the single enemy sentry guarding it, and advanced warily inside, pistols in hands, towards the sound of voices. They found themselves in a room full of German officers clustered around a table laden with a large ham. The battalion commander rose to the occasion. "Stop!" he called to his astonished audience. He leaned forward to seize the ham: "I'll take that." The Americans were uncommonly lucky. Other units endured hard fights at Cap de la Hague.

THE REDUCTION OF A "FORTRESS" that Hitler had ordered to resist for months gave sufficient exhilaration to the Allies to mask the bitter disappointment of their commanders when they received the first reports from Cherbourg harbour. There, Bradley's engineers found one of the most comprehensive and ruthless demolition programmes in the history of war. The OVERLORD logistics plan called for Cherbourg to discharge 150,000 tons of stores by July 25. In reality, the port had received less than 18,000 by that date. It was late September before it approached the full operational capacity, by which time almost every harbour in France and Belgium was in the hands of the Allies. The drive for Cherbourg thus failed to achieve its principal strategic purpose of accelerating and securing the Allied build-up.

In the years since 1944 there has been interminable debate about the respective fighting power of the British and American soldier, and its shortcomings as revealed in Normandy. Despite the fine performance of Collins's VII Corps in gaining Cherbourg, each army at large had found it difficult to work up the driving power, the killing force, necessary to break through well-positioned German forces on the battlefield. It ill became either army in Normandy, however, to seek to harp upon the shortcomings of the other—the British sluggishness in gaining Caen or the poor performance of some American divisions in the *bocage*. The truth seems self-evident—that the best British and American units were very good indeed, and perfectly comparable with each other.

The German Army: Stemming the Tide

For every soldier of imagination in the German army, the battle of Normandy represented the last struggle of the war which offered a frail chance of final victory. From all over Europe, throughout the month of June, hundreds of thousands of men, thousands of tanks and vehicles, crawled painfully along the devastated rail network and finally over the roads lined with slit trenches to provide a ready refuge from the inevitable fighter-bomber attacks, to bolster the precarious German line.

On June 6, the Allies had inflicted upon the Germans one of the greatest tactical surprises in the history of warfare. In the weeks that followed, they maintained the greatest of all strategic deceptions by the FORTITUDE operation, diverting attention to the Pas-de-Calais. When Rommel reached his château headquarters after his dash across France on June 6, he issued a prompt and formal protest to Hitler's headquarters about the lack of air and naval support for his battle, but warned Jodl, Hitler's Chief of Operations, that he was still convinced that the main Allied effort would come elsewhere. This mistake imprisoned almost the entire German Fifteenth Army in the Pas-de-Calais until late July. Rommel's efforts meanwhile were dedicated to stemming the Allied tide, throwing into the line every new unit as it reached the battlefront. Above all, he was compelled to employ his armoured forces as links of steel in the sagging chain around the perimeter, rather than being able to concentrate them in the rear for a major counterattack. The armoured divisions reached Normandy first, because they possessed far greater mobility than the infantry, many of whom travelled the last hundred miles to the front on foot. Tanks were immensely effective as strongpoints, but were almost invariably lost wherever the Allies gained ground. They could not be replaced.

Furthermore, each effort to move troops west to meet the threat to Cherbourg was prevented by more urgent needs closer to hand. A sense of desperation began to overcome Rommel. "The invasion is quite likely to start at other places too, soon," he wrote to his wife. "There's simply no answer to it. I reported to the Führer yesterday. Rundstedt is doing the same. It's time for politics to come into play. It will all be over very quickly."

Hitler's visit to Rommel's Soissons headquarters on June 17 enabled him to work his customary magnetic spell upon his field marshal, overcoming the workings of reason. Rommel allowed himself to be encouraged by news of the V-1 offensive on England, lifted by the promise of yet more dramatic new weapons to follow. He was also regaining confidence as he saw the German front stiffening and holding around Caen and Caumont, the panzer formations inflicting heavy casualties upon the Allies and parrying their attacks. The fall of Cherbourg made little impact upon him, for he and von Rundstedt had privately written off the town from the moment Carentan was lost.

On June 28, at the height of the struggle around Caen and the Odon, Rommel once again saw Hitler, this time in Berlin, at the Führer's behest. Hitler's intention, plainly, was again to stiffen the resolve of his commander. He was enraged when Rommel persistently attempted to bring home to him the terrible reality of the situation in Normandy. At last, Rommel said, "*Mein Führer*, I must speak bluntly. I cannot leave here without speaking on the subject of Germany." Hitler said abruptly, "Field Marshal, be so good as to leave the room. I think it would be better like that." It was their last meeting. Once again, the encounter had served to harden Rommel's faltering determination.

On July 2, von Rundstedt resigned his command, after an abrupt hint from Berlin that his health was plainly no longer adequate to his task, and was succeeded by Field Marshal von Kluge, a leathery Prussian veteran of the Eastern Front who immediately sought to assert his own authority over Rommel and to re-establish his command's confidence in their own ability to defend Normandy. Yet by July 13, Rommel was telling Admiral Ruge, "The tragedy of our position is this—we are obliged to fight on to the very end, but all the time we're convinced that it's far more vital to stop the Russians than the Anglo-Americans from breaking into Germany." He judged, with remarkable accuracy, that the German front in Normandy must collapse within a month.

Since June 6, he had lost 2,360 officers and over 94,000 men, while receiving only 6,000 replacements. He had lost two hundred and twenty-five tanks and received seventeen, in addition to the new formations arriving at the front. The ammunition position remained critical. Yet every Allied tank and aircraft lost was replaced within a few hours. "Everywhere our troops are fighting heroically," he reported to von Kluge on July 15, "but the unequal struggle is drawing to its close."

It was at about this date that Rommel began to put out feelers to his commanders about the possibility of some form of negotiation with the Allies, for the first time. Hellmuth Lang was witness to one conversation at which Dietrich, Hitler's old chauffeur and devoted follower, shook Rommel's hand and declared, "You're the boss, *Herr Feldmarschall*. I obey only you—whatever it is you're planning." Then Rommel and his aide climbed back into the big

Horch staff car and raced away towards his headquarters. At around 6:00 pm, near Vimoutiers, a British Typhoon caught them, wounding Rommel's driver and sending the car careering into a tree, throwing its passengers into the road.

Rommel, terribly injured in the head, had ended his career as a battlefield commander, and would be forced to suicide three months later on the evidence of the July 20 conspirators. The field marshal had never been party to their plans, but the evidence that they had considered him a suitable figurehead to lead negotiations with the Allies was sufficient to ensure his death sentence. Von Kluge succeeded him, remaining Commander in Chief West while also assuming command of Army Group B.

THROUGHOUT HIS TENURE of command in Normandy, Rommel directed the defence of the German front to formidable effect, filling the critical gaps and rushing forward units to stem dangerous Allied attacks. But there was no evidence in his handling of the battle of a great commander making brilliant strokes which confounded the enemy. Rommel played the part of a firefighter with all the energy at his command, and it is difficult to see how any other commander could have achieved more, given the limitations of his resources and orders.

Once the Allies were firmly established ashore, the only sane strategic course open to the Germans was precisely that which Hitler's madness would not allow—a progressive, carefully ordered retirement, causing the Allies to fight hard for every gain. The Germans would have been relieved of one immense handicap if they could have fought beyond the range of Allied naval gunfire. Southern France could have been abandoned, releasing invaluable forces to support the decisive battle in Normandy.

As things were, however, Hitler's generals were never permitted to assess their military predicament freely, and to act in accordance with their findings. Every act of military planning was conducted within the straitjacket of Hitler's manic instructions, running contrary to reality and logic. The German generals were conducting a campaign in which they had no faith after the first days, by methods wholly inimical to all their instincts and training. It is difficult to believe that anything they might have done, in these circumstances, would significantly have altered the course of events.

1. One of the greatest perils in Normandy was dust, which could bring down a deadly rain of enemy fire.

2. British Sherman tanks pass through St. Aubin in pursuit of the enemy, on the afternoon of June 6.

3. US infantrymen in an attack on a Norman village.

4. After a month of bitter and repeated attacks, the ancient city of Caen was tragically reduced to ruins.

THE GLORY OF GERMAN ARMS in Normandy—and it was glory, in however evil a cause—was gained by the officers and men at divisional level and below, who held the line against the Allies under intolerable conditions for more than two months. And no division fought with more tenacity than that of the Hitler Youth, the average age of whose soldiers was eighteen and a half.

"It was a situation for despair, but there was no alternative but to keep one's nerve," said Colonel Heinz Guderian, son of the great panzer leader and senior staff officer of 116th Panzer Division. "One had to hold before one's eyes the memory of Frederick the Great, and perhaps also to think of the words of that American general who said that the man who wins a battle is he who can remain standing until the last five minutes."

Fritz Langangke's tank platoon of 2nd SS Panzer Division was posted in reserve early in July, when they were suddenly ordered forward in a crisis move to meet a new American breakthrough. He asked for the position of the main battleline and was told that this was unknown. Late in the evening, he led his five Panthers cautiously forward, each commander straining his eyes and ears, above the roar of his engine and the squealing of the tracks, for a hint of the enemy. At last there was a rattle of small arms fire against the hull of Langangke's tank, and he concluded that he had come far enough. The platoon pulled back to deploy on each side of the road, hull down behind a hedge. "It was a pretty tight night," said the German. The crews sat absolutely silent in their tanks, listening constantly for movement in front of them. At dawn, despite their careful camouflage, one of the ubiquitous American Piper Cubs pinpointed them, and artillery fire began to fall around the position. Conventional wisdom demanded that the tanks should fall back at nightfall, but Langangke understood that there could be no such refinements here, where the tanks were being employed as strongpoints and where their moral support was essential to stiffen the infantry even of an SS division.

The tank platoon held its position for two weeks, under constant artillery fire. At night, when they risked crawling out of the vehicles for an hour or two of merciful release, they could hear the American convoys moving up with supplies, and hear American voices across the still summer air. Once, the Allied troops attempted an infantry attack in a fashion which astonished the German veterans. They marched forward in long, leisurely files towards the Panthers "as if they were going to a carnival." The SS opened a withering fire, and the attack crumpled.

Yet it would be absurd to give the impression that the German soldier found Normandy an easy, or even a tolerable battle. While many men said later that it was an incomparably less terrible experience than the war in the east, hurling themselves again and again into action against the great steamroller of Allied resources shook even veterans very deeply.

2nd Panzer Division reported in July on the difficulties they faced: "The incredibly heavy artillery and mortar fire of the enemy is something new, for seasoned veterans as much as for the new arrivals from reinforcement units. The assembly of troops is spotted immediately by enemy reconnaissance aircraft and smashed by bombs and artillery directed from the air; and if, nevertheless, the attacking troops go forward, they become involved in such dense artillery and mortar fire that heavy casualties ensue and the attack peters out within the first few hundred metres. The losses suffered by the infantry are then so heavy that the impetus necessary to renew the attack is spent.

"Our soldiers enter the battle in low spirits at the thought of the enemy's enormous superiority of *matériel*. The feeling of helplessness against enemy aircraft operating without hindrance has a paralysing effect; and during the barrage the effect on the inexperienced men is literally soul-shattering. The best results have been obtained by platoon and section commanders leaping forward uttering a good old-fashioned yell. We have also revived the practice of bugle calls."

It is important to emphasize that by no means the entire German front in France was in the hands of these elite formations. Many German infantrymen, in fact, were happy to seize an opportunity to be taken prisoner. They developed what they themselves called sardonically "the German look", ever craning upwards into the sky, watchful for fighter-bombers. They prayed for rain and cloud to keep the *jabos* away from them. Their greatest luxury was the capture of a few American soup cubes or tins of coffee. They were jealously scornful of the Allies' material riches. Few German soldiers even of moderate units, it is fair to say, felt great respect for the fighting qualities of their enemies. Corporal Adolf Hohenstein of 276th Infantry said that his men were constantly puzzled, when they faced the Americans, by their reluctance to exploit success.

"We felt that they always overestimated us. We could not understand why they did not break through."

Undoubtedly the Germans were much more efficient than the Americans in making use of available manpower. In a panzergrenadier division in 1944-45, 89.4 per cent of the men were fighting soldiers, against only 65.56 per cent in an American division. In June 1944, 54.35 per cent of the German army consisted of fighting soldiers, against 38 per cent of the American army. Even the British, who possessed nothing like the Americans' vast supply of manpower, traditionally employed officers on a far more lavish scale than the German army, with its emphasis upon NCO leadership.

Events on the Normandy battlefield demonstrated that most British or American troops continued a given operation for as long as reasonable men could. Then—when they had fought for many hours and suffered many casualties, or were running low on fuel or ammunition—they disengaged. The story of German operations, however, is marked by repeated examples of what could be achieved by soldiers prepared to attempt *more* than reasonable men could, to try to do more than had been asked of them.

The German soldier was denied the sustaining force granted to the Allied armies—the certainty of final victory. But, as Corporal Hohenstein claimed, he and others were motivated above all by, "two words—'unconditional surrender'. If for the rest of my life I was to chop wood in Canada or Siberia, then I would sooner die in Normandy." There is no doubt that President Roosevelt's insistence upon a public declaration of the unconditional surrender doctrine was of immense value to the Nazi propaganda machine: it stifled many Germans' private hopes of some honourable escape after the war. They believed that defeat in Normandy, and beyond that defeat in Europe, would inaugurate a new dark age for Germany. There is little doubt that the natural obedience and dedication of the German soldier exceeded any such qualities among most men of the Allied armies. He was a soldier, and therefore he fought.

The Battlefield

By the last days of June, the battle for Normandy had become a struggle involving more than a million men pitted against each other on a front of scarcely a hundred miles. The Allied armies required 26,000 tons of stores *a day* to sustain them in action.

By August, the numbers would be over 2,000,000. Every man who approached the French coast that summer was overwhelmed by the panorama of shipping that met his eye, the ferries shuttling out to the transports with cargoes of dejected German prisoners, the huge caissons and heavily gunned piers of the two Mulberry harbours which had been constructed in Britain and then towed across the Channel.

In fact, there will always be grave doubt as to whether the Mulberries justified the enormous cost and effort that was put into them. Their scale fascinated and impressed contemporary servicemen but recent researchers have focused much more closely upon the American achievement of unloading stores at a greater rate directly across the beaches than had been managed across the Mulberry before the American harbour was wrecked in the "great storm" of June 19-23. The storm itself, treated by some chroniclers as a veritable cataclysm, has also been the subject of modern dispute. At no time, it has been pointed out, did the winds exceed force six, a moderate blow by nautical standards. The inability of the Mulberries to withstand it—for the British harbour was also severely damaged—seems to reflect more upon the strength of the structures rather than upon the nature of the gales. It is likely that Allied unloading operations could have been shielded from the sea just as effectively merely by sinking the screen of blockships and creating a network of piers, rather than by devoting the labour of 45,000 men to building the Mulberries. Some of the same doubts apply to another celebrated innovation, PLUTO—Pipe Line Under The Ocean—a device for pumping petrol direct from England to the armies in France. It was forty-one days before PLUTO was in position. A few weeks later its submerged couplings gave way and a new line had to be laid from Dungeness to Boulogne. This began to yield 700 tons of fuel a day only in January 1945.

Inland from the beaches, newly arrived men gaped at the vast dumps of fuel, ammunition, supplies, the parked ranks of brand-new tanks, vehicles, guns that crowded every field. Uncamouflaged, their existence was a formidable tribute to the Allies' absolute command of the air.

The rear areas were littered with signs—divisional symbols and direction markers: cautionary, KEEP TO SWEPT PATH or roughly daubed, FRONT LINE NO VEHICLES FORWARD OF HERE, or simply

85

DUST MEANS DEATH: among the greatest perils was the dust thrown up by speeding convoys, bringing down a deadly rain of German artillery fire. Infantry cursed the proximity of their own tanks or artillery for the same reason, and took pains to avoid occupying positions near a major signals unit, for fear of German radio locators and the fire that they could call down. Every German signaller testified to the carelessness of Allied soldiers on the air, especially the Canadians and some American units, whose easy chatter provided priceless intelligence.

Among the fighting soldiers, there were few diversions between battles except strolling in the fields or visiting a nearby village to buy milk or eggs; they could write home; drown themselves in the ubiquitous calvados and cider; play cards; or talk interminably. Most Normans treated the fighting armies with impartial disdain or occasional kindness, but it was not remarkable that so many French families were shocked and appalled by the cost of liberation to their own homes, for there was looting among both the Allied and German armies. Hundreds of soldiers paid the price of recklessly ignoring warnings about German booby traps, failing to see tripwires between hedges and charges linked to tempting booty on abandoned farmhouse tables.

Some soldiers found solace in religion. Frank Svboda, a Presbyterian chaplain with the US 79th Division, was moved by the manner in which his services were attended impartially by Protestants, Jews, and Catholics clutching their rosaries. Good chaplains were greatly prized by their units, but bad ones—of whom there were many in the Allied armies—were detested for the hypocrisy with which they offered their blessings from the rear echelon. Frank Svboda felt that the best aid he possessed in cementing relations with his men was a little axe he had bought in England, and which they found invaluable for hacking off the stubborn hedgerow roots as they dug foxholes. "Chaplain pass the hatchet!" became a unit catchphrase.

With the coming of night, men lay down to sleep beneath the stars, wrapped in a blanket in their foxholes or the nearest ditch. Most tank crews stretched out a tarpaulin from the hull of their vehicle and slept beneath it. Some felt safer lying under the tank itself, although enthusiasm for this practice diminished when the bad weather came and a number of men were found in the morning crushed by the vast weight of steel subsiding into the soft ground

86

above them as they slept. The mosquitoes plagued them, and made a laughingstock of the cream issued for their suppression. There were other natural miseries: swarms of flies and wasps; the dysentery from which many men suffered despite the heavy use of chlorine in the water; and the lice.

For the gunners, the greatest strain lay in the shattering noise of their own artillery, and the physical sweat of shifting ninety-five-pound 155mm projectiles day after day, stripped to the waist and working like automatons through the bombardment before a big attack. In fact, their risk of death or mutilation was small—very small, by comparison with that of the infantry.

Much the most hazardous gunnery task was that of forward observer, either working with the infantry, spotting from the steel towers erected around Caen, or flying an American Piper or British Auster. The pilots droned slowly up and down the line at 120 mph, normally 1000 feet up and 1000 yards behind the front. They seldom glimpsed men below, more often the quick flash of German guns or a brief movement of vehicles. Then the pilot called his battery: "Hello Foxtrot 3, I have a mike target for you." When the guns warned him that they were ready, he called the firing order and watched the ground below for explosions. Then he radioed any corrections, until shells were bracketing the target. One British spotter pilot, Captain Geoffrey Ivon-Jones, said he developed a personal affection for some of the batteries for which he spotted, above all the 79th Scottish Horse, which prided itself on its smartness. Circling above them in action, the pilot could see the tiny figure of the gun position officer standing with his battery, giving the signal to fire with a sweep of his white silk handkerchief.

Tragic accidents were part of the small change of the battle. One day, spotting for a warship, Ivon-Jones found that the naval gunners were reading the directional "clock" messages upside down, and shelling British positions. He and the other pilots flew perhaps four or five forty-minute sorties a day, ever watchful for German fighters. Some Allied fliers became so accustomed to regarding every aircraft as friendly that the Luftwaffe could spring lethal surprises. "What are those, Geordie?" Captain Harry Bordon asked his observer. "Spitfires, sir," came the cheerful reply, seconds before five ME109s shot them down.

Although the Luftwaffe possessed no power to impede Allied operations seriously, it was still capable of causing considerable

1. While the British struggled to capture Caen, the Americans launched their drive to cut off Cherbourg and extend the western sector south of St. Lô. Here, GIs advance behind cover of a tank.

2. A US mortar crew directs its fire on enemy positions.

3. A German Tiger tank lies abandoned on the road to St. Lô after repeated dive bombing attacks by British Typhoons.

4. Normandy was a battlefield of hedges and ditches, a succession of nightmarish dashes between islands of cover.

irritation, and even acute fear, among men living and working on their principal targets, the beaches. Each night up to fifty Luftwaffe aircraft droned overhead, bombing at random yet with the near certainty of hitting something in the vastly crowded perimeter. The Americans called the night visitation "Bedcheck Charlie", and lay down in their gas masks, because of the great smokescreen that was ignited to shroud the piers from enemy bomb aimers. The German pilots called the invasion coast "Golden City", because of the dazzling array of tracer lacing the darkness offshore.

After the enormous initial excitement of the landings, the quick capture of Bayeux, the dramatic seizure of Cherbourg and clearance of the northern peninsula, the mood among the men of the Allied armies slowly changed, stiffened as the lines of battle congealed. Among the greatest strains on them was the sheer length of the summer days—from 4:45 am to 11:15 pm in the first June weeks. Men discovered that they could sleep on their feet under bombardment, in their tanks, on the march. Fatigue, and the struggle to overcome it, ruled their lives.

For the tank crews, even in battle, there were hours sitting motionless, closed down beneath their hatches, firing an occasional shell. Inside their hulls, they were vulnerable only to direct hits from artillery or mortar fire, but they were often more ignorant than the infantry of what was taking place around them.

The tank men pitied the infantry, their bodies naked to every form of high explosive, just as most foot soldiers preferred the comfort of their slit trenches to facing the enemy in a vast, noisy steel box which seemed to ignite instantly when hit. Tank crews could carry all manner of private comforts and extra rations with them, and despite strict orders against cooking inside the tanks in action, all of them did so, brewing up on the floor of the turret.

Inevitably, every forward unit suffered a steady drain of casualties from snipers, mortaring and artillery fire, which both sides employed daily to maintain pressure upon each other. It is important to remember that throughout the campaign, even in sectors where neither side was carrying out a major offensive, there were constant local attacks.

To emphasize the immense weight of firepower that the Allies employed in support of their movements, it is worth mentioning a minor operation near Cristot on June 16. Throughout the night of June 15-16, the German positions to be attacked were subjected to harassing fire. In the early morning of June 16, naval guns fired on the objectives, and Typhoons rocketed and strafed them. A squadron of tanks provided covering fire for the assault from the flank, while a company of heavy mortars shelled selected German positions. The attack itself was supported by seven field regiments of 25-pounders, and four regiments of medium guns. At noon on June 16, the attacking battalion advanced two companies at the normal infantry pace of twenty-five yards a minute, a troop of tanks accompanying each company. At 1:15 pm the battalion passed through Cristot, where it reorganized. They found seventeen German dead in the village, and two armoured cars and one soft-skinned vehicle destroyed. The British had lost three killed and twenty-four wounded. A few hundred yards of fields and ruins had been gained, at uncommonly small cost in British life. But the weight of firepower that had been deployed to make it possible was staggering.

Snipers were detested: their activities provoked as much irrational resentment as the killing of baled-out tank crews or parachutists in mid-descent. Both sides habitually shot snipers who were taken prisoner. "Brad says he will not take any action against anyone who decides to treat snipers a little more roughly than they are being treated at present," wrote the First Army Commander's ADC in his diary. Much has been made of the shooting of prisoners by 12th SS Panzer and other German units in Normandy, yet it must be said that propaganda has distorted the balance of guilt. Among scores of Allied witnesses interviewed for this narrative, almost every one had direct knowledge or even experience of the shooting of German prisoners during the campaign. In the heat of battle, in the wake of seeing so many comrades die, many men found it intolerable to send prisoners to the rear knowing that they would thus survive the war, while they themselves seemed to have little prospect of doing so. Many British and American units shot SS prisoners routinely, which might explain why so few appeared in POW cages. The 6th King's Own Scottish Borderers never forgave or forgot the action of a wounded SS soldier to whom Major John Ogilvie leaned down to give water. The German drank, then shot the British officer.

Beyond those who left the battlefield as prisoners or never left it alive at all, hundreds of thousands of men were more or less seriously wounded. Indeed, it became an astonishing achievement for an infantryman who had landed on D-day to remain with his unit uninjured into July. As the doctors and medical teams handled hundreds of cases each day—aided by unprecedented facilities, and above all by the miracle of penicillin—they found that many lightly wounded men were deeply relieved to escape the battlefield with honour. For most men, the need to continue the job to sustain their own self-respect was the principal motivating force.

In the field hospitals, doctors and nurses toiled over the procession of wounded men laid before them in the tents, cutting away mudstained battledress and bloody boots to reveal the interminable tragedies beneath. "Stepping over splinted limbs and stretcher handles," wrote Sister Brenda McBryde, "we moved to the next man, a penetrating wound of the chest, needing a large firm dressing to contain those ominous sucking noises, and another pillow to keep him upright. Lieutenant Colonel Harding, one stretcher ahead with Audrey Dare, kept up a running commentary: 'Stomach here. Put him number one. Quarter of morphia, Sister, straight away. Two pints of blood, one of plasma . . .' Gunshot, mortar blasts, mines, incendiaries. Limbs, eyes, abdomen, chest. He chewed his pencil. Who had priority? Of all these desperately wounded men, whose need was the most urgent?"

Although "battle fatigue" and other psychiatric casualties never reached epidemic proportions in the British army, every unit in Normandy suffered its share of men who found themselves utterly unwilling to endure more. One morning as Charles Mundy and his fellow troop commanders of the 22nd Dragoon Guards stood in their turrets on the start line before an attack, they were astonished to hear the silence broken by a brief burst of Sten gun fire. A man had simply shot himself in the foot rather than endure the assault. A company commander in Major Randall Bryant's battalion of the US 9th Division reported to him, to declare flatly, "I've had it. You can do anything you want, but I won't go back." Men seldom despised or scorned those who were driven to these acts—they merely pitied them, and prayed that they themselves might not be driven to such extremities.

Every infantryman feared falling victim to a TOT—Time on Target, an artillery shoot carefully synchronized to concentrate the fire of an entire battery or regiment at a precise moment. Major Randall Bryant was walking across an orchard near St. Lô, his closest friend Captain Charles Minton beside him. "Suddenly everything was exploding. There was blood all over me, and a helmet on the ground with a head inside it. It was Minton's. Three young 2nd lieutenants had just joined us, straight from the beach. I had told them to sit down and wait to be assigned to companies. They were dead, along with six others killed and thirty-three wounded, in a shoot that lasted only a matter of seconds."

The ambitions of most men in Normandy were pathetically simple: to survive, to finish the job, and to go home.

BY EARLY JULY, the struggle for Normandy was inflicting almost equal dismay upon the German, British and American armies—the first having overwhelmingly greater cause for it. The defenders knew that their forces were being relentlessly ground down, and that they could not hope for tolerable replacements. Many of their difficulties of manpower, armour and supplies were known to the Allies through ULTRA. Yet it was small comfort to read the Germans' gloomy signals about their predicament when, on the battlefield, the effectiveness of their resistance seemed in no way diminished. Meanwhile, the invaders were growing visibly weary, and the problem of infantry casualties, a matter of concern to the Americans, had become an issue of crisis for the British. Already battalions had been broken up to fill the ranks of others in the line. Now there was a threat of disbanding entire divisions.

After the excitement of the capture of Cherbourg, a new southward American offensive began on July 3 in driving rain, mist and low cloud. In the first days, it bogged down amidst all the now-familiar difficulties of untried formations and stubborn defensive tactics destroying momentum.

Meanwhile on the eastern flank, the British Second Army was fighting CHARNWOOD, a tough, slow-moving battle that did at last gain its men a large part of the ruins of the old city of Caen, which had recently borne the brunt of a massive air attack. The infantry had won through to the bank of the River Orne, but they could go no further, and the Germans still held the critical high ground of the Bourgébus Ridge to the south.

Further west, 43rd Wessex and its supporting armour were fighting for Hill 112, the commanding position beyond the Odon which had been lost in the last stages of EPSOM, at the end of June. It was a battle of shattering intensity even by the standards of Normandy. Even so, the hill was held only briefly before being lost yet again to a German counterattack.

MONTGOMERY WAS NOW compelled to endure a crisis of confidence in his leadership which would have cracked the nerve of a more sensitive man. He had always been the object of animosity within the headquarters staff in England, and unloved by many of Bradley's Americans. Now, even the American press had become openly impatient about the lack of progress in France. It was being suggested that the Western Allies were content to mark time while the Russians did the hard fighting to defeat Hitler's armies. Even more dangerous to Montgomery's position was the growing impatience of Churchill, who had convinced himself that if there was no rapid breakthrough after D-day, it might be a year or more before the Allies reached the Seine. The prime minister was at pains to remind Eisenhower, a few days after the landings, that the supreme commander had only to express his dissatisfaction with any British officer "no matter what his rank" for him to be removed.

With all these dangerous currents swirling in his rear, in the caravans of his tactical headquarters, shrouded by camouflage netting in a Norman field, Montgomery sat amidst his pet puppies and canaries and pondered the course of the battle. And, on July 10, he approved a plan to employ massed armour in a final attempt to break through the German defences overlooking Caen.

The details of Operation GOODWOOD were settled: all three British armoured divisions would attack under the command of General O'Connor's VIII Corps, along a corridor blasted open by massed bomber forces. The aim was to strike fast through the German defences while the enemy were still reeling from the air bombardment, seize the Bourgébus Ridge and then race on southwards across the great sweep of open country beyond. The tanks would drive headlong for Falaise. Meanwhile, the Canadian infantry would attack south from the centre of Caen, in an effort to secure the rest of the city.

Every previous operation that Montgomery had mounted in Normandy was skilfully conceived, and offered a real prospect of success. Yet from its inception GOODWOOD was flawed. The plan relied heavily upon surprise to gain the high ground which dominated the British line of advance, yet called for the movement of 8,000 tanks and armoured vehicles across the Orne to the assembly points. Moreover, only narrow corridors in the minefields would be available through which the tanks could move forward. But most damning of all, the Germans were expecting them. Long before the tanks began to roll from the start line, German intelligence had achieved one of its few important battlefield successes in Normandy, alerting Rommel to the imminent British move against Bourgébus. General Eberbach of Panzer Group West reacted by adopting perhaps the most formidable defensive deployments of the entire campaign: five lines of tanks and anti-tank guns, directly confronting VIII Corps's axis of advance.

Between 5:30 and 8:30 am on the morning of July 18, one of the greatest-ever air bombardments against ground forces was unleashed upon Panzer Group West, by bombers of the RAF and USAAF. Tanks were hurled bodily into the air or buried by earth and rubble, men deafened and stunned for days or blasted into fragments, guns were wrecked and twisted on their mountings, fuel and ammunition exploded.

Nevertheless, one of the great surprises of warfare in the twentieth century has been the power of soldiers to survive even overwhelming concentrations of high explosive and emerge to fight with skill and determination. So it was now with the men of Panzer Group West. The leading British units of 11th Armoured Division jumped off promptly at 7:30 am and made rapid progress at first, then found themselves meeting heavy, stiffening resistance. As British units crossed the Caen to Vimont railway embankment and attempted to push on towards Bourgébus, they met ruthless German tank and anti-tank fire. The vehicle carrying 11th Armoured's sole RAF forward air controller was knocked out in the first two hours, causing the loss of close air support for the advance. Meanwhile, several armoured divisions had been seriously delayed by the huge traffic jam of vehicles moving along the corridor through the British minefields, losing a total of one hundred and eighty-six tanks in the day. Without support, the British spearhead of 29th Armoured Brigade was already in serious trouble, only 12,000 yards from its start line.

The Canadians were particularly bitter about the disappointments of the battle, even though in fact they had gained most of Caen. "GOODWOOD had been sold to us as a big deal," said Corporal Dick Raymond of 3rd Canadian Division. "To see those Shermans puffing into black smoke gave us a sick feeling in the stomach. It seemed a futile, clumsy thing." The Canadian operation on the GOODWOOD flank cost 1,965 casualties, and the Germans remained in absolute control of the Bourgébus Ridge. Two days later, after further brutal fighting, 7th Armoured Division gained part of the ridge, but heavy rain and mud now made the closure of the operation inevitable, and the German line was still unbroken. The Allies had suffered 5,537 casualties and lost four hundred tanks. So prodigious were Allied reserves of *materiel* that replacements reached almost every armoured division within thirty-six hours. The restoration of Montgomery's prestige would take a great deal longer.

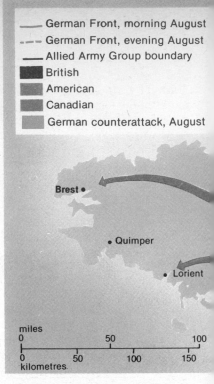

The Great Allied Breakout

MONTGOMERY'S BEHAVIOUR throughout this period seemed dominated by the belief that he could afford to spurn Eisenhower, whose unfittedness for field command was apparent to every senior officer. It is undoubtedly true that even Bradley, the most loyal and patient of men, was irked by Eisenhower's inability to "read" the battle that was taking place in Normandy. The supreme commander laboured under a vague misapprehension that he himself could best serve the Allied cause by touring the touchline like a football coach, urging his generals to keep attacking more or less simultaneously.

Eisenhower's personal lifestyle, journeying between fronts with a ragbag of sycophantic staff officers, his Irish driver, his mistress, and occasionally his newly commissioned son and cosseted pet dog, was more suggestive of an eighteenth century European monarch going to war than of a twentieth century general.

Yet Dwight Eisenhower was the supreme commander of the Allied armies, the man upon whom hung the fervent hopes of two governments for the unity and success of their armies. His charm and statesmanship had impressed, even moved, all those who

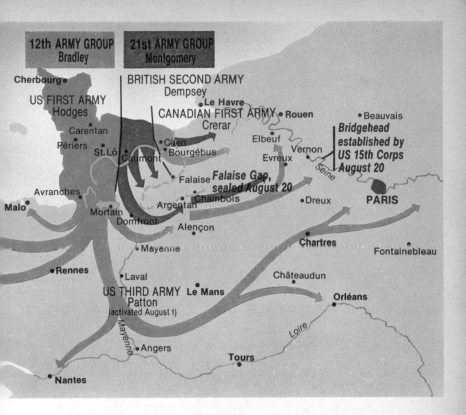

12th ARMY GROUP
Bradley

21st ARMY GROUP
Montgomery

Cherbourg

US FIRST ARMY
Hodges

BRITISH SECOND ARMY
Dempsey

Le Havre

CANADIAN FIRST ARMY
Crerar

Rouen

Beauvais

Carentan

Périers

St. Lô

Caumont

Caen

Bourgébus

Elbeuf

Vernon

Evreux

*Bridgehead
established by
US 15th Corps
August 20*

Seine

Avranches

Falaise *Falaise Gap,
sealed August 20*

Malo

Mortain

Domfront

Chambois

Argentan

Alençon

Dreux

PARIS

Mayenne

Chartres

Fontainebleau

Rennes

Laval

US THIRD ARMY
Patton
(activated August 1)

Le Mans

Châteaudun

Orléans

Mayenne

Angers

Tours

Loire

Nantes

worked closely with him. Montgomery's inability to establish a personal relationship with the American, to confide to him his own private hopes and fears for the battle, cost him dear. He made the error of believing that the supreme commander could be side-stepped, deluded, soft-talked into leaving himself, Montgomery, the supreme professional, to fight the war. He might indeed have been successful in this had his armies on the battlefield fulfilled his early hopes in Normandy. But when they did not, it was Eisenhower, fretting impotently in England, who bore the impatience of the American press, the doubts and fears of the politicians, the charges of failure of generalship which the ignorant attributed to him. There is no doubt that by late July, Eisenhower was weary to death of his ground force commander.

Admittedly, it is impossible to imagine that Montgomery could have been sacked without inflicting an intolerable blow to British national confidence: he whom propaganda has made mighty, no man may readily cast aside. But it is difficult to guess what new pressures and directives might have been forced upon the commander in chief of 21st Army Group had not the perspective of the Normandy campaign now been entirely transformed by the Americans' Operation COBRA.

The Breakout

Throughout the first half of July, while the British and Canadians were fighting their bitter battles around Caen, the Americans were enduring equal pain and frustration in their efforts to disentangle themselves from the clinging misery of the French hedgerows. "We were flabbergasted by the *bocage*," said General Quesada of IXth Tactical Air Command, who was working daily alongside Bradley. "Our infantry had become paralysed. It has never been adequately described how immobilized they were by the sound of small arms fire among those hedges."

It had become brutally apparent to every man in First Army that service in an infantry unit or tank crew was almost a sentence of death. 90th Division suffered 150-per-cent officer replacements and over 100 per cent among enlisted men, in its first six weeks in action. Typical tank casualty figures showed that in June alone, the 746th Battalion lost forty-four out of fifty-one, in twenty-three days of action.

Yet, even as First Army's difficulties seemed at their greatest, the transformation of American fortunes was at hand. Together with General Collins of VII Corps, Bradley had conceived a new plan. To clear the way for a major offensive, Collins's men began to push forward to the St. Lô to Périers road. By July 20, they had reached positions commanding it. On July 18, the Americans had gained the vital heights of St. Lô. The battle for the shattered rubble of the town was one of First Army's outstanding feats of arms in the campaign. The German 352nd Division, whose presence had wrought such havoc with American plans at the beachhead on June 6, was now in ruins, and the stage was set for the supreme American military achievement of the Normandy campaign, Operation COBRA.

IN CONTRAST TO THE USUAL American preference for broad front assaults, COBRA was to be a narrow, concentrated attack on a 7,000-yard front, immediately preceded by a massive air bombardment. The fighter-bombers would concentrate on hitting forward German defences in a two-hundred-and-fifty-yard belt immediately south of the road. General Spaatz's "heavies" would bomb to a depth of 2,500 yards behind the German front, accompanied by the artillery fire of a thousand guns. Breakthrough would be followed by a turn to the right, enveloping five or six divisions.

The Americans' principal secret weapon for COBRA was the "Rhino"—a set of steel tusks welded onto the front of many of the Shermans, which had been found capable of battering a path through the Norman hedgerows in heartening fashion. It is difficult to overstate the importance of the Rhinos, for they restored battle-field manoeuvrability to Bradley's armour. Henceforth, while the German tanks remained restricted to the roads, the Shermans possessed the power to outflank them, across country.

COBRA was launched on July 25, following a short delay caused by torrential rain. At 9:38 am the fighter-bombers opened their first twenty-minute assault on the German front line. Behind them, high above the dust and smoke, 1,800 heavy bombers of 8th Air Force droned slowly towards the target area, their glinting wings watched by thousands of expectant young Americans below, massed ready to move when the airmen had finished.

"As we watched," wrote the war correspondent Ernie Pyle, "there crept into our consciousness a realization that banks of exploding bombs were easing back towards us, flight by flight, instead of gradually forward, as the plan called for. Then we were horrified by the suspicion that these machines, high in the sky and completely detached from us, were aiming their bombs at the smokeline on the ground, and a gentle breeze was drifting the smokeline back over us!"

Bradley had asked that the bombers attack east-west, out of the sun and parallel to the front, to reduce the risk of short-bombing or "creepback" as the British called it. The airmen, for their own reasons, came in north-south. Despite desperate efforts by the ground troops to identify their positions with yellow panels and smoke markers, there was wild bombing by 8th Air Force, with appalling consequences for the men below. Some enraged American units opened fire on their own aircraft, a not uncommon practice by all the armies in Normandy when they suffered at Allied pilots' hands. The entire command group of the 9th Division's 3rd/47th Infantry was wiped out. Maddened men were forcibly carried to the rear. Others merely ran blindly from the battlefield. Maimed men lay screaming for aid.

Amid the shambles created by the bombing of their own forward areas, VII Corps's attack began hesitantly, men moving slowly forward to discover to their dismay that the Panzer Lehr division before them was battered, but still unbroken. Units found themselves entangled in protracted firefights against strongpoints and networks of foxholes held by the customary German mix of a handful of tanks, a body of infantry, and the inevitable 88mm guns.

Yet even in these first encounters, General Collins found cause for encouragement. While the German positions were resisting fiercely, they did not appear to form a continuous belt of defences. They could be outflanked, bypassed. In contrast to the meticulously prepared succession of defensive positions with which the Germans on the Bourgébus Ridge met GOODWOOD, here they retained only a crust. It was a tribute to the efforts of the British and Canadians that von Kluge's fears and principal forces were still decisively fixed upon the eastern flank, around Caen. General Fritz Bayerlein of the Panzer Lehr division was enraged to receive a visit from a staff officer of von Kluge's, conveying the field marshal's order that the St. Lô to Périers line must be held; not a single man must leave his position, for a battalion of Panthers was on its way. Bayerlein said flatly, "Out in front every one is holding out. Every one. My grenadiers and my engineers and my tank crews—not a single man is leaving his post. They are lying silent in their foxholes, for they are dead. You may report to the field marshal that the Panzer Lehr division is annihilated." Bayerlein's remarks were only slightly exaggerated.

By the afternoon of July 25, Collins had learned enough about the vulnerability of the Germans to risk giving the order for his mobile columns to start moving. The offensive was gaining momentum with every hour. Sergeant Hans Stober and his company of 17th SS Panzergrenadiers had been ordered to hold their positions for twenty-four hours. "But we found that American units in company strength had bypassed us. There was no choice but to order us to withdraw." So it was, as darkness fell, for thousands of German soldiers the length of the line.

Next morning a sense of exhilaration such as they had not known since Cherbourg was overtaking the Americans, who were dashing through villages which welcomed them with all the warmth of civilians whose homes and possessions had not been devastated. The infantry clung to the tank hulls and sat up in the trucks, waving wildly to French onlookers as they raced southwestwards, the blackened German vehicles by the roadside testifying to the efforts of the fighter-bombers clearing the roads in front of them.

But the offensive now entered a new and bloodier phase. As the American columns lay strung out over miles of unfamiliar country, German units began to fight with all their customary ferocity to escape entrapment. At last von Kluge was moving reinforcements from the eastern flank. On the night of July 29, American elements found themselves fighting for their lives near St. Denis-le-Gast, against a panzer column which had smashed through their lines in the darkness. Other men of the same American units were attacked near Cambry the same night, and fought for six hours. But now First Army knew that they were dominating the battlefield, that the German assaults reflected the thrashing of desperate men rather than a threat to the American front.

Lieutenant Fritz Langangke of 2nd SS Panzer was ordered to rendezvous with a paratroop unit at a crossroads which was to be held open until evening. He arrived to find no sign of the infantry, and was reinforced only by a single tank, that of his company commander. They camouflaged the Panthers and deployed to cover the road. A Sherman appeared, Langangke fired, but the first round missed. While the American seemed to hesitate, Langangke fired again and hit. The Sherman's commander was still standing uncertainly upright in his turret when his tank caught fire, and the second Panther accounted for the two behind it. Mist, most unusual for the season, was drifting across the road, and Langangke was shocked to see Germans moving out of the haze towards the Americans with their hands up. They were the infantry he had expected to meet—"They had taken their chance to finish the war."

On July 30, General Rose's 2nd Armored approached the town of Percy, which lay in a hollow surrounded by hills. At about 4:30 in the afternoon, a cluster of American tank commanders and infantry officers were at the bottom of the hill preparing to advance, unconscious of serious opposition in the area. Some of the tank crews were out of their vehicles, cheerfully milking cows in a field.

Suddenly the entire area erupted under German mortar fire. Wounded and dying men lay scattered in the grass as the Americans hastily deployed their tanks to move up the hill. As they paused to breast each hedge, one or two tanks were hit and burst into flames. The tanks poured fire into every hedge in front of them, but Lieutenant Phil Reisler of 2nd Armored could see infantry dropping around his Sherman "like in some terrible war film. I saw one tall, very thin man drop his rifle and start to run away down the hill. Then I caught sight of holes in his head, and he crashed full-tilt into an apple tree. He was running dead, like a chicken. I'll never forget the dedication of those men of 4th Infantry, walking up that hill over their dead buddies like British redcoats attacking in Revolutionary War days. It was magnificent. We got to the top with about ten tanks and about thirty-five foot soldiers."

But the Americans could far better afford losses of this kind than could the Germans. As von Kluge's men at last recoiled, spent, further east the Allies were pressing forward. On July 30, the British VIII Corps launched Operation BLUECOAT south from Caumont towards Vire and Mont Pinçon, while the US V Corps advanced on their right. For the British, any satisfaction at the extraordinary loosening of the flank was soured by the discovery that XXX Corps and 7th Armoured were performing feebly. Montgomery sacked the two commanders concerned.

COBRA, on the other hand, had been a vast success, the achievement preeminently of Collins. This passionate, intolerant, impatient soldier had once again demonstrated his unique qualities as a corps commander. All the American virtues of speed and energy had at last come into play on the battlefield. It is highly doubtful whether an operation resembling COBRA could have been launched earlier in the campaign. Its pre-essentials were a degree of battle wisdom that First Army only attained after weeks of painful experience, and an erosion of German strength that had taken much hard fighting to bring about.

At this pivotal moment in the Allies' fortunes, a long-scheduled shift in the American command structure took effect. General Courtney Hodges assumed command of First Army. Patton's Third Army formally came into being. Bradley stepped up to exercise overall command of the American forces, now designated 12th Army Group. The stage was set for one of the most dramatic American strategic movements of the war.

The Open Flank

By the last days of July 1944, the German army in Normandy had been reduced to a condition in which only a few fanatics of the SS still entertained hopes of avoiding defeat, far less of achieving victory. Any faint hope of replacements being found for the huge casualties in the west vanished in the wake of the Russian offensive against Army Group Centre, which had destroyed twenty-eight German divisions in five weeks.

Von Kluge reported to Hitler: "Whether the enemy can still be stopped at this point is questionable. The enemy air superiority is terrific, and smothers almost every one of our movements. . . . Losses in men and equipment are extraordinary. The morale of our troops has suffered very heavily under constant murderous enemy fire, especially since all infantry units consist only of haphazard groups which do not form a strongly coordinated force any longer."

Wholesale collapse of morale was bringing about huge surrenders of units swamped by the American advance. Sergeant Hans Stober admitted that even in 17th SS Panzergrenadiers, from mid-July, shellshock—hitherto an almost unrecognized condition in SS units—became a problem. It was astonishing that the German east-west front held together at all. Yet the surviving fragments of the old elite units still disputed the Allied advance at every stage.

The reverberations of the July 20 bomb explosion at Hitler's headquarters echoed through the upper ranks of his army. After the assassination attempt, Hitler's chronic mistrust and scorn for his generals became manic. On July 30 his Chief of Operations, Jodl, placed before him an order "for possible withdrawal from the coastal sector", which was in reality a blueprint for the evacuation of France. Hitler brushed it aside, saying that it was not at present necessary. The next day he sent General Warlimont to be his personal agent at von Kluge's headquarters, to ensure that the wavering field marshal precisely executed his orders.

It was ironic that many officers whose confused sense of honour had convinced them that they should not be party to the bomb plot now suffered bitter consequences because that same sense of honour had prevented them from betraying the plotters to Hitler. A chasm widened between the fanatical loyalists and those despairing of victory. The SS were increasingly obsessed by the conviction that

1. German troops drag a field gun through the undergrowth.

2. A brutal encounter between a German Mark I tank and a Norman shop.

3. Soon after D-day Hitler released the panzer reserves which proved formidable opponents in the *bocage*. Here, a Panther crew is seen rearming.

the anti-Hitler plotters were contributing directly to their misfortunes on the battlefield, while Hitler himself raged that the lack of *Panzerfausten* in Normandy was clearly the consequence of sabotage by the Quartermaster-General, Wagner, one of the dead plotters. There will, in fact, never be conclusive evidence one way or the other, but it remains far more probable that the failures and difficulties were genuine accidents and errors of war, and that the German army in France was on the edge of catastrophe because of its ruin on the battlefield and the demented strategy of Hitler, not because it had been betrayed from within.

For the Allied armies, the battle now took on a new character. Hitherto, while generalship had naturally been important, the progress of the campaign depended overwhelmingly upon the ability of British, American and Canadian units to seize ground from their German opponents. Henceforth, while hard fighting still lay ahead, Normandy became a commanders' battle. It was the decisions of the generals that determined the manner in which events unfolded in August, their successes and failures which brought about the position that was achieved by September.

THE AMERICAN "RIGHT TURN" into Brittany at the beginning of August was led by General Patton, who won the admiration of the world for the energy and ruthlessness with which he forced his army through Avranches and on their dash westwards. Bradley, however, like many veteran commanders, had no patience with Patton, and was exasperated by the Patton legend. Although he himself had authorized it, he wrote of Third Army's great sweep: "Patton blazed through Brittany with armoured divisions and motorized infantry. He conquered a lot of real estate and made big headlines, but the Brittany campaign failed to achieve its primary objectives." Bradley referred to the seizure of the western ports in a usable condition.

The fruits of the dash into Brittany were intoxicating for the men riding in the tanks and trucks—an almost unopposed swing across country already largely in the hands of the French Resistance. Yet most of the Germans in the region were given time to withdraw into Brest, whose defences held until September 19. Far more serious, the vital turn east towards Mayenne and Alençon, beginning the rolling up of the main German front in Normandy, was delayed.

There is little doubt that the commitment of such large forces in the west was ill-judged, when resistance was so slight and—after the example of Cherbourg—the prospect so small of the ports being of early use. If the Germans had now behaved rationally and begun a full-scale retreat east, then Bradley could indeed have been accused of losing his armies a great prize. But, driven on by Hitler's delusions, they did nothing of the sort. They prepared a major counterattack at Mortain, and even following its failure they were so slow to begin pulling back that Bradley's divisions had all the time they needed to reach around behind the German rear.

From the moment on the night of August 6 that ULTRA provided a brief warning to Bradley's headquarters of the Mortain counterattack, the Americans perfectly understood it as an opportunity, not a threat. The Germans had plunged enfeebled forces into battle against powerful American formations which were not merely confident of withstanding them, but expected utterly to destroy them. Bradley said, "This is an opportunity that comes to a commander not more than once in a century. We are about to destroy an entire German army."

Hitler had personally dispatched plans for the armoured attack. "We must strike like lightning," he declared. "When we reach the sea the American spearheads will be cut off. Obviously they are trying all-out for a major decision here, because otherwise they wouldn't have sent in their best general, Patton. . . . We must wheel north like lightning and turn the entire enemy front from the rear." It will remain one of the great enigmas of history that the German generals should have borne obediently with fantasy such as this.

The commander in chief of Army Group B, too weak to reject the plan as absurd, determined that if it was to be launched at all, the armour must move immediately, before US envelopment had rendered any move impossible. Thus it was impossible to bring up any additional panzer forces from the east in time to support the Mortain thrust, which attacked with only one hundred and forty-five tanks and thirty-two self-propelled guns.

After some promising early gains, during the morning of August 7, the Germans were quickly in deep trouble: out of the sky came the first of the greatest concentration of fighter-bombers yet deployed in the west: Thunderbolts supported by the RAF's rocket-firing Typhoons. The promised Luftwaffe air cover never materialized. Almost every approaching German sortie was intercepted by Allied fighters. The ground attack, begun with little hope even amongst the most formidable remaining formations of the German army, foundered in disarray and destruction. Far from creating even temporary relief from the threat of encirclement, von Kluge's divisions had driven themselves deep into the destructive embrace of the Americans.

HITLER, WITH HIS unerring instinct for reinforcing failure, now did so yet again. In the south, for a hundred miles from Domfront to Angers there was only one panzer and one infantry division in the Americans' path, along with a few security battalions. Yet Hitler ordered even this panzer division to be shifted north for a renewed attack towards Avranches on August 10. Its commander called this movement "a death blow not only to Seventh Army but also to the entire Wehrmacht in the west." Von Kluge said simply: "It is the Führer's order." As late as August 9, von Kluge could readily have executed the only sane movement open to him, a withdrawal to the Seine covered by a sacrificial rearguard. Hitler, and Hitler alone, closed this option to him, and presented the Allies with their extraordinary opportunity. The climate within the German High Command plumbed new depths of fantasy. When General von Cholitz reported to Hitler, fresh from the front near Avranches, he was informed that the Führer was about to hurl the Allies into the sea. The general concluded that "the man was mad".

The Road to Falaise

Through most of the campaign in northwest Europe, while there were tensions between the American and British High Commands, and each army possessed a large stock of jokes about the other, there was no real ill will between the soldiers. But during the weeks between the start of COBRA and the march to the Seine, many men of the British and Canadian armies found the glaring newspaper headlines about the American breakout a bitter pill to swallow. They received newspapers from England only a day or two after publication, and saw photographs of jubilant American infantry, helmets pushed back and weapons slung, waving as they rode their tanks through liberated villages alive with smiling civilians. Above all, they read of the light opposition that the advance was meeting, while they themselves were pushing slowly forward on their own front, with much pain and at heavy cost.

108

The British VIII and XXX Corps were attacking on an axis southeast from Caumont, still in dense country, while the Canadians moved directly south from Caen towards Falaise, facing an unbroken German line with overwhelmingly greater armoured strength and *nebelwerfer* support than anything the American Third Army encountered. Tank and infantry cooperation were now much improved, with the armoured divisions reorganized to integrate tanks and foot soldiers within their brigades. If there was less of the flamboyant spirit of the landings, there was much more professionalism. Most of the Scottish units which in June so eagerly sent forward their pipers to lead the men into battle had long ago dispensed with such frivolities. There were too many pipers who would never play another pibroch.

Then, on the night of August 7, preceded by a massive air attack, Canadian II Corps, under Lieutenant General Simonds, launched a renewed offensive southwards towards Falaise: Operation TOTALIZE. Simonds, who had commanded a division in Sicily, was to prove one of the outstanding Allied corps commanders in Europe, a dour, direct officer who brought unusual imagination to bear on every operational plan for which he was responsible. It was Simonds who now decided to make his attack across open country in darkness, to use seventy-six converted self-propelled gun-mountings to move his infantry, to employ a sophisticated range of electronic equipment and illuminants to guide his men to their objectives. There was to be no delay in following up the bombers.

At 11:30 pm the assault forces crossed the start line, led by navigating tanks and flails. They rumbled forward into the great dust-cloud raised by the bombing in four columns, each of four vehicles abreast. Bomber Command had done its job, guided by coloured marker-shells, with astonishing accuracy—there were no casualties among Allied troops and 3,462 tons of bombs had fallen on the villages in the path of the attack. By first light the early objectives had fallen. German counterattacks were repulsed, and the Typhoons were out in strength, aided by Mustangs and Spitfires flying sweeps over German approach roads. At about 12:50 am, the first of four hundred and ninety-two Fortresses of 8th Air Force began to launch a new wave of support attacks. The bombing was wild, and Allied troops suffered over three hundred casualties.

Now came the familiar, depressing indications of an offensive losing steam. German positions which had been bypassed, and were expected to collapse when they found themselves cut off, continued to resist fiercely. Canadian II Corps had advanced more than six miles, but Falaise still lay twelve miles ahead. Night attacks by Canadian battlegroups were driven back with substantial loss. The familiar screens of German 88mm guns inflicted punishing losses upon advancing armour.

Both the Polish and Canadian armoured divisions spearheading the Allied attacks were in action for the first time, and this increased their difficulties and hesitations. By August 9, Simonds's staff were exasperated by the persistent delays that appeared to afflict almost every unit movement, and the repeated episodes of troops and tanks firing on each other. A fierce German counterattack completed the chaos. The British Columbia Regiment lost almost its entire strength: forty-seven tanks in the day, together with one hundred and twelve casualties. The infantry of the Algonquins, who had been with them, lost one hundred and twenty-eight.

It is an astounding reflection upon the relative weight of forces engaged north of Falaise that by the night of August 10, the German tank strength was reduced to thirty-five, while the Canadian II Corps, even after losses, mustered around seven hundred. Yet on August 10 it was decided that nothing less than a new full-scale, set-piece attack with massed bomber preparation would break the Canadians through to Falaise. But it was evident that the Canadians were not performing well, handicapped by undermanning and leadership problems, and on August 11 Simonds was obliged to order his armoured divisions to pull out of the line, to be relieved by infantry formations.

It was now, with the disappointing breakdown of TOTALIZE, and the Canadians bogged down north of Falaise, that Montgomery missed what was probably his last opportunity to conduct a major switch of forces in time to hasten the closing of the German pocket. Had he fully recognized the Canadians' difficulties and shortcomings he might have rushed tested British formations southeastwards to support them. It may be, of course, that he was reluctant to impose new strains upon British divisions which had already suffered so much; or even that he doubted whether they would do any better than the Canadians. But for whatever reasons, he left the vital drive to meet the Americans at Argentan entirely in the hands of General Crerar's Canadian First Army, which had vividly demonstrated its shortcomings in the past four days.

TWO WHOLE DAYS were spent entirely in preparations for another big set-piece attack on Falaise, Operation TRACTABLE. It is easy to understand the impatience of the Americans waiting outside Argentan to close the gap from•the south, so conscious of time slipping away. TRACTABLE at last jumped off at 11:42 am on the morning of August 14, shielded by a smokescreen, which made navigation difficult. The brigade commander of the leading Canadian tanks was mortally wounded in the first hour, causing serious control problems in the action that followed. In addition, "short bombing" by Bomber Command caused over three hundred casualties among the assault troops, and had a severe effect on morale. And more seriously, the Germans had found a copy of Simonds's orders on the body of a scout car commander. They had redeployed with exact knowledge of the Canadian lines of advance.

Eventually, however, on the evening of August 15, the Canadian 2nd Division reached positions a mile from the edge of Falaise, but only after the Germans had disengaged and pulled back in front of them. They cleared the shattered town on August 17, some fifty Hitler Youth fighting to the last in the *école supérieure*.

It was now that von Kluge at last issued the order for a full-scale retreat eastwards out of the shrinking pocket. At midday on August 16, he had declined to execute an order from OKW for a counterattack, which he declared was utterly impossible. Although a withdrawal was at last authorized by order of the Führer later that afternoon, on the evening of August 17 von Kluge was relieved. On his way back to Germany he killed himself. He left behind an extraordinary letter affirming his undying devotion to the Führer, final testimony to the German officer corps's obsession with loyalty. Suicide, for an astonishing procession of German senior officers who failed in Normandy, became the final expression of their own retreat from reason. Von Kluge was succeeded by Field Marshal Walter Model. The supply of senior officers willing to attempt to implement their master's deranged will seemed limitless.

FOR THE ALLIES, time had now become critical in blocking the German army's escape. Yet while the Americans stood at Argentan, the Canadian and Polish armour edged south with agonizing sluggishness. The gap through which German vehicles and infantry were pouring in headlong retreat had now narrowed to a few thousand yards. Yet the principal labour of destroying the forces

1. The end of the
Cherbourg
campaign: General
von Schlieben
surrenders on
June 26, 1944.

2. An American
paratrooper keeps
his German prisoner
at bay.

3. German troops
are flushed out of a
farmhouse.

4. The face of defeat:
a prisoner being
searched by a British
military policeman.

3

4

within it was being borne by the Allied air forces. The fighter-bombers, flying 2,000 to 3,000 sorties a day throughout this period, inflicted massive losses. The pocket was being closed too late, however, to prevent the escape of some of the most dangerous elements of the German army, including some of its most dedicated officers, who lived to lead men through many more battles.

The ragged remains of two German divisions and a handful of tanks had held all Crerar's Canadian First Army for thirteen days, from the opening of TOTALIZE to the closing of the gap at Chambois, east of Argentan—a distance of barely thirty miles across mostly open country. Now, blackened vehicles, blackened corpses, blackened buildings and hedgerows scarred every acre over which the fighter-bombers had passed. The wounded were merely gathered where they might be tended by their captors when the Allies reached them—there were no more drugs and few enough doctors. Men ate what they could find in shattered vehicles or farmhouses—every surviving building was crowded with stragglers hunting food, or shelter from the interminable shelling and bombing.

On August 22, it was concluded that all significant German forces west of the Allied lines were dead or in captivity, and the battle for Normandy was over. The Allied armies could make free with the ruins of St. Lambert and Coudehard, Chambois and Trun, the ghastly killing ground of the Falaise Gap.

The Aftermath

Some Germans had already been fortunate enough to get back to their homeland before the collapse in Normandy came. Lieutenant Schaaf and his gunners of the 1716th Artillery had been sent back to re-equip with new guns when those which they had fired since June 6 became worn out with ceaseless use. Corporal Kortenhaus of 21st Panzer was still in hospital after catching his foot in his tank track. But the mass of the German army in Normandy remained, to endure in the Falaise Gap one of the great nightmares of military history. Pounded by shells from north and south, fighter-bomber strikes from first light to dusk, the long columns of men, horse-drawn carts and the few surviving tanks and vehicles struggled slowly eastwards, past their unburied dead by the roads and in the fields, the stinking carcasses of countless hundreds of horses and cattle, the ruins of Panthers and half-tracks, field cars and trucks, the last hopes of Hitler's armies in France. Kurt "Panzer" Meyer, outstanding combat commander and fanatical Nazi, escaped, according to his own account, "guided by a French civilian". It is not difficult to picture the means of persuasion Meyer brought to bear. Yet even the iron Meyer described later how he climbed out of his vehicle amidst the shambles of the Gap, "my knees trembling, the sweat pouring down my face, my clothes soaked in perspiration." He and his men represented, at one level, the utmost perversion of National Socialism. Yet at another, they command reluctant respect. No formation caused the Allies such deep trouble in Normandy, until the end, as 12th SS Panzer.

Lieutenant Fritz Langangke of 2nd SS Panzer had been driving since the beginning of August in a hastily repaired tank with chronic overheating problems. Its collapse on the start line for the Mortain counterattack probably saved his life, and the same Panther carried him eastwards as the line crumbled, sustained by petrol drained into a canvas bucket from abandoned vehicles. In the final days of the pocket, the Panther's engine caught fire for the last time. The crew blew it up and started walking: "We just kept going along with the rest of the German army."

Colonel Kurt Kauffmann, the operations officer of Panzer Lehr, similarly walked out of the pocket in the clothes he stood up in, the entire divisional headquarters and its documents having been lost in the American breakthrough. He was to find himself posted to the Eastern Front for speaking openly about the hopelessness of the military situation.

Corporal Adolf Hohenstein of 276th Infantry marched eastwards out of the pocket with a handful of men, having lost all contact with his unit. They came upon a château where they paused to gaze sadly upon the wonderful library, torn open to the elements by shellfire. Around noon on August 20, they were lying in a field wondering desperately how to cross the flat ground ahead, littered with dead horses, burning vehicles and wounded men, and still under furious shellfire. Suddenly the firing stopped. There was a rumour, probably unfounded, that there was a local truce while a German hospital was handed over to the Allies. They seized their moment and hastened through the smoking chaos. Many men, said Hohenstein, were no longer seeking to escape, but merely lingering in the hope of making a safe surrender. St. Lambert was crowded with

115

fugitives who had abandoned their weapons and clutched only sheets to assist their efforts to give themselves up.

At 5:00 am on August 21, Hohenstein's group approached the village of Coudehard, its houses burning quietly in the early light. They heard voices. They strained their ears, to discover from the shelter of the trees to which army the men belonged. At last they moved cautiously forward until an unmistakably German accent called "Halt!" They had reached the new German lines. "After Normandy," said Hohenstein, "we had no illusions any more. We knew that we stood with our backs to the wall."

AS THE FIRST ALLIED FORCES moved into the pocket, gathering up prisoners in their thousands, they were awed by the spectacle that they discovered.

"The roads were choked with wreckage and the swollen bodies of men and horses," wrote Group Captain Desmond Scott. "Bits of uniform were plastered to shattered tanks and trucks, and human remains hung in grotesque shapes on the blackened hedgerows. Paper was scattered around where several mailbags had exploded. I picked up a photograph of a smiling young German recruit standing between his parents, two solemn peasants who stared back at me in accusation. . . . Strangely enough it was the fate of the horses that upset me most. Harnessed as they were, it had been impossible for them to escape, and they lay dead in tangled heaps, their large wide eyes crying out to me in anguish. It was a sight that pierced the soul, and I felt as if my heart would burst. We hurried back to the sanctuary of our busy airfield near Bayeux."

Most Allied soldiers found that now, for the first time, in the midst of their own crushing victory, they could spare pity for the defeated enemy. Trooper Dyson of the Royal Artillery Corps watched the lines of prisoners shuffling through the forward area, "some of them old men wearing overcoats down to their ankles." Like many Allied soldiers, he took a German's belt for its eagle buckle, then felt ashamed because the man's trousers fell down. "I looked at them all, and somehow it seemed unbelievable that they were the Germans, the enemy—some mothers' sons."

THE FALAISE GAP could be accounted properly closed only on August 21, when tanks of the Canadian 4th Armored Division linked up with the Poles at Coudehard, and the Canadian 3rd and

116

4th Divisions secured St. Lambert and the northern passage to Chambois. Three hundred and forty-four tanks and self-propelled guns, 2,447 soft-skinned vehicles and two hundred and fifty-two guns were counted abandoned or destroyed in the northern sector of the pocket alone. The battle for Normandy had cost the German army a total of 1,500 tanks, 3,500 guns and 20,000 vehicles. They had lost around 450,000 men, 240,000 of these killed or wounded. The Allies had achieved this at a cost of 209,672 casualties, 36,976 of these killed. British and Canadian losses amounted to two thirds those suffered by the Americans. Some 28,000 Allied aircrew were also lost either over Normandy, during the vast campaign of preparatory bombing, or in battles against the German airforce and aircraft industries.

Since few episodes in the Normandy campaign have provoked such a torrent of criticism as the Allied failure to close the gap south of Falaise more speedily, it seems worth emphasizing that the portion of the German forces which got away was tiny by comparison with that which was destroyed. Only twenty-four tanks, sixty guns and something over 20,000 Germans escaped the pocket. Furthermore, it may reasonably be argued that any Allied attempt at envelopment before the German forces had been brought to the brink of destruction by attrition would have cost the attackers dear. A British or American breakthrough southwards in June might have been very heavily punished by a German counterattack.

The Allies in Normandy faced the finest fighting army of the war, one of the greatest that the world has ever seen. The quality of the Germans' weapons—above all tanks—was of immense importance. Their tactics were masterly: stubborn defence; concentrated local firepower from mortars and machineguns; quick counterattacks to recover lost ground. Units often fought on even when cut off, which was not a mark of fanaticism, but of sound tactical discipline when such resistance in the rear did much to reduce the momentum of Allied advances, as in GOODWOOD, the final attack on Caen.

An ethos, a mood, pervades all armies at all times about what is acceptable within them, what is expected of them. The ethos within the Allied armies in Normandy in 1944-1945 was that of men committed to doing an unwelcome but necessary job for the cause of democracy. The ethos of the German army, profoundly influenced by the threat from the east, was of a society fighting to the last to escape *götterdämmerung*.

All this Montgomery and Bradley understood perfectly well, and shaped their plans and expectations accordingly. They had not been sent to Normandy to demonstrate the superiority of their fighting men to those of Hitler, but to win the war at a tolerable cost—a subtly but importantly different objective. Their business, and their difficulty, while accepting this and acknowledging the difference in mood and spirit between their own soldiers and those of Hitler, was to persuade their armies to do enough—albeit, just enough—to prevail on a given battlefield and in a given action. This they were at last able to do, inflicting a crushing defeat upon their enemies.

A good case can be made also that the Allies' disappointments and delays in gaining ground eventually worked to their advantage. Just as in Tunisia more than a year earlier, Hitler's manic reinforcement of failure caused him to thrust division after division into the cauldron for destruction. By the time the breakout came, no significant forces lay in front of the Allies before the German border. Paris fell on August 25, Patton crossed the Meuse on August 31 and was at Metz, on the Moselle, the next day. The Guards armoured division reached Brussels on September 3 after advancing seventy-five miles in a single day. 11th Armoured reached Antwerp, finding the port intact, on September 4.

Although, at this juncture, there were perhaps one hundred German tanks on the entire Western Front against over 2,000 in the Allied spearheads, through another herculean feat of organization, the German line was thickening everywhere by mid-September. The battles in Holland and along the German border would so often seem to belong to a different age from those of Normandy that it is startling to reflect that Arnhem was fought less than a month after Falaise; that within weeks of suffering one of the greatest catastrophes of modern war, the Germans found the strength to halt the drive of XXX Corps, now commanded by General Horrocks, in its tracks, to prolong the war until May 1945. But although this phenomenon reveals the same staggering qualities in Hitler's armies that had caused the Allies such grief in Normandy, it is also another story.

Max Hastings

Ever since leaving school Max Hastings has been an avid student of warfare—both in libraries and on the battlefield. A scholar at Charterhouse and at University College, Oxford, he has reported for the BBC and national newspapers from more than fifty countries, seeing action in Vietnam, Angola and the Middle East. But his greatest opportunity to study military affairs, and one that helped him greatly in the writing of *Overlord*, came quite unexpectedly two years ago.

Max Hastings recalls how in April 1982 he was embarking on this book, "seeking to make the leap of imagination that is essential to books of this kind, to conceive what it was like to crouch in a landing craft approaching the hostile shore at dawn on June 6, 1944. By an extraordinary fluke of history, less than two months later I found myself crouched in a British landing craft 8,000 miles away. In the weeks that followed I had an opportunity to witness an amphibious campaign whose flavour any veteran of 1944 would immediately have recognized." Max Hastings's award-winning reports from the Falklands, where he landed with the marines and took part in most of the principal actions of the campaign, made him a household name almost overnight.

Coming from a family of writers—his is the third generation—Max Hastings has already written eight books, mostly on military themes. In 1980 he won the Somerset Maugham Prize for *Bomber Command*, his study of the strategic air offensive in the Second World War. He has also written a biography of the great seventeenth century Scottish commander Montrose, and another, of an Israeli commando officer killed leading the Entebbe raid.

Now thirty-eight, he lives in Northamptonshire with his wife and three children.

The
CHILDREN'S
GAME

A CONDENSATION OF THE BOOK BY
David Wise

ILLUSTRATED BY JOHN SOLIE
PUBLISHED BY ST. MARTIN'S/MAREK, NEW YORK

Seven years ago secret agent Bill Danner walked out of the CIA. He had been one of the best operators in the spy business, but after a long career of intrigue and deceit he had definitely had enough. And now all he cares for is his lovely eleven-year-old daughter Carrie and the remote fishing camp that he runs in the Canadian wilderness.

Suddenly, the CIA want Danner to return, to uncover a mole within the Agency, leaving him with little choice but to plunge back into a world that he has grown to despise. As the dangerous game of espionage threatens all he holds dear, Bill Danner vows to change its rules.

A leading authority on the CIA and international espionage, David Wise brings an unmistakable stamp of authenticity to this thrilling tale.

Chapter 1

The bears, as expected, had been excellent. The lead bear came gliding into the ring on roller skates, pirouetting gracefully to the music. Another followed him, riding on a bicycle. Then more bears roared in on motorcycles as the crowd began to clap rhythmically. The trainer was a genius: the bears were the true stars of the Moscow Circus.

Seated in the first row, Yuri Vladimirovich Kalin, general secretary of the Communist Party and president of the Soviet Union, joined in the applause. He loved the circus and enjoyed all the acts. The bears, the monkeys, the leopard that rode a horse. He especially liked the blonde aerialist in her little red tights, working without a net high above the arena.

Kalin looked at his watch. The moment he was waiting for was almost at hand. His favourite act of all. He turned to his right and patted his pudgy married daughter Galina on the knee. "*Milaya,*" he said, grinning like a child. "My dear. *Seychas budut klouny.* Time for the clowns."

IT WAS COLD AND GREY in Vienna, and the cobblestones glistened in the early morning rain. Stein leaned into the chill wind and held the paper bag close to protect it. He turned into the Haslingergasse and made his way to an ancient apartment house in the middle of the block.

The imposing building, now badly in need of repair, stood as a shabby reminder that this had once been an upper-middle-class neighbourhood. The glass-sided lift, which required a coin to operate it, was not in the lobby. Someone had forgotten to return it from the top floor. Stein shrugged. He would walk, and it would save a schilling.

Very slowly he mounted the stairs to the third floor. He was a short man, almost thirty pounds overweight, and the climb had been getting harder of late. At the landing, he fumbled for his key, opened the door, and entered the apartment. Carefully he took two croissants out of the sodden bag and put them on a plate. He lit the burner under the espresso pot.

It wasn't just the stairs, Stein reflected as he waited for the water to boil; everything was getting harder. It was not like the old days. After the war, during the four-power occupation of Vienna, one could see agents for each side sitting at adjoining tables at the cafes along the Ringstrasse. In those days he was prosperous; he collected from everybody for the same secrets. Now the Americans were paying him less than eighty dollars a month. His wife, Lili, worked as a waitress and, with tips, she made far more in one week than he made in four. It was humiliating.

The coffee was ready, and he poured himself a cup, adding a dollop of thick cream. He sat down heavily and sighed. The business wasn't fun any more. Yet, if all went well, today could be a turning point. His life could change.

It depended on Vlasa. This morning, in her office, she would be changing the printed circuit board on the Czech embassy's coding machine. It was a four-by-six-inch plastic card, and all she had to do was run it through her copying machine. In three seconds the pattern of the delicate little ridges of metal would be captured. If she didn't lose her nerve, he would meet her in the gardens of the Schönbrunn Palace at noon. In the meantime there was nothing he could do but wait.

As he ate his breakfast, Stein thought back over the past six weeks. Not without pride; he had handled the operation perfectly. He was jarred from his reverie by the doorbell. He was not expecting anyone. Lili was not due back from work until late in the afternoon.

He went to the door but did not open it. *"Ja, bitte?"* he asked.

"Postman," a voice answered cheerily. "Express letter for Herr Stein."

Stein opened the latch on the peephole, looked through, and relaxed. It was a postman in the familiar blue uniform. *"Einen Moment, bitte,"* he grumbled as he fussed with the lock.

The postman, a heavy-set middle-aged man, smiled and handed him a clipboard and a pen. "Sign here, please."

As Stein wrote his name on the form, the postman reached into his leather mailbag and removed a .22-calibre automatic.

When Stein looked up, the gun was pointing straight at him. He stepped back and tried to slam the door, but he was not quick enough. The man fired twice. Stein heard no sound but felt unspeakable pain explode within him. Then he fell to the floor.

THE HELICOPTER dipped low over the river, and the pilot gestured towards the scattering of houses set among trees along the far bank. His only passenger, a big blond man in a business suit and sunglasses, had to shout to make himself heard over the noise of the engine. "Blackville?"

"Right. Won't be long now," the pilot said. He wondered about his passenger. The man was an American, clear enough, but almost every outsider who flew in to this part of Canada came to fish. The blond man wasn't even carrying a rod. Still, his money was good. When he had chartered the chopper at Fredericton, he had peeled off five hundred-dollar bills from a fat roll.

The pilot swung south and followed the river upstream. Within a few moments he found the clearing the American had described. They zoomed down towards the tree line, and seconds later the helicopter was hovering over the clearing, its whirling blades strewing grass, pine needles and dirt in every direction. Off to one side the pilot could see a man waiting in a jeep.

The chopper landed on its skids. The blond man stepped out, ducked his head to clear the blades, and ran towards the jeep as the helicopter roared aloft.

The blond man, whose name was Larry Gates, got into the jeep beside the young driver. They rode in silence for a time along a bumpy track. Gates was uneasy about the mission that had brought him from Washington to the remote New Brunswick wilderness. He was under great pressure from his superiors to succeed in his task.

They had been driving south, parallel to the river, for about half an hour when Gates saw some buildings through the trees. The

125

driver stopped, and Gates climbed out. Before him were half a dozen rough-hewn log cabins set among firs and maples, and a larger building that served as a lodge, dining room and cookhouse. A terraced lawn dropped steeply towards the river, and a long flight of wooden steps led down from the buildings to the water. The camp appeared to be empty, but Gates had expected that. It was midmorning: the fishermen and their guides would be out on the river.

Gates headed down the steps. Two long canoes were moored beside the bank, and a man who looked to be a guide was bent over one of them, tinkering with a small outboard motor. He straightened up as Gates drew near. He wore chest-high rubber waders and a tartan shirt, and he had an open face with a ready grin for the stranger.

Gates was unsmiling. "Where's Danner?" he asked.

"Upriver a ways. I can take you." The man indicated the second canoe, and Gates got into the bow. The guide sat in the stern and started the motor. The canoe began moving up the wide river.

They had gone about a quarter of a mile when Gates saw a man in waders standing about five feet offshore. As the canoe veered towards him, the man snapped his rod back, then forward, in a practised motion, casting out sixty or seventy feet of line. The canoe touched shore, and Gates jumped out awkwardly, spattering mud on his shoes and trouser turn-ups. The guide swung the boat around, waved, and headed back towards camp.

The angler in the water had his back to the shore, and he paid no attention to his visitor as he began reeling in. He was a handsome man, with even features, and dark hair just beginning to be flecked with grey. He was a shade under six feet tall, with a muscular, athletic frame.

"Danner," Gates said. "I need to talk to you."

The man turned for the first time. "No kidding," he said.

Gates licked his lips. He had known this wasn't going to be easy. "Can we talk?"

"You'll catch a hook standing there."

Gates moved to his left. Danner twitched the rod, then brought it forward gracefully, and the line shot out over the river.

"It's important, Bill," Gates pleaded.

"Not to me." Danner seemed intent on watching the fly as it floated downstream just under the surface.

126

It was late June and the sun was hot. Gates loosened his tie. "We thought you still cared about your country. Enough to listen."

Danner turned. "I care," he said angrily. "I love my country. You and your friends know that." His voice became calm now as he reeled in again. "It's the CIA I don't love."

"The agency's part of the country. We need your help."

Danner wondered why they had sent Gates as their messenger boy. He had worked with him on occasion, and considered him a mediocre officer. Gates wasn't dumb, just unimaginative. Not that it mattered. It had been seven years, and there was no way Danner was ever going back.

He whipped the line over his shoulder and cast forward again. "You do any fishing?" he asked.

"Naw. Not really."

"The Atlantic salmon isn't like any other fish. He can run up to three feet long and weigh twenty-five pounds. When he strikes— well, you've got your hands full."

Gates sat down on the bank. If Danner wanted to talk fish, he'd go along for a while.

"Nobody can really explain their migration," Danner said. "How they find their way thousands of miles from the North Atlantic to the tiny stream where they were born. My own guess is that they go mostly by their sense of smell. But maybe they use the sun, even celestial navigation."

Gates tried again. "I've brought a message from Dixon Hadley. He wants you back. There's something wrong at the agency."

"There's a lot wrong. That's why I got out."

"You don't understand," Gates said. "This is recent. Just the last few months. The whole place is tied up in knots. Hadley's a wreck. His hands are starting to shake."

Danner reeled in and changed the fly. The river was slightly high from the spring rains. It meant the fish would be moving along at a good clip, not lingering in the pools; a heavier hook might help.

"I'm not authorized to give you any details," Gates continued, "but our operations are going bad all over. Agents are being blown right and left. The Soviets seem to know what we're doing even before we do it."

Danner cast again. The line made a whooshing noise as it flew out over the water. There was no other sound except the quiet murmur of the river.

"The pattern is clear," Gates went on. "Somebody is deliberately sabotaging operations. There's a mole in the agency. We want you to find him."

Danner had started to reply when the fish struck, and the fibreglass rod bent double.

"Good Lord!" Gates jumped to his feet.

Danner fought to keep the rod up. The salmon was taking the line downstream. As the two men watched, the great fish leaped out of the water, a flash of silver in the sunlight. "He's a big one," Danner shouted. He was grinning. "Twenty-two pounds easy."

With enormous strength, the fish was making its run downstream, jumping as it went. Each time the salmon leaped, Danner lowered the tip of his rod to create a little slack. But as he watched the line intently, the salmon turned and headed back upriver. He reeled in fast.

Not even the drama of the struggle between man and fish discouraged Larry Gates. "You wouldn't have to come back for long. Maybe only six months."

"You don't need me," Danner said, keeping his line taut. "It's a job for Counterintelligence."

"We do need you," Gates said. "You were the best."

Gates was not exaggerating. In his twenty-year career, William Danner had become a legendary figure inside the Central Intelligence Agency. He was known, quite simply, as the best agent in the Clandestine Services. Until seven years ago, when he walked out of his office at headquarters and never went back. His detractors whispered that he was a burnt-out case. Danner knew better. He understood the reasons for his disillusionment. Some of those reasons were private and seared indelibly on his soul.

The salmon had reached a point about opposite where Danner stood. Suddenly the fish turned and rocketed downriver once more. Danner released the handle of the reel.

On the bank, Gates was still pleading. "We can't trust anyone in the agency for this job. He might turn out to be the mole."

Danner shrugged. He wished Larry Gates would go away. He was trying to concentrate on the fish.

"Come back on temporary assignment," Gates said. "We'll pay you whatever you want. The sky's the limit."

"No. I've put in my time." He was reeling in again, and now the fish, exhausted, turned over and showed its side. It was the moment to bring him into the net. Danner glanced over his shoulder. "Here, make yourself useful. Hand me that net."

Gates picked it up and stepped out onto a flat rock a couple of feet from shore. He passed the net to Danner. Then he lit a cigarette. This was the part he dreaded. There was no telling how Danner might react. Gates spoke, but his tone was no longer friendly. "If you don't come back," he said abruptly, "we'll poison the river and kill the fish."

Danner, still playing the salmon, turned to stare in disbelief.

"We won't kill you," Gates went on, "but we'll ruin you. No more hotshot New York executives will come here to fish at a thousand dollars a week. If you move somewhere else, we'll find you there and do the same thing. William Danner won't be able to earn a living anywhere."

Twenty years. He had given them twenty years and it wasn't enough. They couldn't let him live his life. They had to track him down, here in the wilderness, with a threat to crush him. "You wouldn't dare!" he said, his anger breaking with full force. "What makes you think I won't go public and expose your threats?"

Gates looked unperturbed. "Who would believe you? An ex-spy with a grudge against the agency and a wild story about killing fish. Acid rain kills a lot of fish up here; you won't be able to prove anything."

The salmon was only a few feet from shore now. Despite his fury, Danner was determined to land him. He slipped the net below the surface of the water. Holding the rod high in his right hand, he manoeuvred the thrashing fish towards the mesh. It was a critical point at which many a salmon broke free. He dipped the rod to give some slack to the line. In another moment the enormous fish, bright silver and red, gills heaving, was landed.

"There," Danner said. "He's in the net."

"Yes." Gates smiled. "So he is."

Chapter 2

For three days afterwards Danner tried to deal with Larry Gates's visit by putting it out of his mind. He busied himself with the routine of running the fishing camp. He played the genial host to his guests, answered the mail, checked food shipments and supplies.

129

And he went fishing with Carrie, his eleven-year-old daughter, who lived with her mother in California and had come to spend part of the summer with him.

When Danner walked out of the CIA, he had not been sure what he would do. He knew only that he wanted something far removed from the agency, both spiritually and geographically. He had always loved the outdoors, and his thoughts had turned to Canada's Maritime Provinces, where he had worked during the summers of his college years. With his savings, and a bank loan, he had been able to buy this old fishing camp near Blackville. He had remodelled it with his own hands and slowly got it back into shape. Now, out of his past, the agency threatened to destroy all he had struggled to build.

He had told no one of Gates's visit, not even Carrie. But this morning, he knew, he would have to talk to her. She had breakfasted in the kitchen with him and the guides and then skipped off somewhere—perhaps to play with her cat, Mr. O'Malley, who liked to hang around in front of their cabin.

Danner found the grey-and-white cat licking his paws and luxuriating in a warm patch of sunlight. There was no sign of Carrie. Then from above him he heard a giggle. He looked up and spotted his daughter, grinning at him from twenty feet overhead, in the branches of a maple. "I should have known," he said, smiling back. "The monkey banana girl."

Carrie made a face. He saw she had split a winged maple seed and had pressed it against the bridge of her nose. She was a pretty girl, with light freckles under her blue eyes, and a straight, chiselled nose. She had got that from Francesca. She wore faded jeans, a polo-neck shirt and old sneakers, and her blonde hair was held in place by a slide made of rainbow-coloured beads. She was still half tomboy, but fast growing out of that, Danner thought. In a few weeks she would be twelve.

"Planning to spend the morning up there?"

"It depends on what we're doing today."

"I'm taking you fishing. And you can pick the spot."

"Terrific!" Carrie scrambled down and ran to get her rod. She knew the river almost as well as Danner did, and she had learned to cast a fly with almost as much accuracy, although not as far. Danner was proud of her skill. More than that, the fishing was something that brought them together.

Down at the landing, Carrie climbed into the bow of a canoe and Danner got in the stern. "Where to?" he asked her.

"The Cains. Beyond the little island, to the ledge."

The Cains was a tributary of the Miramichi River, and there was a long, flat ledge of rock about two miles upstream, where one could fish and talk and catch the sun. It was their special place. Danner started the outboard and they were quickly under way.

When they reached the ledge, he moored the canoe. For half an hour they fished, saying little. They were enjoying the morning together, the warmth of the sun and the summer sounds, the birds chattering in the branches. Danner put his rod aside and sat down on the rock, just watching Carrie.

"Dad, you know what I was thinking?"

"What?"

"That summer is like a scoop of chocolate ice cream. It's delicious, but you have to remember to enjoy each mouthful. Otherwise, before you know it, it's over."

Danner nodded. "Life's like that, too."

She thought about that a moment, and said, "I really love it here. And the best part is I've still got five whole weeks before I have to go back to California."

"Carrie." Something about his voice made her turn and look at him sharply. "Come and sit with me for a minute." She reeled in her line and came over.

"Carrie, you remember the work I used to do, a long time ago?"

"Sure. You were a spy."

"I was an intelligence officer."

"Same thing." Carrie tossed a pebble into the river. "Why did you stop?"

"I didn't like it any more."

"Were you a spy for a long time?"

"Yes, for a long time. Even before I knew your mother."

"I wish you would call her Mom, or Francesca. I don't know why you always say 'your mother'."

"I'm sorry. You're right. I'll call her Francesca." Danner hesitated. "Carrie, a man came to see me on Monday. From Washington. I have to go back there for a while."

"To be a spy again?"

"Sort of."

"But you don't like that any more. You said so."

"Well, I have to go back. I don't want to, but I have to. And that's the point. You can't stay here. I can't leave you with a bunch of guides. They don't know anything about kids."

The blue eyes were suddenly filled with tears. "But I don't want to go back to Santa Barbara now."

"It's nice there in the summer. You can go horseback riding. Maybe Richard will take you sailing."

"Richard's OK, but he's not my real father. It's not the same as being with you."

"I know. But we'll have to fly to Montreal the day after tomorrow. I'll put you on a flight to Los Angeles, and I'll go on to Washington. I'll call your mother this afternoon so she can meet your plane."

"Francesca."

"Sorry. I goofed again."

He wiped away her tears, and suddenly she broke into a grin. She took the maple seed from her nose, leaned over, and stuck it on Danner's nose. She pushed back to admire the effect, then started giggling. "I'll bet James Bond never wore a maple wing on his nose," she said.

Danner laughed and took her in his arms and hugged her for a long time. "I love you, Carrie."

"I love you, too, Daddy." In their embrace the maple seed brushed loose and fell onto the rock. Danner picked it up and stuck it in his shirt pocket.

"Why d'you do that?" she asked.

"It might bring me luck," he said.

As HE DROVE IN from Washington National Airport in his hired car, Danner's mood alternated between rage and resignation. One moment he was pounding the steering wheel, furious to find himself capitulating to the agency's threat. The next moment he was calm, assuring himself that he had no option.

The rolling hills of northern Virginia swept by, luxuriant and green in the early summer. They were a bittersweet reminder of all he had hoped to put behind him for ever.

He thought, with a sudden surge of tenderness, of the scene at the Montreal airport when he had had to put Carrie on the plane to California. She had made him swear to take good care of the cat, Mr. O'Malley. Then they had kissed goodbye, and she had gone off through the gate with her flight bag, her teddy bear named Edward,

132

and a large chocolate ice-cream cone, which had started to drip down the sides. He smiled at the memory.

But the present intruded. The boys in the agency were clever; they had threatened him not with physical harm but economic destruction—his most vulnerable spot. As a retired intelligence officer, he received a monthly pension cheque. But he depended on his income from the fishing camp, and even that was seasonal. Unlike so many other veterans of the Clandestine Services, Danner did not come from a moneyed east coast family. He had no independent means with which to meet the mortgage on the camp, the payroll and other expenses, and child-support payments to Francesca. If the agency waged all-out economic warfare against him, it would certainly win.

He was on the George Washington Memorial Parkway now, driving south along the Potomac River. He let his mind wander back to the beginning, when he had first arrived at the CIA as a gung-ho junior officer trainee. It was 1957, and he was just out of Dartmouth. He had gone through several weeks on "the Farm", at Camp Peary, Virginia, the CIA's secret training base for its agents. There he had learned the tradecraft of a spy—bugging, wire-tapping, microdots, dead drops, safe houses, codes, invisible writing, lockpicking, and all the rest. He had gone through rugged paramilitary training as well, learning to shoot with pistols, rifles and submachine guns. He had loved it all.

He looked in the rearview mirror. A girl in a red MG was tail-gating, trying to nudge him into the right-hand lane. Smiling a little, he slowed down and made her go round on the right. He got a glimpse of her as she zoomed by, noting that she was dark-haired, pretty, and driving too fast.

Camp Peary seemed a million years ago. Danner wondered whether he could be the same man who had come off the Farm ready to save the Western world. He had thought he would be protecting his country, a cold warrior in the secret service of the United States. What could be more glamorous, noble and exciting?

His disillusionment, he realized, had been gradual. The first doubts had come with the trauma of Lisa's death in Berlin. Although he had been in charge of the operation, he had been officially absolved of any blame. But that would not bring her back, and the ache, the sense of loss, would not go away, ever.

He left the parkway at the CIA exit. In a moment he was at the chain-link fence and the guard hut. "William Danner," he told the guard. "I'm expected." He handed over his driver's licence.

The guard checked a list and directed him to the visitors' car park. "I know where it is," Danner said.

He turned left, and soon the greyish-white headquarters building came into view. He parked, got out, and walked up the front steps. To his right stood the familiar bronze statue of Nathan Hale. Danner noticed that the pavement was crumbling around the base. Headquarters was getting a little seedy.

Inside the lobby, he crossed the big grey-and-white seal of the Central Intelligence Agency inlaid in the marble floor. At the front desk, another guard examined his driver's licence, made a phone call, and finally waved him up a short flight of stairs to the reception lounge. There he signed in, and a clerk handed him a visitor's badge, which he clipped to his lapel.

Waiting for him was a blonde woman, who led him through a small anteroom and into a private lift. They got off at six and walked down the hall to a door that said DEPUTY DIRECTOR FOR OPERATIONS. The DDO was the man in charge of the Clandestine Services, handling covert operations and espionage for the CIA around the globe. He was one of the most powerful men in the world; yet his name was virtually unknown outside these sterile, guarded corridors.

As Danner entered the office, Dixon Hadley was rising from his desk, smiling broadly.

"Danner," he said, "good to see you." He extended a moist hand, waved him to a chair, then sat down again. The woman left, and closed the door behind her.

The DDO was a somewhat heavy-set man in his fifties, with sandy hair, a pink face, and thick, horn-rimmed glasses that accentuated his fussy, academic manner. He had once taught philosophy at Yale but had given up the good, the true and the beautiful for the darker ambiguities of the CIA. His penthouse office was furnished in executive modern, with a lot of dark wood and chrome. The east wall was entirely glass, and the morning sunlight poured in.

"Well," Hadley began with a satisfied air, "we were very pleased that you've agreed to come back."

Same old Dixon, Danner thought. Always polite. "I'm here," Danner said simply.

Hadley smiled and cleared his throat. "Well, as Larry Gates

134

undoubtedly told you, we've been having a bit of trouble. We thought perhaps you could help."

Danner noticed that Handley's hands really were shaking. Gates had been right about that.

"To come to the point," Hadley went on, "our operations are being blown everywhere. An agent was shot in Vienna. We had an incident in Madrid. In Tokyo the first secretary of the Soviet embassy was all set to defect to us when, at the last moment, the Soviets whisked him onto an Aeroflot jet for Moscow."

"With a connecting flight to the Gulag," Danner observed.

"No doubt." Hadley leaned forward and lowered his voice. "There's a peculiar and extremely awkward aspect to the whole thing. In each city where an operation has been blown, one of our retired or dismissed agents has been seen. Or some personal trademark has been evident."

Danner tried to suppress a faint smile. He was not a man who was easily surprised. But he had not expected this. "You mean a former Clandestine Services officer?"

"Yes. Exactly. One of our old boys."

Danner was becoming intrigued, in spite of himself. "What sort of trademark?"

"I was coming to that." Hadley was at his most professorial, Danner thought. "Vienna station has been running an agent for several years, code name MS/Skylark, true name Max Stein. He's low level, long past his prime. What he provides is mostly chickenfeed. But about three months ago he stumbled onto something. He was fishing for secretaries from the Czech embassy. He figured that when the weather was nice, some of the secretaries might eat their lunch nearby, in the gardens of the Schönbrunn Palace. They're very beautiful. The gardens, I mean."

"So that's where MS/Skylark brought *his* lunch."

"Precisely. He showed up every day for two weeks, and nothing happened. Then, bingo. A woman actually sat down on his bench. A homely thirty-five-year-old named Vlasa Radek, a butcher's daughter from Bratislava. Unmarried, and no prospects." Hadley paused for effect. "And she worked in the code room."

Danner whistled. "Love at first sight," he offered.

"Just about. Stein struck up a conversation and started romancing the woman. They met again the next day and went on a tour of the palace together. She was looking for a father figure, an older man who would take her to dinner, flatter her, and most of all, pay attention to her."

"Who was the case officer handling him?"

"Tyler Ashford. He's under consular cover in our embassy. He told Stein not to rush things, but Stein knew that. He took her to concerts, museums, the opera. He waited until the right moment. Then he told her he wanted the circuitry on the code machine."

"How did she react?"

"She was shocked, of course. But he gave her some double-talk about having a partner in his import-export business who was manufacturing code machines for commercial use. He told her they could get the edge on their competitors if they knew the wiring on a sophisticated diplomatic machine."

Danner looked sceptical. "And she believed that?"

"It took a while, but in the end she agreed."

Danner could visualize the board, a little plastic card about one sixteenth of an inch thick, laced with slightly raised metal ridges. Its circuitry formed the heart of the code machine.

"It was Vlasa's job to change the circuit board each month," Hadley explained. "All she had to do was get it to a photocopier. Once we had a copy of the board, we could have cracked their code."

"How was she going to get this out of the embassy?"

"In her lunch hour, in a brown paper bag. She would meet Stein in the gardens at noon. They would each lunch, and MS/Skylark would gather up their rubbish afterwards to dispose of it."

"And we'd have our copy, covered with mayonnaise."

"Yes, only it didn't work out that way. On the morning it was supposed to happen, our Austrian friend was alone in his apartment. He answered the doorbell, signed for a special-delivery letter, and was shot. He lived, but barely. It was hours before his wife found him, unconscious on the floor. One of the bullets severed the nerves in his leg. He's permanently crippled now. Gets around in a motorized wheelchair. We bought it for him."

"That was generous."

"We thought so. The point is, the fake postman used a .22-calibre pistol. The impersonation of a postman and the calibre of the gun are quite familiar to us. The hit had Nick Rossi's trademark. And Rossi left the agency four years ago."

Danner mentally pulled out Rossi's file. Nicholas Aldrich Rossi, age about fifty. Skilled marksman. Princeton graduate. Mother an American, of east coast establishment family. Father an Italian aristocrat.

"And which of our former agents was in Tokyo when that operation was blown?" Danner asked.

"Tracy Thatcher. Thirty-six hours before the Soviet defector was set to come out, Tracy checked into the Okura Hotel, registering as the representative of a fictitious business firm."

"When did Tracy retire?"

"He didn't. He was fired by Admiral Turner in the Hallowe'en Massacre in 1977, five months after you left us."

"And someone was spotted in Madrid, too?"

"Yes. Kermit Gardner. He came through as a tourist the week before a very embarrassing story about our operations surfaced in *Mundo Obrero*, the Communist Party weekly. Gardner was fired from the agency at the same time as Thatcher."

It had become apparent to Danner, as he listened, that some of the old boys were up to no good. These were the now-ageing spies, the prestigious, often wealthy graduates of Harvard, Yale and Princeton, who had formed the heart and soul of the agency during the 1950s and 1960s. There had been great glamour in secret work in those days. And the CIA appealed as well to the puritan heritage of these scions of the WASP establishment, to the sense of service and duty with which they had been inculcated since childhood. This group of men, bound together by class values, old school ties, and supreme self-confidence, had formed the core of the Clandestine Services, the agency's dirty tricks department. They shared a belief that they could set aside ordinary rules of morality in the higher interest of the state.

In 1977, however, the old boys had fallen upon hard times. Congressional investigations and news stories had focused on abuses by the intelligence community—drug testing on innocent Americans, wire-tapping, assassination plots. In the shake-up that followed, hundreds of old boys were dismissed or forced to retire. The action—swift, unexpected, and somewhat mysterious, Danner remembered—took place on October 31, and so became known as the Halloween Massacre. Some of the most powerful secret agents in the world were swept away. Experienced CIA hands, men who had run important divisions and bureaus, were suddenly unemployed and left railing at the injustice.

137

Against that background, the implications of what Hadley had been telling him were mind-boggling. "What do they want?" Danner asked.

"We don't know," said Hadley.

"Who's running them?"

"That's one of the things we want you to find out."

"But not the most important thing."

"No. Quite obviously, someone inside the agency—someone with access to our plans for covert operations—is betraying those plans. We have to find him."

"There are still some old boys inside the agency. They weren't all fired, were they?"

"Well, I suppose I would qualify as one," Hadley said with an awkward laugh. "No, not all of them walked the plank. But we've already given lie-detector tests to two dozen people. The polygraphs say they're all innocent. Including me."

Danner looked out at the thick cover of trees that surrounded headquarters. He wondered why the agency relied so heavily on lie detectors, since anyone who took a tranquillizer could beat the machine. He wished he were out on the Miramichi. "I'll come back for a while," he said. "But on my own terms."

Hadley brightened. "Name them."

"One, a free hand to poke anywhere inside the agency and get anything I want. Two, complete independence: I'll be taking orders from no one. Three, the director himself must agree to the terms. And I want to hear it from him."

"Done." Hadley rose. "I'll take you in to see him right now."

"As far as money is concerned," Danner added on the way down the hall, "whatever my old job pays will be OK."

"Fine, fine."

A moment later they were being ushered into a huge office with floor-to-ceiling picture windows covered by white metal blinds. As they entered, CIA Director Brooks Jordan rose from the black leather swivel chair behind his antique mahogany desk. He was tall, with cold grey eyes that looked at the world through rimless glasses. His hair seemed whiter than Danner remembered. But it had been seven years.

"Hello, Bill," the director greeted him, shaking hands. "Good to have you aboard again."

"You didn't give me much choice."

"I do apologize," Jordan said. "But we have rather a large problem." He sat down and motioned them into chairs by the desk. "Your job, put simply, is to find the mole."

"And when I do?" Danner asked.

The director smiled. "Leave that to us."

Chapter 3

A week later Danner had settled in. He rented a one-bedroom apartment in Alexandria, Virginia, about twenty minutes from CIA headquarters in Langley. He had a telephone installed, with an unlisted number. The agency provided him with a car.

At Langley he was given a small office on the fourth floor and an identity badge that showed his photograph against a blue background. He was also issued with a set of formal credentials in a leatherette folder with a gold CIA seal on the cover and Director Brooks Jordan's signature inside. In the halls and in the cafeteria he ran into a few of his old colleagues. To those who asked, he said simply that he was doing some consulting.

In midweek he telephoned the fishing camp. He had left Andy, his head guide, in charge, and he wanted to see how he was doing. He gave Andy his address and phone number in Alexandria but instructed him not to give them to anyone.

He missed Carrie a lot. He started to phone her, then decided to allow her a little more time to readjust to being back with Francesca and her stepfather. On Thursday he drove to Georgetown and bought three T-shirts and a new fishing-rod for Carrie, and had everything posted to California for her birthday.

By Friday he was feeling lonely and at a loose end. It was pouring outside—a summer cloudburst, accompanied by thunder and lightning. Instead of driving home at the end of the day, he got off the parkway at Arlington and pulled up in front of a red brick apartment building.

In the lobby, he gave his name to an elderly blue-haired woman at a desk, asking her to ring Mr. Green. She announced him, and he took the lift to the fifth floor.

Before he reached the apartment, Sam Green had the door open. "Bill," he said, his pudgy face beaming, "I can't believe it. Come in."

"Hello, Sam. Nice of you to let me in out of the rain." He

139

surveyed the short, thickset man, who had dark hair, bushy eyebrows, and the beginnings of a pot belly. Sam had been Danner's closest friend in the agency.

"Sit down. Have a drink." Green indicated an armchair opposite the couch. "You still drinking Scotch?"

"On the rocks, with a twist of lemon," Danner said. He did not drink a lot, except when his leg bothered him, which it did on damp days like today. He had twisted his knee badly in Berlin, more than twenty years ago, and Scotch was the best way to ease the pain. Or so he told himself.

Green bustled about in the kitchen, getting the ice, then joined Danner in the living room and handed him a drink. "Now, what in the world blasted you out of the north woods?"

"I was called back in for a little consulting. There are problems in my old shop. More I cannot say, and even that's too much."

Green waved the subject aside. "I've already forgotten it. But I'd give anything to know how they got you back."

Danner took a sip of his drink. "Gentle persuasion," he said. "Tell me, how are things in the technical division?"

"Very interesting," Green said. "We've got some birds up there that are shooting incredible stuff." Sam was a photo interpreter for the CIA. His job was to analyse the pictures, magnified many times, that were taken by US spy satellites. His speciality was the Soviet Union. If the Russians changed the location of any of their missiles, Sam Green knew about it within twenty-four hours.

He said, "We're getting fantastic detail of Kalin's dacha, outside Moscow." Yuri Kalin, at the age of seventy, was still firmly entrenched as the leader of the Soviet Union. "There's a solarium on the roof. The photos show him cavorting with his mistress, who wears a purple bikini." Sam laughed. "But what about you? Do you ever miss the business?"

"Never. I put it behind me. At least I thought I had."

"I know how you felt," Green said. "But I don't think I'd have the guts to up and quit like you did."

"I'm forty-eight, Sam. I put in twenty years with the agency, my best years. What have I got to show for it? A broken marriage, and a background that no corporation would want."

"You're not blaming the agency for the divorce?"

Danner took a gulp of his drink before he replied. "Look, you're a bachelor. Marriage is out of your orbit. I'm not saying Francesca left

140

me because of the agency. But she hated the secrecy, resented it bitterly. She said I couldn't share my life with her."

Sam nodded. "That's true of so many agency marriages."

"There were times when I had to leave for weeks, even months, and I couldn't tell her why," Danner said. "The agency was like a mistress, and Francesca was always jealous." He rattled the ice cubes in his glass. "The real trouble started in the summer of '72, when I was posted to Madrid. Francesca was pregnant with Carrie, and I could only give her three weeks' notice of the move. It was hot that summer, and nerves were frayed. One night we had a fight. Francesca was screaming. She said the CIA was compartmentalized for secrecy. She said I had compartmentalized my soul."

Sam was silent. He stared at his shoes.

"Maybe she was right," Danner said. "Anyway, we hung in there until 1976, when the divorce came through." He finished his drink. "I don't blame the agency. On the other hand, it might not have happened if I'd been working for IBM."

"You'd have been bored to death."

"Maybe, but when I left the agency, I tried the corporations. Guys I went to college with are at the top of the corporate world now. But they weren't able to do much for me. I couldn't put anything down on my job application. I could say I had worked for the agency, and that was about it." He paused. "I like it up in Canada," he said. "No one bothers me."

"Me neither," Sam said. "When you're a specialist, a technical expert, people leave you alone."

"I know. But I couldn't have stayed. I came to feel more and more that all of us in the agency were just children playing secret games. It didn't seem like work for grown-ups."

"Some of it has to be done."

"A lot of it would be better left undone. Most of our covert ops, for starters."

Sam's eyebrows went up. "Are you trying to put Dixon Hadley out of business?"

Danner laughed. He got up and walked to the window. The rain was still coming down. He turned back to Sam. "Maybe you can help me catch up on a little history."

"Sure. Ancient or modern?"

"Modern. What do you know about the Hallowe'en Massacre? Did they really fire eight hundred of the old boys?"

"The press overplayed it. Only two hundred and forty-three were canned. The rest retired."

"What was the reason for it?"

Sam shook his head. "You hear different rumours. Some of them were just getting old. Living off their reputations and connections. But there may have been more to it than that."

"Brooks Jordan was deputy director of the agency then, wasn't he? He qualifies as an old boy. And he survived."

"That's right," Sam said. "And now he's number one."

"Interesting," Danner said.

"Very." Green looked at his watch. "Listen. I'm invited to a party at Sandy Berens's place over in Rosslyn. Sandy's nice. She works with me in Imagery. Why don't you come along?"

Danner shrugged. "OK. Why not?"

They drove to Rosslyn in Sam's car, and in a few minutes he pulled up at a high-rise overlooking the Potomac. When they walked in, the apartment was crowded with people. The stereo was turned up high. A pretty, brown-haired woman in tight designer jeans and a knitted top came over. "Sam!" She threw her arms round him and gave him a kiss.

"I brought a friend. This is Bill Danner. Hope you don't mind."

"Are you kidding? He's handsome." To Danner she said, "I'm Sandy. The bar's on the terrace, if you can fight your way there." She pointed out towards the balcony.

They threaded their way through the people who were dancing in the centre of the room. An athletic-looking man with an open shirt, a gold chain, and a lot of black curly chest hair bumped into Danner, spilling some of a drink on his jacket. "Hey, sorry, pal," he said.

"He agency?" Danner asked Sam.

"Yeah. A Security hood." Like a lot of agency employees, Sam was not fond of the Office of Security or its staff. They administered the lie-detector tests that all CIA workers had to take periodically, and they constantly nitpicked about open filing cabinets, burn-bags, and other regulations.

Everyone at the party was agency. Employees were encouraged to socialize among themselves. But when Danner looked around, he saw no familiar faces. Most of the people were younger than he was, in their early thirties.

He and Sam were skirting the dance floor when Danner's eye was drawn towards a strikingly beautiful woman dancing with a man in a blue blazer. It was the girl he had seen in the red MG on his first day back. She wore white trousers, leather sandals, a purple silk shirt and gold hoop earrings. She was deeply tanned and her hair was jet black, her eyes bright green under dark lashes. She danced effortlessly to the music, and a lot of people were watching her. Danner figured she was around thirty.

"Who's *that?*" he asked.

"Julie Nichols," Sam replied. "She's taken, I think. She's dancing with Turk Wilcox. He's with Soviet Russia division."

They made it to the balcony, and Danner got a Scotch and water at the crowded bar. The rain had finally stopped. The night was cool for early July, and the trees along the river smelled fresh. He and Sam were enjoying the air when a voluptuous red-haired woman pulled Sam off towards the dance floor. Danner stepped over to the railing and stood looking out at the Potomac.

"Are you counting the stars?"

The husky, pleasant voice came from behind his right shoulder. He turned and saw the woman he had spotted on the dance floor. "No," Danner said. "The years."

She laughed. "There can't be that many."

"Then I'll stop counting. My name's Bill Danner." He could see Turk Wilcox waiting for drinks at the bar.

She smiled, and her teeth were white against the tanned face and the black hair. She was even prettier close up.

"I'm Julie Nichols." She extended a hand. It was soft, yet firm, and Danner held it a fraction of a second longer than necessary. "Are you *the* William Danner?"

He laughed. "I was this morning."

"I've heard of you. Everyone has. But I thought you'd left us."

"I'm back for a while." He smiled. "Do you drive a red MG?"

The green eyes widened. "How did you know?"

"You shouldn't tailgate. It's dangerous to get too close."

She looked puzzled. "Where—"

"About ten days ago," he said. "On the George Washington Parkway. I made you go around."

"Oh, I remember. I was annoyed with you. But I'm quick to forgive." The radiant smile again.

Danner couldn't help looking at her figure, the trim hips and legs. "You dance very well," he said.

"Is that an invitation?"

"If you like," he found himself saying.

Turk was eyeing them now, but he was still stuck in the queue at the bar. They squeezed through the crush inside and started to dance. She moved sensually, gracefully, and she was very near him, their bodies almost touching. She looked up at him challengingly. "Is it dangerous to get too close?"

He started to reply when Turk came up to them with two drinks. "Vodka and tonic," he said, handing one to Julie.

"Oh, thanks," she said. "Turk, this is Bill Danner." The man nodded and gently steered her away. She smiled a goodbye.

Danner headed for a corner that looked slightly less crowded. There, a slim, owlish-looking man with thick glasses was chatting with an intense, dark-haired woman in a beige suit.

"I'm Winckelmann." The man extended a hand towards Danner. "Office of Medical Services. And this is Dr. Quimby from Psychiatry."

"Bill Danner," he told the man. "You a shrink, too?"

"I'm a urologist," Winckelmann said.

"Ah," said Danner, not knowing how to make small talk with a urologist and not particularly wanting to. The agency had physicians of all kinds, who were cleared to treat its personnel. In particular, the CIA had its own psychiatric staff. It would not do to have covert operators spilling secrets to non-agency doctors.

Dr. Quimby broke in. "Murray was just saying how he'd give anything to get a specimen from Kalin."

"Why Kalin?" Danner asked.

"We could tell a lot," Winckelmann replied. "My specialty is urinalysis—looking for sugar for diabetes, protein that can be evidence of nephritis, red or white cells for kidney or bladder trouble. Or to see if someone's on medication. That kind of information about Kalin could be very important."

"I see," said Danner.

"In Psychiatry," Dr. Quimby said, "we prepare psychological profiles of world leaders. We did a profile on Kalin." She looked grave. "I think something serious is going on. His behaviour has been increasingly erratic. He's becoming withdrawn, cancelling Politburo meetings. That behaviour alternates with periods of hyperactivity and enormous energy."

"What about his megalomania?" Winckelmann asked.

"According to the reports I read, it's increasing. He believes in his

144

own infallibility and brushes aside the views of his advisers. He may be a borderline psychotic."

Well, Danner thought, she might be right about that. He'd heard it was the prevailing wisdom inside the agency that the Soviet leader had been acting dangerously screwy.

Winckelmann was shaking his head. "It's so important to get a specimen from Kalin."

Before the doctor could warm to his subject, Danner excused himself. Turning away, he practically collided with Sam, who had his arm round a young and tipsy secretary from Computer Services. "Time to go," Sam said. "I'll drive you back to my place so you can pick up your car."

"Fine with me," Danner said. He looked around and saw Julie Nichols talking to someone a few feet away. He smiled as he brushed past her, then realized she had slipped something into his hand. He put it in his pocket.

Sam dropped him off at his car. Driving home, he reached into his jacket and took out a matchbook. He flipped it open and saw a phone number written inside. He wondered whether he would call her. Meeting her had been exciting. It disturbed him, because he had not expected to enjoy anything about being back.

Chapter 4

Danner dawdled over coffee in his office until it was almost time for his appointment with Dixon Hadley. He had spent the morning studying damage assessment reports on the sabotaged operations, and now he needed answers to some questions.

At four minutes to eleven he took the lift up to the sixth floor. As he walked down the corridor, he saw a blind man with a guide dog coming from Hadley's office. The man was prematurely grey and wore dark glasses. Danner realized it was Roger Jellison.

Jellison had been brought in by the CIA to solve a peculiar problem. Despite the complex phone system used by the agency, when anyone at headquarters placed a long-distance call to someone outside the government, it was handled by the telephone company like any other call. A record of it was automatically registered on a tape that was fed into a computer at the phone company's accounts department, and every month the CIA was billed like any other customer. If the phone company or its computer were penetrated by some hostile intelligence service, the people whom the agency had called could be traced and identified.

There had seemed no way round the security problem until someone discovered Jellison. The blind man had perfect pitch, and he was used to whistle the numbers of ultraconfidential calls illegally. He could exactly match the highpitched musical tones that activated long-distance and overseas calls. These bypassed the telephone company's computers and could not be traced.

Now Jellison halted, listening to the footsteps. "Danner, is that you? I thought you had retired."

"Hello, Roger," Danner said. "I'm just back on temporary duty." He was not surprised that Jellison knew him, even after seven years. The blind man could do things like that.

"Well, nice to see you."

Danner remembered that Jellison had a disconcerting habit of using that phrase. "Nice to see you, too, Roger," he said.

He had to cool his heels for five minutes in Dixon Hadley's outer office. When he was finally admitted, Hadley rose, shook hands, and directed him to a chair. Danner looked around, squinting, because there was, as usual, too much sunlight streaming into the room. "How are you getting along?" the DDO asked.

"Just easing back in. I've been reading the reports. I guess for openers I need to know more about the Hallowe'en Massacre. Who got fired, and why."

Hadley sighed. "It's a long story," he said. "You remember Farrell and Griffin. They quit the Clandestine Services and peddled what they'd learned to the highest bidder."

"And the highest bidder turned out to be Libya's Gaddafi."

"Unfortunately. They became millionaires by selling him explosives disguised as ashtrays, coat hangers, even kettles. They also got a fat contract to train his people as terrorists."

"What's that got to do with the Hallowe'en Massacre?"

"Everything. The director found out that six of our people, then employed by the agency, were working with Farrell and Griffin. The director went off the pad. He decided the old boys were to blame."

"Were they?"

"I suppose some of them were. After all, they had been running the Clandestine Services for years."

147

"So the director drew up a little list."

"Oh, not personally. He turned the job over to Brooks Jordan, who was then deputy director. Brooks drew up the list."

Danner leaned forward. "And he fired a lot of old boys?"

Hadley smiled faintly. "He had an assistant do that. Of course Jordan was in the background, pulling the strings. And when the dust settled, he ended up on top. The director resigned, and Jordan was appointed to succeed him."

Danner asked, "How did you survive? Surely you're as much a card-carrying old boy as any of those who were fired."

"Brooks and I were in the same club together at Yale." Hadley lowered his voice. "But the truth is, I don't know how secure Jordan's position is with the president now."

"I see." Danner looked out at the trees. "I guess I should know who was shaken out. I'd like a copy of the list."

The DDO looked dubious. "Of *all* names?"

"I have to start somewhere."

Hadley sighed. "All right, I'll see what I can do."

Danner got up to leave. "I'll also need Nick Rossi's file from Personnel. I want to find out more about that Vienna operation."

Hadley made a note on his pad. "There's one other thing," he said after a slight hesitation. "It was indiscreet of Sam Green to discuss Kalin's solarium activities with you. The source of that information is highly sensitive."

Danner, stone-faced, made no reply, but he was furious. So he was under surveillance. Knowing that sooner or later he would call on his old friend, they had even bugged Sam. He *had* been away from the business, Danner realized. He had almost forgotten what nice people he worked for.

DANNER WALKED DOWN a corridor towards the rear of the building. When he came to Imagery, he pushed open a door marked RESTRICTED AREA: DO NOT ENTER. The code letters on his ID badge permitted him to go almost anywhere at headquarters.

He found Sam sitting in a darkened room in front of a huge screen that cast an eerie green light on his face and body. A photograph filled the screen. Sam was peering intently at the image and entering numbers into a computer keyboard. Danner watched silently for a moment until Sam became aware of his presence and turned. "Sneak up on a guy, will you?"

148

"I just didn't want to interrupt," Danner said. "What have you got there?"

"Missile silos," Green replied. With a metal pointer he indicated an area near the centre of the screen. "They're camouflaged, but you can see the faint outlines. There. SS-18s, Mod. 4. Kalin's biggest. Range, sixty-eight hundred miles. It would only take one of these to vaporize Washington."

"You've brightened my day, Sam. What are you keying in?"

"Data for image enhancement. The computer improves the picture, gives us measurements of objects in the photograph, and tells us whether anything's changed since the last time our satellite passed overhead." He moved his pointer. "These latrines, for example. They've added a new one. That means they're bringing in more people. We're trying to figure out why."

Danner hesitated. "Sam, I dropped by because there's something you ought to know. They're bugging your apartment."

Sam looked at him. "You're kidding. How'd you find out?"

"Hadley's reading the traffic. He said you shouldn't have told me about Kalin and that girl in the solarium."

"Oh, man, this place really is Disneyland, with all the Mickey Mouse that goes on." Sam shook his head dolefully. "I should have listened to my mother and gone into business."

Danner laughed. "I'm sorry. The bug is my fault. But I thought you should know."

"Well, thanks." Green sighed.

Danner said goodbye and walked back along the corridor. He spent what was left of the day in his office, flipping through reports on past investigations of suspected moles inside the agency. He was surprised at how many such investigations had taken place; it seemed the search for double agents inside headquarters was almost constant. But the files provided no leads to the mole who was currently giving Dixon Hadley the shakes.

CHARLIE'S WAS TUCKED AWAY in Georgetown, along the Potomac River. With low ceilings, a few small spotlights, and a soothing décor, it was the place to go for jazz and supper. Danner had chosen it, and Julie was pleased.

They ordered a bottle of white wine; it was cold and dry, which felt good, because outside it was typical Washington weather for late August, very hot and muggy. Julie was wearing a white summer dress decorated with splashes of bright colours; it set off her black hair and her tan dramatically. She looked beautiful by candlelight.

"It took you a while to open the matchbook," she said.

Danner laughed. "I don't smoke." He had waited more than a month before he had rung her, persuading himself it was because he was busy.

"Do you like being back?" Julie asked.

"I'd rather be fishing."

She laughed. "Then why are you here?"

"They made me an offer I couldn't refuse."

"I see." Her green eyes searched his for a clue to his meaning, but found none. She took a sip of her wine. "You haven't told me what you're doing."

"A little consulting for the DDO. He's having some problems and thought I could help. And you?"

"I'm in SO," she said.

"That must be new," said Danner. "I don't know it."

"Special Operations," she explained. "We're covert, but we're not really part of Clandestine Services."

Their food came, and they stopped talking until the waitress had gone. Then Danner asked, "What do you do in SO?"

Julie hesitated before answering. "Research," she said.

"From the name of the unit," Danner said, trying to sound casual, "I thought it might handle terminations."

She shook her head. "We don't do any now. But we have to be able to."

Danner recoiled. Did this beautiful woman really believe the agency should kill people? He wondered if she herself could carry out such an order. "I don't agree," he responded. "I don't think anyone appointed us God."

"Suppose a termination could prevent World War Three?"

"There are exceptions to every rule. But as a general proposition, I'm against it."

"In a war people get killed. Espionage is a kind of war."

Danner was becoming irritated. Dropping the subject, he asked, "What sort of research do you do?"

"I work with the Central Cover staff. We're trying to build up our commercial cover. It doesn't take the opposition very long to know who our people are in an embassy."

Danner nodded. He didn't know whether to believe her.

"I locate and analyse mid-size American companies that do a lot of business in the Middle East and Africa," she went on. "Then I try to persuade them to hire some of our people. We pay their salaries, of course, and no one except our contact knows they work for us."

"And SO runs operations as well?"

"Some."

Danner decided not to press further. "Where are you from?"

"Everywhere," she answered. "I was a foreign service brat. Wherever my father was posted, we went with him. I was recruited for the agency in my senior year at Bryn Mawr. By my English professor."

They listened to a guitar doing an intricate jazz solo with a lot of improvisations. Then Julie asked, "And what about you? How did William Danner become a legend?"

"I'm not feeling much like a legend. I've been out of it for a number of years."

"Tell me more," she said. "I want to know all about you."

"There's not much to tell. I grew up in a little town in Vermont. White River Junction. My father was a railway engineer. He was away a lot because of his job. But he set great store by education. He encouraged me to read a lot as a kid. And I ended up at Dartmouth, on a scholarship."

"What was your mother like?"

"Irish, with a temper to match. Raised three children on very little money and taught us to fight for what we wanted."

"When did you join the agency?" she asked.

"Right out of college, like you did. I signed on in 1957. After my junior officer training, I was posted to Berlin for two years."

"And after that?"

"A series of posts. Latin America, Africa, Europe. In between, I worked at headquarters."

"Why did you quit?" Julie asked.

"Lots of reasons. My marriage had broken up, for one. And I'd changed. I didn't believe in the agency any more."

"Why?"

"I guess it began in Berlin. There was an operation. We lost someone. I don't think it was worth it. And after a while so much of what we do began to seem pointless. For example, in the Third World we spent incredible energy trying to recruit Soviet defectors. We squandered so much time and money."

Julie shook her head. "But the objective was worthwhile."

"Yes and no. Suppose we get one. Is he a plant? We can never be sure. The more he tells us, the greater the possibility that Moscow Centre is building him, giving away real secrets to make us believe. You end up trusting no one, suspecting everyone."

"But surely the Russians have already tried to plant a mole in the agency. Do you think they've succeeded?"

Danner grew silent. Julie was edging into areas he wasn't supposed to talk about.

She sensed his mood. "Am I getting too close again?"

"No," he lied. "I just can't answer the question." She was smart, he realized, as well as beautiful.

The waitress came, and they ordered coffee. They lingered for a long time over it, listening to the music. But it was getting late, and Danner asked for a bill. He hated to leave. He had been enjoying the evening, the music, Julie.

They walked out into the warm night, but neither of them felt like going home. "Let's go to the kite store," Julie said impulsively. He took her hand; it seemed natural enough. They strolled up towards M Street and found the store, and Danner bought her a Japanese dragon kite with a fifty-foot tail.

"First windy day, we'll go and fly it," she said. "Down by the Washington Monument."

"It's a date. Provided you bring the picnic."

"If you'll bring the wine."

"I'll have to sneak it in," he said. "They don't allow booze in the monument grounds. Park Service rules."

"You see? You're not really against covert operations after all."

Danner laughed. "Touché." He put his arm round her waist. He hadn't felt this good about a woman for a long time, and it scared him. Warning lights were going off in his head. Julie was a lot younger than he was, and he was breaking his rule. He had decided, after Lisa, never to become involved with anyone else who worked for the agency. It was safer that way.

"I guess it's time to take you home," he said.

They went back to the car, then drove south along the river to Alexandria. Julie had the downstairs apartment in a weathered brick house in Old Town. They parked nearby, and when she invited him inside for a brandy, he accepted.

She found a bottle of cognac in a kitchen cupboard and poured

152

some into two crystal brandy goblets. In the living room, she put a record on; they sat down together on a white couch opposite the wide hearth.

They sipped their brandy slowly, and she drifted closer and rested her head on his shoulder. In a moment he had his arms round her. The smell of her perfume mingled with her breath, and he kissed her as she lightly moved her fingers up and down his back.

When Danner left, he wanted to break into a dance. Her kiss had been full of promise. Walking towards his car, he felt happier than he had for a long time. Even though he knew it probably wouldn't last. It never had.

Chapter 5

Danner was staring out of his office window, wondering whether he had been given an impossible assignment, when the telephone rang. It was Hadley's secretary. "He'd like to see you for lunch. Can you come up now?"

Hadley kept him waiting the usual five minutes before joining him in the reception area. Then they walked down the corridor to the executive dining room, where they found a table near a window. Hadley was full of himself because he had accompanied Brooks Jordan to the White House that morning to brief President Lansing Forbes on the situation in the Persian Gulf. Over the years, Danner had noticed that otherwise intelligent men came away from the Oval Office on a sort of high; they seemed to be tingling for several hours.

"I have a question for you," Danner said over his chef's salad. "I'd like to know what Special Operations does."

Hadley looked at him quizzically. "I'm not sure that you need to know that."

Danner reminded him of their arrangement. "I'm cleared for everything," he said.

Hadley paused, then said, "SO was established six years ago, as a follow-up to Executive Action."

Danner understood. Executive Action had been set up during the early 1960s to handle assassination planning. For a while Hadley had run the EA unit.

"SO can handle terminations," Hadley continued. "It carries out operations controlled by the director."

153

Danner could see why the deputy director had been reluctant to discuss Special Operations. The unit was outside his patch. They talked further, and Hadley made it clear that even as chief of the agency's clandestine activities, he was told about SO's work only in vague terms.

"Do they do any research?" Danner asked.

Hadley shrugged. "I suppose so." He stirred his coffee. "I've got the list of old boys you wanted. Everyone fired in the Hallowe'en Massacre. Also Nick Rossi's file. I'll give them to you after lunch."

"Good."

Hadley lowered his voice. "I'm afraid our troubles are continuing. In London, several of our people have been blown. Their names were published in *Private Eye*. We'll have to pull them out."

"Same business?"

"I'm afraid so. One of our old boys was seen checking into a London hotel about two weeks before the names surfaced."

"Sorry to hear it," Danner sympathized.

The deputy director shook his head. "What we need to know," he said, "is where you plan to start."

Danner could understand why Hadley was getting edgy. The calendar had slipped into September and he wasn't making much progress. Danner drummed his fingers on the table. "Vienna," he finally replied. "I want to retrace that operation. Find out everything possible about it. I can stop off in London and Madrid on the way in. I'll want to see MS/Skylark, of course."

"That may be difficult. He's rather bitter. And his wife extremely so. But I'll see what I can do."

They left the executive dining room and walked back to Hadley's office. The DDO handed over two file folders, both labelled TOP SECRET in red letters. Danner took them back to his own office, where he flipped through the list of dismissed CIA men.

Then he opened the file headed ROSSI, NICHOLAS ALDRICH. Its contents were like a guide book through the darker pages of the agency's past. Rossi had been the agency's contact with the Mafia in a Castro assassination attempt. He had been involved in the plot to kill General Schneider in Chile. He had fired a shot that nicked Qaddafi in the jaw, although the Libyans hushed up the incident. But what interested Danner most was a notation near the end of the file. For the last two years of his agency service, Rossi had been assigned to Special Operations.

THE TELEPHONE was ringing insistently on the table next to the bed, and Danner wondered vaguely if he'd overslept. He'd been out late with Julie the evening before. They were seeing each other almost every night now. He half opened his eyes, looked at his clock radio, and saw that it was only a little after six am.

He groped for the receiver. " 'Lo," he croaked.

The voice sounded far away. "Mr. Danner?"

"Andy, how are you? How's everybody?" It was the guide whom Danner had left in charge of the fishing camp. He was delighted to hear Andy's voice, despite the early hour.

"I'm fine. We've been busy."

Danner chuckled. "Well, what's up that couldn't wait until I've had my coffee?"

Andy hesitated. "It's your wife, Mr. Danner. Your ex. She called a little while ago and asked to talk to you. I wouldn't give her your number. You said not to give it to anybody."

Danner sat up, alert now, a little stab of fear in his belly. "Did you say a little while ago? It's only three o'clock in the morning in California."

"Yes, sir. She sounded kind of upset. Said she had to talk to you right away. So I said I would get a message to you."

"OK, thanks, Andy. You did the right thing."

He hung up and dialled Francesca. She answered on the second ring. The throaty, normally confident voice he knew too well. Only this time she was crying.

"Bill, thank God! Maybe you can do something."

"Take it easy. What's the matter?"

"Carrie's gone. I'm sure she's been kidnapped."

"Oh, no." Danner felt as though someone had kicked him in the stomach. Carrie gone! "Tell me what happened."

Francesca was sobbing. Finally she managed to stop. "Yesterday she didn't come home from school. Usually she goes over to her friend Jessica's for a while. I didn't start to worry until it got to be six o'clock. Then I called Jessica's mother. Carrie hadn't been there."

"Damn!" He felt an enormous pressure in his chest, like a deep-sea diver who'd come up too fast.

"So I checked some other friends' houses. Carrie hadn't been to any of them. Then I called the police." Francesca started to cry again.

"Take it easy," Danner repeated. "Were the cops any help?"

She blew her nose. "They came to the house. They wrote everything down. Then they called a few hours later to say some kids had stumbled on Carrie's bike in Toro Canyon Park, covered with brush."

"Toro Canyon? That's almost four miles out of her way."

"I know. I tried to tell them."

"Has anyone called? Has there been a ransom note?"

"No. The detectives are treating it as a missing person case. Just another runaway kid. Happens all the time, they said."

"She's a happy kid," said Danner. "She'd have no reason to run away. She didn't leave a note or anything?"

"No. Nothing. And she didn't take any extra clothes to school. I checked her room."

"What about her bear?"

"Edward is in his usual place on her bookcase. You know she wouldn't go anywhere without Edward." She cried again, and Danner waited for her to stop.

He was terrified by the news, because he recognized it for what it must be—a kidnapping by professionals who were sending him a message. He thought of the wrenching fear Carrie must have felt, the awful terror. Other dreadful thoughts crowded in. He had got Lisa killed in Berlin; and now Carrie?

"I'm afraid it's a warning," Danner said. "Someone is trying to get me to stop something I'm doing."

"What do you mean?" Francesca asked sharply. "Bill, what are you talking about?" He could hear Richard in the background trying to calm her.

"I can't tell you any more."

Francesca exploded. "It's just the same old garbage," she screamed. "It's all a big secret. Agency business. Well, this time it's our *daughter!*"

Danner felt the knot growing in his chest. He took a deep breath. "Look, I'll do everything I can to find out who has her. I'll fly out there. I'll talk to the police." Even as he said it, he knew it wouldn't do any good. Whoever had Carrie wasn't going to be caught by the county sheriff.

DANNER SHOWERED, shaved, and had a quick breakfast. A few minutes later he was driving as fast as he could, weaving in and out of the morning rush-hour traffic.

156

As he drove, Danner concentrated on who would have a motive to abduct Carrie. The most likely kidnapper was whoever was betraying the agency's secrets. The mole. That would mean that the mole knew about Danner's investigation and was signalling to him to stop.

But there were other possibilities. The agency itself, on orders from Brooks Jordan or Dixon Hadley, could have engineered the kidnapping as insurance. To make certain he pressed ahead vigorously with his mission. The agency's motive would be the exact opposite of the mole's.

It was equally possible that Carrie had been snatched by renegade old boys—the former agents who were working with the mole. Like the mole, they would want Danner to stop his investigation.

One other organization would have an interest in acquiring leverage over him, Danner knew—the KGB. The Russians were reaping the benefits of the blown operations. If the mole had warned them of his own danger, the Soviets might well risk a covert operation on US soil. It would not be the first.

One, the mole. Two, the agency. Three, the renegade old boys. Four, the Russians. There was no way to know which of them had his daughter. Dear Carrie, Danner thought, what have I done?

He left the parkway at the CIA exit, held up his badge at the guard's hut, and swept through the gate. He parked, and trotted into the lobby. Passing quickly through another checkpoint, he took the lift up to Dixon Hadley's office.

Hadley's secretary frowned when she saw Danner. He was not expected. "I'm afraid he's in a staff meeting," she said.

"Pull him out," Danner ordered.

From his grim expression, she realized he meant it. "I'll tell him you're here," she said noncommittally.

Danner paced the reception area as he waited. He was still pacing when the deputy director appeared.

"Hello, Bill," Hadley said calmly. "Where's the fire?" He held open the door to his office and motioned Danner inside.

"What the hell is going on?" Danner demanded.

"You tell me," Hadley countered. "I thought by now you'd be on your way to Vienna."

"You're going to say you don't know why I'm here."

"That's right," Hadley said.

157

"Damn!" Danner slammed his fist down on the desk. "Carrie's disappeared."

"Your daughter?" Hadley sounded genuinely surprised. "No wonder you're upset. That's distressing news."

"She didn't come home after school yesterday. It's clear to me she's been kidnapped. By professionals. The timing isn't coincidental," Danner declared.

Hadley removed his horn-rimmed glasses and slowly massaged his eyes. "I'm sorry," he said. "This is a . . . complication."

"I thought you might know something about it."

The DDO looked shocked. But that didn't mean a thing, Danner knew. In the agency you were trained to lie, with facial expressions as well as words.

Hadley put his glasses back on. "It wasn't us," he said.

"How can I be sure?"

Hadley sighed. "You can't. But if it were us, we'd tell you. There wouldn't be much point otherwise, would there?"

"I guess that's true," Danner admitted.

"Besides, we don't kidnap children."

"Well, someone has," Danner said.

"The mole," Hadley suggested.

"Or the embittered old boys. Or the Russians."

"All of those are possible, I'm afraid."

"It doesn't matter. Whoever has Carrie wants me to stop what I'm doing. So I'm going to stop. And hope they let her go."

"They might," said Hadley. "Or they might kill her."

"OK," Danner replied. "You have any better ideas?"

"Yes," Hadley said. "Let's assume you're right. This was done by professionals. The only leverage you have over them is to keep after the mole. You may smoke the kidnappers out. They may show their hand, make contact with you or your wife."

"And if they do?"

"If they do, there's a chance of finding them. If they don't, there's none at all. We'll put tracing equipment on your phone and on your wife's, if she agrees. You'll have the agency behind you. If there's any contact, we'll move fast."

Danner thought it over. Despite his anguish, he knew he must reason clearly. Hadley's argument was self-serving; the DDO desperately wanted him to stay. But it also made a kind of sense. "All right," he said.

158

Hadley looked relieved. "You've made the right decision."

"I'm flying to Santa Barbara today," Danner said. "I promised her mother. Francesca," he corrected himself.

"Of course. Get one of the pool secretaries to arrange it." It was Hadley's way of saying that the trip was company business.

"I'll be there for a day. Then I'll fly back here and leave for London. I'll spend two days there, and two in Madrid. I should be in Vienna on Tuesday, a week from today."

"Good. I'll notify the stations. I've already cabled Ashford in Vienna. And I've instructed him to pave the way with MS/Skylark."

Danner left and walked down the corridor, his mind churning. Back at his desk, he wondered whether he had done the right thing. If his decision was a mistake, the cost was too horrible to contemplate. He telephoned Julie and told her he had to go out of town but planned to be back on Thursday.

Then he drove out to National Airport, scarcely conscious of where he was driving. He thought only of Carrie. He had received a letter from her just four days earlier, forwarded from New Brunswick by Andy. She had sounded very happy, and thanked him for the birthday presents. She had been going sailing with Richard and Francesca. She had spent a whole day roller-skating along Cabrillo Boulevard, all the way to the bird refuge and back four times. In her letter she had enclosed a strand of purple wool, three feet long. It was for Mr. O'Malley.

"CAPTAIN BLANCHARD has turned off the seat-belt sign," the flight attendant announced. "You are free to move about the cabin if you wish."

Danner stretched out and eased his seat back, glad to have the California trip behind him. It had been even harder than he had expected. The most painful moment had come when he stood alone in Carrie's room, looking at Edward Bear sitting forlornly on the bookcase.

Francesca had been much more composed than in her initial, grief-stricken phone conversation. She agreed to let the agency put the tracing equipment in. But she was still bitterly angry at Danner and blamed him for Carrie's disappearance. He couldn't argue. He knew she was right.

He had confined himself for the most part to filling her in on his meeting with Detective Radley Walker of the Santa Barbara sheriff's

159

department. The detective had been very sympathetic but said no leads had developed as to Carrie's whereabouts. He pointed out that at any given time the department had ten to fifteen cases of missing juveniles. Usually, he said, they turned out to be runaways. There was no evidence of foul play. And in the absence of any kidnap evidence, such as a demand for ransom, the department could only treat Carrie's disappearance as a missing person case.

Danner had been appalled. A child was gone, and it was all so casual. But then, perhaps he had no right to be angry with the cops. There was a lot he hadn't told them. And couldn't, any more than he had been able to tell Francesca and Richard.

As soon as the plane landed, Danner found a telephone in the terminal and phoned Julie. She sounded glad to hear his voice.

"I'll be there in about forty-five minutes," he said. "We'll have dinner in Old Town."

"Sounds perfect," she said. "I'll get ready."

Half an hour later he pulled up in front of Julie's house in Alexandria. They kissed in the hallway, and feeling the tension in his shoulders, she asked, "What's wrong?"

"Tell you later. Let's get some dinner first."

They drove to the Fish Market. In the crowded restaurant, they ordered soft-shell crabs and beer.

"Where've you been?" Julie asked.

"California."

"To see your daughter?"

Quietly Danner explained that Carrie was missing. He sketched in the facts but said nothing about his belief that she had been kidnapped. Julie took his hand; her fingers felt very smooth and good in his. "Why didn't you tell me sooner?"

"It isn't your problem."

"It is now. I care about you."

He caressed her hand. "I know you do," he said. He took a sip of his beer. "I leave for Europe tomorrow. Agency business. Of course I'll be back right away if there's any news of Carrie."

"Do you think her disappearance has anything to do with your work for the agency?"

Now he was poised right on the edge. He wanted to tell her. But Julie worked for SO, and so had Nick Rossi. He could either deflect the probe or take her into his confidence. He nodded.

"Oh, no." She held his hand tightly. "Oh, Bill."

160

After that the words came in a torrent. Danner broke all the rules. He didn't really care. He felt under tremendous pressure. There was no one else he could talk to. He told Julie how he had been coerced into coming back, how operations had been blown and that traces of old boys had been picked up in each case. He shared his fears that Carrie had been abducted and went over the list of those with a motive. He explained why he had decided to press ahead with the hunt for the mole, beginning in London the next day.

"If I can, I'd like to help," she said, when he had finished. "Just tell me how."

"All right." Relief and happiness flooded through him. He leaned close, speaking quietly. "Hadley swears the agency had nothing to do with Carrie. Even if he's telling the truth, one unit that could carry out a sensitive domestic operation is outside his control. Your shop. Special Operations."

"All of our operations are in the SO computer," Julie said. "As a researcher, I have access to it."

"That's a break."

"There's a problem. Each operation has a code name. Without the code name, there's no way to call up an operation in the computer. But I'll see what I can do."

"Thanks." Danner paused. She was offering more than he had any right to expect. "You're sticking your neck way out for me. You're sure you want to?"

"I'm sure." She finished her beer. "Take me home now."

"I was thinking the same thing."

He paid the bill, and they drove back to her house. In the living room, Danner took off his jacket and lay back on the couch. It had been a long two days.

Julie came over and gave him a light kiss. "I'm going to miss you," she said.

"I'll miss you, too."

"No, you won't. You'll be too busy." She traced the outline of his lips with her finger. "I think of all the cities in Europe, Vienna is my favourite. I love it. I lived there when I was ten. My father was second secretary in the embassy."

Danner stretched. Julie reached inside his collar and began kneading his neck and shoulders.

"Mmmm," he said, "that feels good."

She smiled. "Would you like me to rub your back?"

"Julie," he murmured. He got up, took her hand, and they walked into the bedroom. And as he held her tightly, he forgot about anything else.

Later, Danner lay with Julie's head cradled against his shoulder, and he told her he loved her, which were words he had not expected to say again.

"I love you," she said. "I love *you*." She rubbed her nose against his cheek like a large, green-eyed cat, then kissed him gently.

In the morning, after they had had breakfast, Danner returned to his apartment to pack a bag. He drove to headquarters and checked in briefly with Dixon Hadley, then picked up his airline tickets from the pool secretary and drove out to Dulles International. Airports were getting to be a habit, he reflected.

His flight for London took off promptly. As the Concorde streaked across the Atlantic, his thoughts returned to Julie, warm and sensual and loving. But something kept nagging at him about their night together, something that was wrong. What was it? Yes, something she had said. In the apartment Julie had said that she loved Vienna. *But he hadn't mentioned Vienna to her*.

Could he have been mistaken? He went back over the evening in his mind. At the Fish Market he had told her he was going to Europe. He had mentioned London, but he had never said Vienna. Perhaps it was simply a coincidence. They had been talking about Europe, and she loved Vienna; it would have been natural enough for her to say so. Or it could mean that she knew where he was going, that SO was monitoring his movements.

If so, was it a slip on her part, or was she trying to tip him off that he was being watched? Whose side was she on? He had shared his anguish over Carrie with this woman, and told her that he loved her. He wondered now whether her "I love you" had been as real as his.

He had to force himself to consider the next question: Had he really met Julie by chance, or had it all been carefully arranged? But that would mean Sam . . . He rejected the idea before it was fully formed. It was too far along the road to paranoia. His meeting Julie had to have been accidental.

His thoughts were interrupted by the steep descent of the supersonic jet. Below him, in the night, he could see the blue runway lights of Heathrow.

162

Chapter 6

Very few people visited Vienna's clock museum on weekday mornings, and the wizened old man who opened the door seemed glad to see Danner. No one else was there.

Danner started to glance at his watch, then realized he didn't have to. All the clocks in the room were ticking, and they told him he was ten minutes early. He began to browse among the exhibits. The floors in the old building creaked with each step.

He stopped to admire a cobalt-blue case clock, an elaborate construction of gilt and bronze topped by two garlanded gold cherubs. Seeing Danner studying it, the museum guard shuffled over and flashed him a gap-toothed grin. "The mistress of Emperor Franz Josef once owned this clock," he confided in heavily accented English. "It was in her villa."

Just then the doorbell buzzed, and the guard went off to answer it. In a moment a tall young man stepped into the room and moved towards Danner, his hand extended in greeting.

"Tyler Ashford," he said. "Sorry to get you over here right from the airport, but the KGB does a rather efficient job of bugging the embassy." Ashford, who had been MS/Skylark's case officer, had a neatly trimmed blond moustache and wore a conservative grey suit, a button-down shirt, and a blue-and-red silk tie. Danner decided he did not like him.

Ashford glanced around. The old man was out of earshot. "Headquarters asked me to show you the file on the Stein operation," Ashford said briskly. "You can come to the embassy to read it."

"I'll do that," said Danner.

"That's the good news. The bad news is that our Skylark won't sing. He'll see you, but he isn't in a mood to be helpful."

The old man came back, and they broke off. "We have another floor above," he told them enthusiastically. "There you find clocks with beautiful birds."

"Very interesting," Danner said. "Do they sing?"

The guard lowered his voice and spoke in reverential tones. "*Ja*. But only the big boss is allowed to wind them up. He has a special key. He comes on Sunday morning and winds them, and all the birdies sing. It's beautiful."

That's what I need, Danner thought. A key to wind up the Skylark.

When the old man had wandered off, Ashford said, "I think I should leave first. No point in our being seen together." He left, and Danner decided to go up to the next floor. There were several elaborate cuckoo clocks, and he stopped to admire a cage containing two mechanical but very lifelike birds with real feathers. He wished Carrie were with him. She would like the birds and the story about the man with the key, who allowed them to sing on Sunday.

THE HOT WATER coming out of the shower in sharp needles felt good against his back. Danner had chosen a small hotel in a quiet side street. He had been going nonstop in London and Madrid for the past four days. He hadn't learned very much; he hoped that here in Vienna he would do better.

He finished showering, got dressed again, and phoned for a taxi. Fifteen minutes later he pulled up outside the American embassy, an imposing rococo building with a colonnaded entrance.

In the lobby, Danner showed his credentials to a receptionist. A secretary came and got him after a few moments. They took a lift upstairs, and she escorted him through wide halls to an empty office. She went out, and returned with a thick file folder. "Call me when you're through," she said as she left.

The folder was labelled MS/SKYLARK and stamped TOP SECRET. The file ran chronologically, beginning with Tyler Ashford's approval of the initial effort by MS/Skylark to make contact with employees of the Czech embassy. On April 2 there was a brief memo from Ashford reporting Stein's successful contact that day with Vlasa Radek. There was a memo giving details of her background, as learned by Prague station, and a message from Dixon Hadley, dated April 7, giving approval for MS/Skylark to proceed with the operation.

There followed a series of memos from Ashford summarizing the progress of Stein's romance, and then a cable to Hadley proposing that on May 5 MS/Skylark make his move and request that Vlasa Radek copy the circuit board of the code machine, with the actual copying to be carried out one week later. A return message—signed by Hadley—approved this timetable, provided that in the case officer's judgment, "the operation could be implemented with minimal risk."

The file then described how Stein had been shot on May 12 by someone in a postman's uniform. A medical report stated that one of the two bullets had entered the leg at an angle, severing the sciatic nerve. Stein was permanently disabled.

There was a memorandum, dated May 12, of a report telephoned in by an airport immigration clerk who worked for the agency. A woman using a passport in the name of Vlasa Radek and matching her description had been put aboard a nonstop flight to Prague at ten o'clock that morning. The rest of the file consisted of cables from Tyler Ashford to headquarters reporting negotiations with MS/Skylark over the size of his disability pension, the "unreasonable financial demands" of Lili Stein, and the purchase of a wheelchair out of Vienna station's contingency fund.

Danner wrote down some dates and MS/Skylark's address and telephone number. Then he closed the file and sat for several minutes, drumming his fingers on the polished table. It was a rotten business, he thought, in which lives, people, were disposable. They were used and thrown away. He hoped to hell that Carrie was all right, wherever she was.

A LITTLE AFTER EIGHT THIRTY the next morning Danner went out by the back entrance of the hotel and walked to the post office next door. Inside, he found an unoccupied phone booth and dialled MS/Skylark's number. It rang several times before a man answered. "*Ja, bitte?*"

"Herr Stein? This is William Danner. I'd like to see you."

There was no reply, but Danner could hear a woman's loud voice in the background. Finally the old man spoke again. "There is nothing I can tell you."

"I'll be there this morning at nine o'clock."

There was a click and the line went dead. Stein had hung up.

Outside the post office, Danner hailed a cab. He was not looking forward to the interview, but it had to be done.

The taxi dropped him at an old apartment building. He took the coin-operated lift to Stein's floor—as Rossi must have done, he thought—and rang the doorbell. He heard the latch swinging away from the peephole and felt someone staring out at him. "William Danner," he announced.

The door opened; a squat, broad-shouldered woman of about fifty-five confronted him. Her eyes were too small for her large, coarse features, and she looked angry. "My husband is a sick man," she snapped.

"I won't tire him. It shouldn't take long."

She hesitated. Then grudgingly she stepped aside and let him in. There were cooking smells in the little apartment. Cabbage, he thought.

By the living-room window a grey-haired man was sitting in a wheelchair. His eyes were hollow and defeated. "You have come all the way from Washington," he said, with a trace of a smile. "But I cannot be that important."

"I'm sorry for your trouble," Danner said. "I wanted to talk to you in person. We're trying to find out what happened."

Lili Stein started screaming. "What happened? You already know what happened! They shot him and crippled him and ruined our life, and you want to know what happened!"

"Please, Lili," Stein remonstrated, as she stamped out of the room, slamming the door. "I apologize for my wife," he said to Danner. "She is very upset. Please." He gestured to a sofa.

Danner sat down. The stuffing was coming out of the cushions, but he pretended not to notice. "I have just a few questions."

"I can't understand it," Stein said, shaking his head. "Everything was going well. Then this . . ." His voice trailed off and he started coughing. Danner could see he was in pain.

"Herr Stein," Danner began. "During the period that you were seeing Vlasa Radek, did you ever detect any surveillance?"

"Of course not. If there had been anything unusual, I would have reported it to Mr. Ashford. I am a professional, Mr. Danner."

"I understand. But after you asked her to copy the circuit board, wasn't there any countersurveillance?"

"The last week, yes. On three nights, when we went out to dinner, your people were in the restaurant. Mr. Ashford told me to expect them."

"Could Vlasa have noticed them?"

Stein shook his head. "No. She was a secretary, not an agent. She saw nothing."

"One of those nights was the last night?"

"Yes."

"And she didn't try to back out, or to warn you in any way?"

"No. She was a little nervous, perhaps, but that would be quite normal. It was understood she would copy the board in the

166

morning. After dinner I took her home. It was the last time I ever saw her."

"I'm sorry it ended this way," said Danner.

"She betrayed me. She must have told them," Stein said, his features sagging. "But it was my fault. At my age, to make the mistake of trusting a woman." Again he shook his head.

"I'm almost through," Danner said. "But I wanted to ask you about the postman. You told our people who interviewed you at the hospital that you didn't hear the gun go off."

Stein nodded. "It was very strange. No sound at all."

"The gun. Did it have a silencer?"

"No."

Danner paused. "Did you tell your wife about Vlasa?"

"Of course not," Stein said quickly.

"All right." Danner stood up. "Thanks for seeing me."

"I had no choice."

"Neither did I."

Danner let himself out of the apartment and walked down the stairs. There were some other locations he wanted to look over before he left Vienna. Outside the building, he hailed a taxi and asked the driver to let him off by Auer-Welsbach Park.

At the park, he cut north on a path that ran beneath the trees. He emerged in front of the Technical Museum, where he stopped to admire a modernistic sculpture of a blue turbine that stood at the entrance. He glanced back. No one had followed him.

He strolled down the block to the corner, crossed the street, and walked until he could see the three-storey, yellow, Czech embassy, with its castlelike ramparts. He went past the building. The single policeman guarding the embassy paid no attention to him. Danner walked for another block, then doubled back towards the gardens of the Schönbrunn Palace.

The baroque gardens were intersected by wide gravel paths that were lined with stately trees. He continued on for a while, then sat down on one of the comfortable green benches, wondering if this might be the same one where Vlasa Radek had chanced upon MS/Skylark.

Danner was a great believer in shoe leather. It was not the first time he had investigated a failed operation, and he always made it a point to visit the scene when he could. He liked to get the feel of a city, the places and the people, to see where they had walked and

167

sat and laughed and loved and lied to each other. As Stein had done with Vlasa.

They had met in the spring, as the trees were turning green, and the ageing spy, to impress his quarry, had pretended to be a successful businessman. The butcher's daughter from Bratislava had responded to him eagerly. For a few sad months there had been some kind of love between them. Now she was probably dead, and Stein was finished. He would go to his grave thinking she had betrayed him. And Danner could not tell him the truth.

He got up and walked back towards the palace. He kicked at the gravel, taking stock of his own situation. It wasn't a lot better than Stein's, he thought. Forced back into the agency, he was caught up again in a world of deception he thought he had finally shed. His daughter was in the hands of his enemies. Julie, the woman he had begun to love, might be working against him. It was even possible that his employer, the CIA, was lying to him about Carrie. Meanwhile, he was no closer to unmasking the mole.

Danner had come to the broad central plaza of the gardens, and he turned towards the Schönbrunn, which Stein and Vlasa had toured at their second meeting. He went inside, bought a ticket, and joined a crowd of tourists.

The enormous palace, the playground of the Hapsburgs for almost two hundred years, was a mélange of inlaid floors, crystal chandeliers, scrolled frescoes and elaborate tapestries. The guide talked in the manner of a robot as they passed through room after magnificent room.

Near the end of the tour Danner and the others crowded into a chamber that contained two enormous mirrors with gilded frames, facing each other at opposite sides of the room. The effect, as the guide pointed out, was to create an endless hall of mirrors, stretching as far as the eye could see.

A group of children jostled each other to get a better look, and as the crowd milled about, a fat woman awkwardly brushed by Danner. It was a full minute before he felt a crumpled piece of paper in his jacket pocket. He knew if he stopped to read it, he would never catch her.

He bolted after her, but the woman had disappeared. He ran back through the empty rooms, beneath bright chandeliers, past more gilded mirrors. But the woman had a good head start and was nowhere to be seen.

He dashed down a staircase that led to the ground floor. As he did so, he caught a glimpse through a window of the fat woman running across the flagstones towards the front gates. Only the fat woman had become a fat man. Somewhere along the way he had shed a wig and a skirt.

Danner ran out into the courtyard. He could see where the man was heading. Just outside the gates a black Peugeot saloon waited, its engine running. Danner was fast, but the fat man had too big a lead. He jumped in beside the driver, and the car shot away. Danner was barely able to catch the last three digits of the licence number.

He reached into his jacket pocket and uncrumpled the paper. When he saw the handwriting, it was as though someone had shoved a knife into the middle of his chest.

"Dear Daddy," the note said. "Please do whatever they say. I want to come home. Love, Carrie."

At the bottom of the paper someone had scrawled, "If you want to see your daughter alive, you will drop your investigation."

Chapter 7

Dixon Hadley lived in Cleveland Park, a Washington neighbourhood of Victorian houses and stately oak trees. Danner had been there once, years ago, at a party, and he remembered a big white house with red shutters. He found it and parked in the drive.

It had been after ten pm by the time he finally cleared customs at Dulles. Nevertheless, he had telephoned Hadley at home. The deputy director had not been thrilled at the prospect of a Saturday morning meeting, but Danner had insisted. Now he walked up to the wide, shady porch and rang the bell. It was answered by Hadley's teenage son, who led him to a broad redwood veranda at the rear of the house.

Hadley was sitting at a wrought-iron table, reading the morning papers over coffee. He got up when he saw Danner. "My wife is still asleep," he said. "But I can manage a cup of coffee if you'd like one."

"Thanks," Danner said. "I would."

Hadley went into the kitchen and emerged with a cup. "Got some news for you," he said.

"Good or bad?" said Danner, sitting down.

"Mixed," the deputy director replied. "I had a call from the watch officer this morning. Ashford gave your three licence-plate digits to our liaison with the Austrian police. It took a while, but they traced the car. It was rented that day by a woman named Grete Wolf, an Austrian national. Her sister, according to our informants, is married to one Otto Bauer, also an Austrian."

"What do we know about him?"

"Otto Hans Bauer is a small-time support agent employed by the KGB in Vienna."

So it wasn't the old boys or the agency. Somehow Danner had hoped it would be. The dangers might be as great, but at least he would know who he was dealing with. "I guess I owe you an apology," he said.

Hadley dismissed the thought with a wave of his hand. "What will you do?" he asked.

"Keep going. You deal with the Russians from strength. Moscow Centre took a risk in kidnapping Carrie. It means they're desperate to protect the mole. My only leverage with the KGB is to keep looking for him."

"It's your decision," Hadley said. "But I agree."

Danner wondered where they were holding Carrie. Perhaps in San Francisco, where they had a consulate. But she could be anywhere by now. And Francesca had still heard nothing from the kidnappers. He felt sick.

Hadley interrupted his thoughts. "I'm anxious to hear what you learned on your trip," he said.

"Not much in London or Madrid. I had better luck in Vienna. To begin with, you're almost certainly right about Nick Rossi. The shooting had to be done by someone who works for the agency, or used to."

"Why?"

"Stein never heard a shot. But the gun had no silencer. That means the hit man used silent ammo."

Hadley nodded. "Of course. A low-signature bullet."

The silent ammunition, Danner knew, had been developed for the agency, and its very existence was highly classified. Yet it worked on a simple principle. There were two reasons why a shot made noise: gas escaping from the shell under enormous pressure, and the sonic boom of the bullet breaking the sound barrier. The silent ammo contained a tiny piston inside each cartridge that forced

171

the bullet out of the barrel at subsonic speed, then sealed the end of the shell case. No gas escaped, and there was no sonic boom.

"Rossi must have kept some ammo when he left us." Hadley paused. "What else did you find out?"

"A lot. It was all in the file. You know the outlines. MS/Skylark meets Vlasa Radek on April 2. Five days later you approve the operation. On April 15 Ashford sends you a cable proposing that Stein put his requirement to Radek on May 5. On May 12, the day it was all supposed to happen, Nick Rossi shoots MS/Skylark, and Radek is hustled aboard a plane to Prague."

Hadley looked puzzled. "I'm not sure I get your drift."

Danner leaned forward. "We're assuming the mole has access to the cable traffic. That means he—or she—must have known that something was going on as early as the first week in April. By the fifteenth the mole knew the target was the Czech code. Yet almost a month went by before anything happened."

The light began to dawn on the DDO. "In other words—"

"If the Czechs had known about the operation all along, they would have pulled Radek out of Vienna earlier. But they didn't. It means *the Czechs didn't know*."

"They may have wanted to catch her in the act."

Danner shook his head. "No. Our side does that to obtain legal evidence. The Czechs don't bother."

"If you're right," Hadley observed, "it means the renegade old boys never told the Czechs until the very end."

"That's the point," Danner continued. "What happened in Vienna means that the mole *is* working primarily through these old boys. Not directly with the Soviets or their friends."

Hadley got up and began pacing about the room. "It also means these old boys control when the Soviets are clued in to our operations."

"Exactly. And there's one thing more. It's obvious the renegade old boys weren't interested simply in blowing the operation. If that was their motive, all they had to do was tip off the Czechs and Radek would have been sent packing."

"Then what were they after?"

"A high-visibility scandal to embarrass the agency. With trumpets and crashing cymbals. They must be hoping that sooner or later the press will hear about it. There's sure to be gossip at headquarters. Some of it might even reach the White House."

Hadley shuddered. "We try to protect the president from details of that sort."

"I can believe it," Danner said.

"They want the director's scalp," Hadley said slowly. "And mine."

"It looks that way," Danner agreed.

IN THE MIDDLE OF THE NIGHT Danner woke up to Julie's kisses. "I'm sleeping," he protested. But she laughed and pulled him against her.

He had not told her yet about the note from Carrie, or about MS/Skylark. They had just wanted to be with each other, away from the pressures of the real world.

After a while they both drifted off to sleep. When Danner awoke again, sunlight was streaming through the white curtains of the bedroom windows. Julie was already up.

He found her in the kitchen, deep in the Sunday comics. "You're sure that's not too heavy for you?" he asked.

"I like Snoopy," she said. "If you don't like Snoopy, you'll have to leave."

"I like Snoopy."

They lazed about the garden for most of the morning. Then Julie packed lunch in a straw basket, and they drove to the grounds of the Washington Monument. They spread a blanket on the grass at the top of the hill and lay in the sun for a while. Then Danner let out the string on Julie's kite. The breeze lifted it quickly and the kite sailed aloft, its long, tapered tail of green, orange and yellow trailing behind the purple dragon head. A dozen other kites dotted the sky.

When the dragon had reached a satisfactory height, Danner tied the string to the handle of the picnic basket. Julie poured them each an illegal glass of wine, and Danner lay back to watch puffy white clouds rolling by.

Julie lay down beside him. "Do you mind if I ask you something?"

"No. Go ahead."

"At Charlie's, that first night we had dinner, you talked about an operation in Berlin. When you began to change. What happened?"

Danner shook his head. "It was all a long time ago. Light years." He gazed at the kite for a moment. "There was a girl. Her name was Lisa Hallam. She worked with me."

"Were you in love with her?"

"Yes. I still think of her sometimes. She's dead."

"What happened?"

"The Soviets were operating from East Berlin, out of a huge compound. Lisa worked there under deep cover, posing as a German national. She was very beautiful. It was an old story, a honey trap, and a KGB colonel fell into it."

"And you were running the operation?"

"Yes," Danner said. "We were building her, giving her material to pass along. It went on for about four months. Then, when the time looked right, she made her move and tried to recruit him. It was risky, of course. They were having dinner at a restaurant. I was in a car with two other officers, parked down the block. When Lisa and the colonel came out and started walking towards his car, she shifted her purse from her right to her left shoulder—the danger signal."

"It meant the colonel wasn't buying it."

"Yes. We started up the car and cut him off. But he was very quick. He ducked into an alley, pushing her ahead of him. He had a gun in her back. We jumped out and ran after them. There were loose bricks and rubble in the alley. I twisted my knee and went down. I yelled to the others to keep going. But we lost them."

"You never saw her again?"

Danner looked away. "Only once. In the morgue. They fished her body out of the Havel weeks later."

Julie touched his hand. "I'm sorry. I shouldn't have asked."

He shrugged. "You wanted to know about me. And that's part of me."

A sudden downdraught sent the kite spiralling into a dive, and Danner quickly untied the string from the basket. Leaping up, he started running down the hill into the wind, holding the string high, while Julie cheered him on. The tail came perilously close to the ground, but Danner managed to save the kite, and it sailed aloft again.

He came back to the blanket only a little out of breath; Julie applauded. "Milady's kite," he said, with a mock bow, handing her the string. She tied it back on the basket. "Now, how about lunch?" he asked.

"Fine with me." Julie spread out the food while he poured another glass of wine for each of them.

As they ate, he looked around. There was no one within earshot. "Did you have any luck with the SO computer?" he asked.

Julie nodded. "I had no trouble logging on. My password for

access is 8L6D4Z. You enter the word 'hometown' to call up domestic operations, or 'stranger' for foreign. I entered 'hometown', and a line of zeros came up on the screen. It meant there were no domestic operations in the computer. The kidnapping wasn't us."

"I know that now. They've made contact." He told her then about the warning he had received in Vienna, the note from Carrie, and the licence plate that led to the KGB. He also told her of his decision to keep going, despite the risks.

She took his hand. "If the Soviets are trying to stop you, they won't harm Carrie. She's no good to them dead."

He wanted desperately to believe she was right. "That's the gamble I'm taking."

It was getting late. Julie packed up the remains of the lunch, and Danner started to pull in the kite.

"Let's let it go free," Julie said suddenly.

"OK with me."

She took a paring knife from the basket and cut the string. The kite soared straight up, its long tail dancing crazily in the wind, until it was only a distant speck in the sky.

ON MONDAY MORNING Danner scanned his list of the old boys shaken out in the Hallowe'en Massacre. The list was too long to go through one by one. He hoped to short-cut the process by seeking out a couple of old agency hands who might have some information.

At noon he went to the Holiday Inn at Tyson's Corner. Sailor Cummins was sitting at the downstairs bar, which was exactly where Danner expected to find him. He was a big red-faced man in his late fifties, with a large pockmarked nose, a thatch of brown hair, and the watery eyes of an alcoholic. When Danner eased onto the stool next to him and ordered a drink, Cummins turned and stared. "Danner," he said. "I don't believe it."

"Hello, Sailor," Danner said.

Time had not improved the older man's appearance. He was called Sailor because years before, as a young agency officer, he had kept a boat in Annapolis. He and his friends would go there at weekends for legendary drinking parties.

"Where you been?" Cummins demanded.

"Fishing," Danner replied. "Up in Canada. And you?"

"Drinking," Sailor said. "In northern Virginia."

Danner raised his glass. "Cheers."

"Down the hatch." Abruptly Sailor leaned his puffy face close to Danner. "If you're in Canada," he said, slurring his words, "how come you're here?"

"Trying to get a piece of the action," Danner confided. "No reason the beltway bandits should get it all."

The beltway bandits were the dozens of research and development firms scattered around Washington, in northern Virginia and Maryland. Staffed mostly by former government officials, the bandits lived and prospered off government contracts, performing research on weapons, electronic warfare and antiterrorism for the Pentagon, the CIA, and other agencies.

"I'm here to make some contacts," Danner said.

Sailor shook his head. "It's all hogwash. We're nothin'. *They* have the power, same as always."

"The old boys." Danner made it a statement, not a question.

Sailor shrugged. "Gotta know the right ones. You want to get in on cushy consulting deals and fat contracts, they decide. They don't like you, forget it."

"How do I get inside?" Danner asked.

"You don't. They come to you."

"Who does?"

Sailor smiled enigmatically. "You're wasting your time, good buddy. Gotta be able to yodel the right tune."

"What do you mean?"

"Gotta be able to talk to the gnomes."

Sailor wasn't making much sense. His head was drooping.

"You're right," Danner said.

"Sure I'm right."

Danner called for the bill and paid it. "Well, so long," he said. "Good to see you again."

Sailor waved goodbye. "It's all hogwash," he said.

That afternoon Danner drove out by the Leesburg Pike into the Virginia countryside, glancing once in a while at the rough map he had drawn from Will Lamont's directions. He hadn't seen Will in years, and he was looking forward to it.

Lamont was a sort of turncoat WASP; he had the money and the social credentials to be accepted in circles that would always remain partially closed to Danner, but he had moved away from that world. He and his wife, Ann, instead chose to live in rural isolation. He had retired from the agency a few years ago to farm and to write poetry.

176

Danner found the blue mailbox where Will said it would be, and turned into the muddy track that led to the house. He was just getting out of the car when Ann appeared on the porch, wiping her hands on an apron and smiling. He bounded up the steps and gave her a hug.

"Will's out back in the barn," she said. "He'll be along in a minute. Come in and sit down."

She led Danner into the kitchen and offered him coffee. "How's Carrie?" she asked. "She must be a big girl by now."

He hesitated. Then he smiled. "She's fine."

Will came in at the back door and greeted Danner. An extremely handsome man, he had the sort of aristocratic, chiselled face that seemed to improve with age. "You haven't seen the farm," he said. "Let me show you around."

He took Danner on a tour of the barn, the stable, Ann's vegetable garden. He then led him over to a small stone storehouse by a cool, clear brook.

"Beautiful place," Danner said. "How's the writing going?"

Lamont smiled. "The muse visits me intermittently. But you didn't come to talk about my poetry."

They sat down on boulders near the storehouse. "No," Danner said. "I'm back in the agency temporarily."

Will's eyebrows arched, but he said nothing.

"It's a long story," Danner said. "I won't bore you with the details. But we're having alumni problems. Apparently some of the old boys shaken out in the Hallowe'en Massacre haven't forgiven the agency."

"That's not surprising. When you take a stick to a wasps' nest, the wasps tend to get angry."

Danner laughed. "I'm told that some of the old boys are more equal than others."

Will nodded. "True enough."

"And that the insiders control who gets consulting jobs and fat contracts. I was hoping you could tell me who they are."

Will looked across the brook to the cornfields beyond. "I've been out for half a dozen years. Ann and I live a nice, quiet life."

Danner understood. "I won't use your name," he promised.

"They made me an offer once," Will said. "They call themselves the Group. I told them I wasn't interested."

"I need names, Will."

"Go see Talbot Braswell. He lives in Georgetown. He's more or less the Group's screening committee."

"But not their leader."

"No. The real power is Wellington Lloyd."

"Lloyd!" Danner knew him; at one time Lloyd had been high up in the covert bureaucracy. "Where does he live now?"

"I don't know. He keeps a very low profile. Perhaps Binky will know, although I doubt he'll tell you."

"Binky?"

"Braswell. That's what everyone calls him." Will looked worried. "Be sure to leave me out of it."

"I haven't even been here," Danner said.

GEORGETOWN was a self-contained world. Its quiet, tree-shaded streets and Federal-style brick houses were the domain of senators, diplomats, Supreme Court justices and syndicated columnists. Beneath the surface charm, everything about the neighbourhood bespoke wealth and power.

Danner had chosen midmorning for his cold call on Binky Braswell. Finding him had not been difficult. He was listed in the telephone book. The problem would be getting in to see him.

Danner came to the address he was looking for: an elegant brick, three-storey house with black shutters. The front door had an expensive brass knocker. He tried it. After a long wait, a woman in a white uniform opened the door. "Good morning," said Danner, flashing his best smile. "I'm from the telephone company. Is Mr. Braswell in?"

She looked him over doubtfully. "Maybe he is in the garden," she said, with a heavy Spanish accent. She pointed to a gate at the side of the house.

Danner thanked her, walked over to open the gate, and headed towards the back of the house. He found Braswell down on his knees, digging in the topsoil with a trowel. He was wearing a broad-brimmed panama hat with a red band, a blue work shirt and dirty khaki trousers. He straightened up at Danner's approach.

"Mr. Braswell? Bill Danner. We met once. Bucharest, I think."

Braswell slowly got to his feet. "Did we? I'm afraid I don't remember." His voice was nasal, cultivated, and faintly disdainful. He kept his work gloves on and did not offer to shake hands. He was grey-haired, in his late sixties, Danner judged.

178

"Mind if we talk?"

"The truth is, I'm rather busy just now," Braswell said.

"I won't take up much of your time."

"Well . . ." Braswell hesitated. "I generally prefer it if my visitors telephone first. But since you're here." He led Danner over to chairs on the patio. He peeled off his work gloves and tossed them on a table. "Would you care for some iced tea?"

"Yes, thank you." Danner marvelled at the patrician manner, the display of good form in the most awkward circumstances. Binky Braswell's smile was elaborately polite.

"I've come to you for some advice," Danner said after Braswell called the maid and asked for tea. "I've been told you're influential. In the Group."

Braswell's eyes clouded over. "My dear fellow, what group? And as for being influential, I'm just a retired government official digging in my garden. I scarcely venture out."

"When did you leave the agency?"

"In October 1977. It was suggested that I retire."

"I left that spring," Danner said. "Before it all happened. I run a fishing camp in New Brunswick now. It's not very profitable. So recently I came back to do some consulting."

Braswell nodded. Danner had the distinct impression that he already knew all of that. The maid appeared with the tea.

"Frankly, I'd like to broaden my options," Danner continued. "Move into a field with more opportunity." He didn't know if it would work. But perhaps the renegade old boys would get the idea that if they could not scare him off, they could buy him off. "I was hoping you might suggest some people I could see."

Braswell stirred his tea with a long, thin silver spoon. "I'm most sympathetic, Mr. Danner. But I wouldn't really know whom to suggest." His tone was polite but cold.

"There was one person in particular I thought I should see. Wellington Lloyd."

"Wellington?" Binky Braswell looked up at the trees and seemed to search his memory. "He and I share an interest in gardening; we're both fond of flowers. He's out of the business, of course. Forced to walk the plank by the admiral."

Outwardly Braswell appeared calm. But Danner thought he detected a tremor in his voice. "I was hoping you would know where he is," Danner said.

179

"I'm afraid not. Haven't seen him for years." Braswell rose from his chair. "I really can't be of much help to you, much as I might like to."

"Well, thanks anyway." Danner sipped his tea, then said goodbye and left as he had come, along the side of the house.

DIXON HADLEY'S office was too warm. The sun was pouring in through the open blinds and overwhelming the air-conditioning.

"The renegade old boys," Danner said. "They're organized. They call themselves the Group."

"I'm not surprised," said Hadley. "Have you been able to find out who's running them?"

"One of the high-level victims of the Hallowe'en Massacre. Wellington Lloyd."

Hadley's eyebrows went up. "He was staff assistant to the former DDO. He knows how *everything* works."

"I want you to help me find him," Danner said. "Fast. He's the key to it all—the blown ops, the mole, my daughter."

"But we don't keep track of ex-employees," Hadley explained.

"What about his retirement cheque? You must be sending it somewhere."

Hadley smiled. "If he's keeping a low profile, you don't think an old fox like Wellington Lloyd would have his cheque sent to his real address, do you?"

"No, it's probably going to a lawyer's office in Tulsa, or some such. But maybe we can trace it from there."

"I doubt you'll have any luck. But you're welcome to try. You might start with Wilbur Ogleby in Personnel."

Danner took the lift down to Personnel, talked his way past a secretary, and was ushered into Ogleby's office. The chief of the retirement section looked to be in his mid-sixties, with silver hair, a precise manner, and rimless glasses. He reminded Danner of a loan officer at a bank.

"I'm trying to find a former employee," Danner said. "His name is Wellington Lloyd. I figure you must be sending him cheques."

Ogleby took off his glasses and rubbed the bridge of his nose. "Mr. Danner, to provide you with information on a specific individual would violate the Privacy Act. I'm afraid that I can't help you."

180

"I'm on special assignment for the director," Danner said. "You can check with the sixth floor."

Ogleby coughed slightly. "Well, there's really no need. The director is a busy man. We'll see if we have a record of your Mr. Lloyd. You understand, of course, that we're doing this confidentially and unofficially."

"I'd like the information as soon as possible," Danner said. "Within the hour."

He took the lift up to his office to wait for Ogleby's phone call. It came within ten minutes.

"Mr. Danner? I have that information you requested. The gentleman in question gets a Treasury cheque sent to him on the first of every month at PO Box 46, Hobe Sound, Florida 33455."

Danner thanked him and hung up. He banged his fist hard on the desk and swore. Hadley was right. Lloyd was too smart to leave any traces. A post office box. It undoubtedly meant that a friend or confederate picked up the cheques and forwarded them to Lloyd, wherever he was.

Danner thought for a moment, then dialled Ogleby back. "What happens to the cancelled cheques?" he asked. "Do they go back to Treasury?"

"I suppose so. You'd have to ask them."

Danner's next call was to the head of the Treasury Department's Cheque Claims division, a man named Al Kelly. He agreed to see Danner and gave directions to his office. Danner found the grey concrete building tucked in next to the Bureau of Engraving and Printing, and took the lift to the fourth floor.

Kelly was a thin, red-haired man, with a raw-boned Irish face and clear blue eyes. Danner showed his credentials and explained what he was looking for.

"A retirement cheque looks like any other Treasury cheque," Kelly told him. "It's a computer card with holes in it, green on the front, buff on the back. We have almost two million former federal employees drawing pension cheques, not counting the military. That's twenty-four million cheques a year."

"What happens after the cheques are deposited or cashed?" Danner asked.

"Each bank sends the cheques along to the nearest Federal Reserve bank. The Fed does three things. It sprays a locator number on each cheque, makes a microfilm copy of the front and back, and creates a magnetic tape of the transaction. The actual cheques go in numbered boxes and get shipped to records centres for storage. The microfilm cartridges and the mag tapes are sent here."

"So the locator number is the key?"

"Exactly."

"But how can you match a name to the locator number?"

"To do that, I need a cheque number and a symbol number."

Danner was trying to follow the complex procedure. "OK, where do I get those?"

"There are eight disbursing offices scattered around the country. Retirement cheques are issued serially, each with a cheque number, and the symbol number tells us which disbursing office issued a particular cheque. CIA's pension cheques are written by the Washington office. We'll call them. Since we know the name on the cheque and the agency the man worked for, it won't take long to retrieve the numbers. Once we have those, I'll query our main computer and get the locator number. Then we're home free."

Kelly called in his secretary and told her what they needed. She was back in only a few moments with the data. "Follow me," Kelly said confidently. He led Danner down the hall and into a room with a small computer terminal. Kelly sat down at the keyboard and entered the information.

In less than a minute the Treasury's main computer responded. "The locator number," Kelly said with satisfaction. He showed it to Danner: B52572641298470. "The letter and the first seven digits give us the number of the microfilm cartridge and the number of the box it's in. The last seven digits tell us the sequence number on the cartridge."

They took the lift down to the ground floor, where Kelly led the way into a huge vault, with a heavy steel door and time locks. Stacked inside on metal shelving were row upon row of cardboard boxes containing microfilm reels. Kelly strode among them like a king in his realm, with Danner at his heels. He stopped at last, pushed a rolling stepladder into place, and climbed up to reach the top shelf. He opened one of the boxes and removed a single reel of film. "The picture of your cheque is on this roll."

In a room across the hall were several microfilm readers. Kelly went to one of the machines, threaded the end of the reel through the rollers, and sat down. Peering into the screen, he advanced the reel until he reached the correct sequence number.

"Got it!" he said triumphantly. He pushed a button, and a piece of paper slid slowly from the machine.

Danner studied the printout. After state and federal taxes, Wellington Lloyd received $1810.37 a month. But it was the back of the cheque that held Danner's attention. The stamp on the bank where the cheque had originally been deposited read, "Schweizerische Kreditanstalt, Zürich."

Gotta yodel the right tune . . . talk to the gnomes. Now Danner understood. Sailor Cummins had been right all along.

Chapter 8

It was clear and cool in Zurich, a good day for walking. Danner crossed the street and made his way along the Limmat River, then cut over to the Kreuzplatz. The flower shop was still there.

So was Felix Tobler, the proprietor, who greeted Danner with a hug and a crushing handshake. Well over six feet tall, Tobler looked more like an ex-linebacker for a pro football team than a florist to Zurich's high society.

"What a wonderful surprise," Tobler boomed out. "Erich did not tell me you were coming."

"Erich doesn't know I'm here. I haven't had a chance to call him." Erich Hoffman was Swiss, a college classmate of Danner's who had returned home to become a professor of English literature at the University of Zurich. It was through Erich that he had met Felix Tobler fifteen years before.

Danner surveyed the shop admiringly. "The roses," he asked, "are they local?"

"Beauties, yes? All are from the Zurich area. Our customers like them."

It was Felix's customers who interested Danner. The shop, the Blumenhaus Kreuzplatz, catered to the city's gold coast, the millionaire financiers and businessmen who lived in their mansions in Zollikon, Küsnacht, Herrliberg, and the other cloistered communities that stretched along the north shore of the Lake of Zurich. When the gold coast needed flowers to adorn its tables, it called Tobler.

While the two men talked, a salesgirl waited on a stout matron who was fussing about some begonias. Felix motioned Danner into a large, sunny back room with a huge worktable on which flower arrangements were prepared. "Here we have privacy," Felix said. "How can I help you, my friend?"

"I'm looking for a man. An American."

"There are many Americans in Zurich."

"This one is wealthy. The sort of person who would buy a house on the gold coast. Your patch. And he likes flowers. His name is Wellington Lloyd. He'd be in his late fifties."

Tobler spread his hands and shrugged. "I know of only one American who has bought on the gold coast. A Mr. Kramer."

"When was that?"

"About two years ago. He purchased the von Bruhler estate in Herrliberg. A beautiful place, right on the lake."

Danner sat down on the edge of the table. "Tell me about Mr. Kramer. You've met him?"

"Not personally. But he is a good customer. He entertains a lot, small dinner parties. Usually on Saturday morning his housekeeper calls and orders an arrangement for the table."

"Can you give me his address?"

"Certainly." Felix lumbered over to a metal card file sitting atop a desk in the corner. He searched through the cards. "Seestrasse 7," he said. "Here, I'll write it down for you."

Danner tried to rein in his mounting sense of excitement. There was no point in jumping to conclusions about Kramer. Yet he knew this could be it. "Thanks," he told Felix.

He said goodbye, then hailed a taxi and took it to the university, which stood on a hill overlooking the river. When Erich Hoffman returned from class, he found Danner sitting in his office.

Erich stared in surprise over the top of his half-glasses, then broke into a broad grin. "Dartmouth's in town again; run, girls, run. How are you, Bill?"

"Fine, Erich. Good to see you." Hoffman was a lanky man, with unruly sandy hair, a rumpled tweed sports jacket and a pipe. He looked every inch the academic.

"So," he said. "What brings you to Zurich?"

"Business. I was hoping you could help."

"If I can, naturally. I never believed you were really running a fishing camp. It was cover, yes?"

184

"No," Danner said. "It wasn't. But I've come back to the agency on a special assignment. Not for long, I hope."

"I see." Erich struck a match and lit his pipe. "How can a scholar of the English poets possibly be of help to an international, let us say, businessman?"

"It isn't your scholarship I need. It's your contacts. In particular, Colonel Zeiss." Walter Zeiss, Danner knew, was high up in the Swiss military intelligence agency. He was also Erich's childhood friend. "I'd like to see him today. Do you think you can arrange a lunch at Chez Max?"

A look of alarm crossed Erich's countenance. "Rather steep for a mere academic," he said. "For Walter, too, I imagine."

"I'm on an expense account. My treat."

"In that case, Chez Max. Let me see if Walter is free." Erich dialled his friend, and a brief conversation took place in Swiss German. He hung up and said, "You're in luck. He will be delighted to join us." Erich made the reservation, and they drove along the shore in his green Volkswagen to the restaurant.

They were seated at their table when Colonel Zeiss arrived. He appeared to be in his mid-forties, with jet-black hair and piercing eyes. He was in mufti: a dark blue suit and a conservative tie.

They chatted amiably, luxuriating in the restaurant's elegant atmosphere. There were flowers everywhere. Danner wondered if they were from Felix's shop.

When the ice had been well broken, Danner showed Zeiss his agency credentials. The Swiss intelligence officer studied them carefully and handed them back.

"I was hoping you could give me some unofficial, back-channel help," said Danner.

"That is not so easily done," Zeiss said. "Why are you not working through your Bern station? They have liaison with us."

"My mission is extremely sensitive."

The *sommelier* brought a bottle of wine, and the colonel, after inhaling the bouquet and taking a sip, pronounced it charming. "Tell me what you need," he said, "and we shall see."

"There is an American named Wellington Lloyd. He banks at the Schweizerische Kreditanstalt, where he probably has a secret numbered account. I need to know as much about him as possible. Including his address."

Walter Zeiss chuckled. "You expect me to get information on this

185

account? Perhaps you would also like me to climb the Matterhorn barefoot?"

Erich looked embarrassed. Danner smiled and said, "I know all about your strict Swiss banking laws. I also know that Swiss intelligence has its sources inside the banks."

The waiter arrived with their lunch. "In any event," Zeiss said when he had gone, "I doubt that your man has such an account. Since about 1978, the major Swiss banks have been very cautious about opening secret accounts for US citizens. There's been too much pressure from Washington about Mafia money flowing into Zurich."

"Lloyd would have opened it in 1977. When he left us."

The colonel's eyes widened. "Ah. Now I understand the delicacy. One of your own." His expression became more sympathetic. "It is a difficult request. Very difficult. But we shall see."

IT WAS DISCONCERTING to hear cowboys speaking German, but the dubbed western was the best thing Danner could find on the television in his hotel room. He had been downstairs for breakfast, and now he was stretched out on the bed, waiting. He had never liked the waiting, but it came with the territory. He tried not to think about Carrie.

Just before eleven the telephone jangled. When he answered it, a voice he recognized said abruptly, "Meet me at the Lindenhof in fifteen minutes." Then the caller hung up.

Danner grabbed his jacket, dropped his key at the desk, and walked to the park. Near the fountain he found Zeiss.

They strolled under the plane trees like two old friends. "Your Mr. Lloyd does have a secret numbered account," Zeiss said. "And it's very active. It has several million dollars in it."

"When was the account opened?"

"Just as you said, 1977. In December."

"Where's the money coming from?"

"Various countries. A lot of it is flowing in from Libya. Mr. Lloyd seems to have high-level oil connections. The money is being disbursed to people all over the world. I did not attempt to write down the names. There were too many."

"I'm very grateful for this much, Colonel."

"We can't afford renegades in our profession, Mr. Danner. I am pleased to have been able to help."

Danner could feel his adrenalin flowing. "There is one more thing. I need Lloyd's address."

"Yes." Zeiss reached into his breast pocket, removed a small black notebook, and began turning the pages. "Here it is," he said. "Your Mr. Lloyd lives in Herrliberg. At Seestrasse 7."

AS HE DROVE SOUTH along the lakefront, Danner was surprised by the seagulls. He had not expected to find them in a landlocked alpine country, far from any ocean. Yet there they were, swooping low over the Lake of Zurich to dive for fish.

Like the other residents of the gold coast, the gulls looked well fed. A Mercedes flashed by, the sixth one Danner had counted in the last few minutes. He felt a little out of place in his hired Fiat.

Soon he was in Herrliberg. From the description Felix had given him, he had no trouble finding Lloyd's house. The Seestrasse was a narrow, busy road parallel to the shore. Most of the houses were on terraced hillsides across the road from the lake. But the old von Bruhler estate was right on the water. Danner pulled onto the hard shoulder and parked.

A whitewashed stone wall, nine feet high, protected the estate. The house was set well back from the road, inside a wide cobblestoned courtyard fringed with flowerbeds. The entrance to the courtyard was secured by a wrought-iron gate topped with spikes.

The house itself had three storeys. It was built of stone, whitewashed like the wall. Danner assumed that the rear of the house overlooked a lawn that sloped to the lake, but because of the high wall, he could not see towards the back from his vantage point on the road.

He got out, approached the iron gate, and rang the bell. A metallic voice crackled from a box mounted on the pillar next to the gate. It wanted to know who he was and what he wanted.

"William Danner," he said. "To see Mr. Kramer."

There was a long silence. Then the voice crackled again. "Herr Kramer is not at home."

"Fine. I'll speak to Mr. Lloyd."

There was another silence, longer this time. Then a buzzer sounded. Danner pushed open the gate and walked across the courtyard. Twenty feet to his right, two enormous Doberman pinschers growled at him. He noted with relief that they were safely behind a chain link fence. At night the dogs probably had the run of the grounds. Floodlights were mounted on the sides of the house.

He rang the bell and waited. The door was opened by a tough-looking young manservant. The voice in the box, Danner guessed. The young man motioned Danner up the stairs and followed a few paces behind. At the top of the stairs, he slipped past Danner and turned left, beckoning him to follow. Danner caught a glimpse of a large living room and a dining room overlooking the lake. Just beyond, on the same side of the landing, was a panelled study.

By the desk in the study, framed in the large windows, with light streaming in behind him, stood Wellington Lloyd. "Danner," he said. "It's been rather a long time."

It was typical of Lloyd, Danner thought. No questions about how Danner had found him, no explanation of why he was living in Switzerland under an alias. Just a polite, casual greeting, as though he had bumped into an old acquaintance.

"Seven years," Danner said. He studied Lloyd. The man was remarkably unchanged. His hair was white, as it had been for years. His face and nose were thin, almost effeminate. The soft brown eyes were masked by grey-tinted glasses. He reminded Danner of a large laboratory rat.

"You're back," Lloyd said. "Or so I hear."

"You keep in touch, then?"

"Not really. I'm a businessman now. I pick up stray bits of gossip, nothing more."

They sat down in armchairs facing each other. Lloyd still had his back to the windows, so that his face was in shadow. Danner had to squint to look at him.

"I should explain right away why I've come to see you," Danner said. "I'm in financial difficulty. I have a fishing camp in Canada, but it's not doing well. The agency brought me back on temporary assignment, against my will. What I'd like to do is what you're doing. Become a consultant for multinationals, the oil companies."

Lloyd didn't nibble. "An admirable ambition. I wish you the best of luck."

"From what I hear, it takes more than luck. I've been told that you control a well-financed network of old boys that calls itself the Group. I hear that without your approval, no former agency people can get major contracts."

"Rubbish," Lloyd said. "It sounds like one of Dixon Hadley's fantasies." He smiled. It made him look even more sinister, behind the tinted glasses. "But if you've come all the way from Washington, the least I can do is offer you a drink."

Danner returned the smile. "I wouldn't mind a Scotch."

While Lloyd went to a bar by the windows, Danner looked around the study. Floor-to-ceiling bookcases lined the walls. A heavy oak desk dominated the area to Danner's left. To his right, in the centre of the room, an expensive-looking Bertoia sculpture, about thirty flexible brass rods pointing straight up in a circular cluster, was mounted on a wooden base.

Lloyd handed him a drink. "I see you've been admiring the house. It's three hundred and fifty years old. The rooms on the ground floor are huge; they're just for formal entertaining."

"You're well protected," Danner said. "Those are fierce-looking dogs. But I noticed they didn't bark at me."

Lloyd smiled again. "They're trained to attack silently."

"I also saw some wine casks in the courtyard?"

"We grow our own grapes. They're fermenting now in vats in the cellar. Those hills across the road are all my vineyards."

"You lead a pleasant life here."

"A quiet one. I congratulate you on finding me. It's not easy. But I'm afraid you have gone to a great deal of trouble for nothing. While I'm sympathetic to your financial plight, there is really nothing I can do to help."

"I'm disappointed," Danner said.

They both got up. Lloyd walked over to Danner and stood very close to him. "I might add that I greatly value my privacy. Interfering with it can prove to be dangerous."

Danner wondered whether it was Lloyd who had tipped off the Soviets about his search for the mole; whether this man standing a foot away was the cause of his daughter's disappearance and his own anguish. He resisted a strong impulse to reach out and throttle Lloyd, to see the soft eyes fill with terror, the terror Carrie must have felt when she was dragged away. But killing Lloyd would defeat his purpose.

"Thanks for the drink," he said evenly. He turned on his heel and left. Downstairs, the manservant silently opened the front door for him. As Danner crossed the courtyard, the two Dobermans, now joined by a third, were still growling. The buzzer sounded as he approached the gate, and he let himself out.

Seestrasse 7 was not a very friendly place. But Danner felt

exhilarated. He had not only found Wellington Lloyd, he had just cased his house.

He drove back into Zurich and went directly to the Blumenhaus. Felix was delighted to see him. "I was afraid you had left Zurich," the florist said.

"No. Just doing a little sightseeing in the suburbs."

"In Herrliberg perhaps?"

Danner smiled. "You said that Mr. Kramer orders flowers on Saturday morning?"

"Yes. Almost every week."

"I'd like to go along with the delivery tomorrow."

"That can be arranged." He called into the back room. "Karl."

A young man in blue jeans appeared. Felix told him, "Tomorrow my American friend will join you in the van. Please do what he says. He will leave with you at eleven for the regular route."

Karl shook hands with Danner. "It will be good that you come," he said. "I can practise my English with you."

"You do a lot better than I do in Swiss German," said Danner.

IT WAS DRIZZLING the next morning when Danner ducked into the flower shop. A white van was parked out front with its back doors open. Karl had already loaded the orders. One of them was for Kramer.

Danner was dressed in work clothes that he had bought the previous afternoon—blue jeans, a denim shirt and a khaki cap. He conferred briefly with Karl. "I'll follow you in the Fiat. Go ahead and make the regular deliveries. When you get to Herrliberg, there's a side street off to the right, towards the water, a block before you reach the Kramer estate. Pull in there, go halfway to the lake, and wait for me."

They drove through the districts of Zollikon and Küsnacht as Karl made his deliveries. It was past noon when he turned into the side street in Herrliberg. A moment later Danner pulled up behind the van and walked over to it.

"The flowers for Kramer," he said. "I'll need them."

Karl opened the back. There was a centrepiece of red roses arranged in a straw basket and covered with greaseproof paper to protect it from the rain. While Karl got back behind the wheel, Danner climbed into the rear and opened the paper, being careful not to tear it. From a box in his pocket he removed a tiny black

190

beetle about one eighth of an inch long. It was made of plastic but was extraordinarily lifelike, with legs, a tiny head, and eyes.

Using tweezers, Danner peeled off a little adhesive strip from the bottom of the insect, then gently inserted the beetle deep into one of the roses. Satisfied that it was adhering to the petals, he carefully replaced the paper so the flowers appeared undisturbed.

He had brought the beetle with him from Langley. It was the latest creation of Electronic Services—a powerful transmitter that would broadcast for up to thirty hours to the voice-activated tape recorder locked in the boot of the Fiat. It was the ultimate to meet Danner's needs—a bug that looked like a bug.

He climbed out and got in the passenger seat next to Karl. "OK," he said. "When we get to Kramer's, I'll stay in the van. If anybody asks about me, just say I'm your new helper."

Karl nodded, started up again, and drove the short distance to the gate. He got out, rang the bell and said "Blumenhaus Kreuzplatz" into the entry phone. The buzzer sounded; he opened the gate, then got back into the van. As they drove into the courtyard, Danner slouched in the passenger seat, his cap pulled low.

The thuggish-looking manservant opened the door. While the man was signing for the roses, Danner observed the house again. The three Dobermans were behind the chain-link fence, watching. He studied the roof and noted that the portion over the north wing was flat.

Karl got into the van and backed out of the courtyard. The servant ran out in the rain to close the gate.

"To your car?" Karl asked Danner.

"No. I'll ride into town with you."

"OK. No charge is extra."

"No extra charge," Danner corrected him.

Karl looked disappointed. "I am needing more practice," he said. "To learn, one must listen carefully."

"You're doing fine," Danner said. "You listen very well." He hoped the bug would do the same.

DANNER SPENT the rest of Saturday waiting. When the rain had ended, he wandered through the narrow, twisting streets of the ancient city. He walked along the Paradeplatz and watched shoppers streaming by.

On Sunday Erich Hoffman drove him out to Herrliberg to pick up the Fiat. Back in town, Danner parked in front of his hotel, unlocked the boot, and slipped the microrecorder into his pocket.

He returned to his room and settled himself in a comfortable chair, preparing to listen to the tape. As a precaution against its being overheard, he used an earphone. The ultra-thin tape could hold three hours of conversation. Danner figured it was more than enough to pick up anything said at the dinner table, where he assumed the roses would have been put as a centrepiece.

He rewound the tape to the beginning. Since the bug was voice-activated, there would be nothing to hear until Lloyd and his guests went into the dining room.

The device worked. The first sound on the tape was Lloyd's voice saying he much preferred a French wine to most of those the Swiss could offer. There was a scraping of chairs and clinking of glasses, and more small talk between Lloyd and a second, slightly nasal voice. Danner knew the second voice, yet he could not place it immediately.

"How are things in Washington?" he heard Lloyd ask.

"Brooks Jordan still has the president's backing," said Lloyd's guest. "But it's wearing thin. Too much has gone wrong. There's beginning to be talk. Stirrings on the Hill."

Danner pushed the rewind button and listened to the last part again. Suddenly he knew whose voice he was hearing. He remembered hearing it in a garden in Georgetown. The second man was Binky Braswell!

There was the sound of a door opening, and a woman's voice—a maid serving dinner. Footsteps—the woman leaving the room. More clinking of glasses and silverware. A cough. Then Lloyd again: "We've accomplished a great deal in the last few months. I think our friend Jordan's days are numbered."

"It would be poetic justice if he were fired by the president," Braswell answered.

"How did things go with Janney? Has he been briefed?"

Danner played the questions over again to be sure he had heard the name right. He had. Richard Janney was President Forbes's chief of staff, a smooth southerner who had managed the presidential primary campaign of Vice-President Prentiss Brock. Brock had lost his presidential bid, but Forbes had selected him as his running mate. Janney, in turn, had emerged as a powerful man in the president's inner circle.

"There wasn't time to go into detail," Braswell replied. "But Janney is aware that operations have gone awry, and he's very disturbed that Jordan has concealed them from the president."

"Excellent. Is he going to talk to Brock?"

There were some interfering noises: Danner could not hear all of Braswell's response. But he could make out the words "the best channel". Then he heard Lloyd boasting that he had kept up contacts "with Prentiss". They had worked well together on "the sixth floor".

Vice-President Prentiss Brock was the best channel. To whom? The president, of course. And Lloyd had remained close to Brock. Now the renegade old boys' objectives were clear.

Danner stopped the tape and thought it through. Prentiss Brock was a former director of the CIA. Word of the agency's fiascos had been deliberately leaked to Richard Janney, who promised to pass them along to the vice-president. Brock, in turn, would tell the president, who would lean heavily on him for advice on agency matters—such as whether to remove Jordan from his post as CIA chief. Prentiss Brock and Richard Janney would then recommend that Jordan be replaced by their friend Wellington Lloyd, an experienced CIA officer.

It all made sense: Tokyo, Madrid, London, Vienna. It was a well-organized plot by some of the old boys to take over the agency. The Soviets, meanwhile, were on the sidelines reaping the benefits. No wonder the KGB wanted to stop Danner. And Carrie, he thought bitterly, was the innocent victim.

He pressed the start button again. Lloyd was still playing lord of the manor, going on about his vineyards. Dessert came, and they began swapping anecdotes about former colleagues. Danner listened impatiently. Then he heard his own name.

"Danner was here." Lloyd's voice.

"I warned you he was rooting around," said Braswell. "Same story he was peddling in my garden?"

"Yes. Offering himself as bait. Claiming he needed money."

"Danner's of no consequence." Braswell's voice was smug. "There's nothing he can do. We're close to the end now."

"We'll see," Danner said aloud.

Over coffee the two men turned to more small talk, more anecdotes. Lloyd offered Braswell a Cuban cigar. Then Braswell's voice: "And we still don't know our benefactor's identity?"

"I haven't a clue. All I know is that the information we're getting is pure gold."

"It's not a voice you recognize?"

"No. And I was warned, when the first one arrived, not to try to find out. Or they would stop coming."

Danner ran the machine back and listened again. ". . . our benefactor's identity . . . not a voice you recognize . . . when the first one arrived . . ." With mounting excitement he realized what it meant. The mole had not risked direct contact. *Wellington Lloyd was getting tapes.*

Lloyd spoke again. "Another one came in two days ago. Right on schedule. Would you like to hear it?"

"Yes, indeed."

Sound of scraping chairs, and footsteps fading away. Danner cursed. He could hear them walking down the hall, probably towards Lloyd's study. The voices were muffled. Then silence.

He listened, but there was nothing more on the tape. He was about to shut off the recorder when he heard quite faintly a weird, unearthly sound. It was unlike anything he had ever heard before. There was some resemblance to church bells, or chimes, but it was not either of those. Maybe Wellington Lloyd is picking up music from outer space, Danner thought. The sound did not recur. There was nothing more. He clicked off the recorder and sat quietly for a long time.

And then he knew.

Chapter 9

The Shanghai Restaurant out on Lee Highway was crowded at lunchtime, as usual. It was a favourite hangout for agency people.

Sam Green was having trouble with his chopsticks. Danner tried not to laugh but couldn't help himself. "Cut it out, Sam. I can't eat if you keep breaking me up. Besides, I'm buying lunch for a reason."

"I should have known," Sam said, switching to a knife and fork.

Danner leaned forward and spoke quietly. "I need a photograph. Can you programme one of your birds to take a picture of a particular house? I want to check out what the roof looks like."

Sam spooned rice onto his plate. "It can be done. But I'll need higher authority."

"Is Dixon Hadley good enough?"

"Yep. You should ask for a STAR—a Special Target Acquisition Request. Where's the house?"

"A suburb of Zurich called Herrliberg: on the north side of the lake. I can give you enough of a description so you can figure out the coordinates."

"No problem."

"How long will it take to get the picture to me?"

"We can reroute our Western Europe satellite for one pass over Zurich. Film capsule recovery in the Pacific. So you're looking at forty-eight to seventy-two hours."

"OK, that gives me three days. Thanks, Sam."

When Danner had paid the bill, they drove back to the agency. Once inside the building, they parted company. Danner took the lift to six and walked to Dixon Hadley's office.

"I've found Lloyd," Danner told him. "In Zurich." He sketched in for the DDO what he had learned.

Hadley looked pleased. "You've done well."

"There's more. He's getting tapes. From the mole."

"So that's it." Hadley scowled. "Under the circumstances, I suppose some counteraction should be taken. It would be of much interest if the material could be examined directly, as it were."

"If you want me to steal a tape, why don't you say so?"

The DDO looked alarmed. "I can't approve anything like that. But if you were to act on your own, it would be in the highest national interest, of course."

"I'll need you to sign for a STAR. I want a picture of—"

Hadley put up his hand, palm out. "Don't tell me any more. I'll sign the request in blank. You fill in the particulars."

"I'll also need some special equipment."

"You've already got authority for that," Hadley interjected. His tone became warmer. "I wish you every success. But if anything should go wrong, well, you understand my position. The operation has not been authorized."

"That's the kind of support I know I can always count on."

"On another matter," Hadley continued. "The telephone monitors have nothing to report from Santa Barbara. There's still been no contact with your former wife by the Soviets."

Danner's heart sank. "All I can do is hope. And keep going."

Hadley shook his head sympathetically. "I'm sorry."

IN HIS OFFICE, Danner dialled Sam and told him that Hadley had agreed to the STAR request. He gave him a detailed description of the house and its location. Then he left headquarters and drove out of the main gate, ahead of the rush-hour traffic.

At his apartment, he sat down by the telephone and started to phone Francesca but thought better of it. There was nothing he could tell her. Instead, he rang Julie and said he would pick her up for dinner. He showered, dressed, and left for her place.

Julie looked terrific. She was wearing a cream-coloured silk blouse and a brown tweed skirt, with a beige cardigan thrown over her shoulders. Danner kissed her lightly.

"Where are we going?" she asked.

"L'Auberge Chez François. We have a reservation for six thirty."

They drove north, then followed a country lane across rolling farmland to the restaurant. It was a cosy place, with dark wooden beams and stained-glass windows. Danner ordered wine, and as they sipped it, he realized how much he had missed her. "I'm making some progress," he said.

She touched his hand. "I'm glad. Where have you been?"

"Switzerland." He did not offer more. He felt very close to her, but ambivalent, too. He had never asked why she had talked about Vienna—he saw little point in confronting her, she would only deny any advance knowledge—but he could not forget it. His love was tempered with caution.

"Any word about Carrie?" she asked.

"Nothing. No further contact."

"It's so frustrating, so frightening. Aren't you scared?"

"For Carrie, terribly. Not for myself. I've never worried much about the physical danger in our work. It goes with the job. Like a movie stunt man, or a window cleaner."

Julie laughed. "I guess that's a good way of looking at it." She picked up her wineglass and twirled it in her hand. "I'm going on a trip," she said. "I'll be gone for three weeks."

He wanted to tell her he would be away, too, but didn't. "Where?"

"The Middle East and Africa. I go about once a year to check out commercial cover arrangements. I have to make sure there are no rough edges."

"Stay away from the sheikhs."

"Don't worry. I mostly talk to financial officers for American corporations. Bookkeepers can be pretty boring."

196

He raised his glass. "To bookkeepers."

Julie's big green eyes looked at him. "There is something else you're worried about," she said.

"Meaning what?"

"You don't give all of yourself when we're together."

Danner wondered if she sensed his doubt about her loyalties. "I give as much as I can," he answered honestly. He wondered whether two people ever trusted each other completely. Or was it only a problem for spies, who were trained to mistrust?

IT WAS TWO DAYS LATER when Sam Green turned up in Danner's office with a manila envelope stamped TOP SECRET. He was whistling. "Got what you wanted," he said. "A beautiful picture. No cloud cover over the Alps."

He removed an eight-by-ten glossy print from the envelope and laid it on the desk. Danner was startled by the clarity of the photo, taken from more than two hundred miles in outer space. The roof of Wellington Lloyd's Swiss villa practically leaped out at him. He could even see the texture of the shingles.

He studied the flat section over the north wing. There were two telecommunications discs on either side of a skylight. "How big would you say that skylight is?"

"Maybe six feet by three feet," Sam replied.

"What's the lock? I can't read the name on the cylinder."

"We're having a special on enlargements this week," Sam said, grinning. "I'll be back."

He returned in an hour with another print and a magnifying glass. "It's a BKS, a high-security German lock, pin tumbler type," he said. "A dead bolt, of course. If someone smashed the glass, they still couldn't open the skylight without a key."

"The pictures are a big help. I really appreciate it."

"No problem." Sam smiled as he let himself out.

For the next forty-five minutes Danner wrote out a list of equipment on a yellow pad. Then he took the list to the Office of Technical Services. The OTS was part of the agency's Directorate of Science and Technology; in their laboratories sophisticated weapons, drugs and espionage equipment were developed.

A secretary ushered Danner into the office of Dr. Louis Weinberg, the wizard of OTS, a legendary—some preferred the word sinister—figure in the CIA. Weinberg had been responsible for developing many of the drugs and poisons used in the agency's assassination plots during the 1960s.

"I've got a shopping list, Lou," Danner said. "I'll need to get the stuff together as soon as possible."

"On whose authority?" Weinberg asked.

"The director and the DDO. You can check with them."

"You might have said so to begin with." Weinberg lit a fat cigar and gave it a puff or two. "What do you need, my boy?"

"For openers, a skeleton key." He put the picture of the lock on Weinberg's desk.

The OTS chief studied it. "On this type of BKS, normally the keys can only be duplicated by the manufacturer. But we can reproduce any key in the world. I'll give the photo to Lockpicking. Unless we run into a snag, you'll have the key tomorrow."

"I'll also need scuba gear—mask, hood, flippers, wet suit, night compass, and buoyancy compensator. I'll pick up the air tank when I get where I'm going."

Weinberg was taking notes. "What else?" he asked.

"A thirty-foot ladder of lightweight nylon rope with grappling hooks at one end. The hooks have to be rubberized. Also, a dart gun and six incapacitating darts."

"Human or animal targets?"

"Dogs. They're Dobermans."

Weinberg turned and took a book down from behind his desk. "Let me check the chart." He studied a page. "All right, body weight seventy-five pounds. What's your required incapacitation time?"

"I need an hour."

"I'd recommend etorphine. It's a paralytic, and our most effective immobilizer. And it's designed for animals."

"And the dosage?"

Weinberg leafed through his book. "Species Canidae. Yes, here it is. Three point two milligrams should do it. That's a little over half a teaspoon. The darts will be very small. But be careful how you handle them, by the way. A drop of etorphine on the skin can kill a human."

"Since it's a paralytic, the dogs won't actually be unconscious?"

"No, they'll be wide awake, eyes open, watching you. But they won't be able to move. Fortunately dogs can't talk. They won't be able to tell anybody what they saw."

"Lucky for me." Danner checked off the items on his list. "I need a small-burst tape recorder for high-speed copying. I'll be making a duplicate of a cassette and I want to do it fast."

"I'll talk to Kerwin in Electronic Services." Kerwin's shop had furnished the beetle-shaped bug that Danner had planted in Wellington Lloyd's roses. "What else?"

"A waterproof torch, a set of lockpicks, some weights, and waterproof pouches for the dart gun, the darts and the tape recorder. Also a knife to strap to my leg over the wet suit."

"That's it?" Weinberg asked hopefully.

"One final item. A sheet of rubber one eighth of an inch thick, cut in a circle, diameter eighteen inches. Around the rim of the circle, two inches in from the edge, I want holes the size of quarters spaced a quarter of an inch apart."

Weinberg looked puzzled. "What the devil is that for?"

"My survival," Danner said.

DANNER CHECKED in to a small Zurich hotel. He did not contact Felix or Erich; if anything went wrong, there was no sense involving them. This time he was on his own.

On the afternoon he arrived, he rented an Audi, but not at the same agency where he had hired the Fiat. After that, he purchased an aluminium scuba tank and had it filled with compressed air. He locked the tank and the special gear prepared by OTS in the boot of the car.

The next morning he drove around the south side of the Lake of Zurich. He parked by the water, and with a pair of binoculars reconnoitred the opposite shore. The Lake of Zurich, like most Swiss lakes, was long and narrow, and he was able to pick out the house easily. There was a small wooden jetty, and the lawn, which sloped gently towards the lake, was not fenced or walled along the water. Wellington Lloyd's fortress was protected only on three sides. But it would take over an hour to swim across.

He drove back round the lake, through Zurich again, then south to Herrliberg. About a quarter of a mile beyond the house he came to a wooded stretch where there were no houses. He parked off the road, then walked through the trees a short distance to the lake. The spot was screened from the road by the foliage. It was ideal. He returned to Zurich, spent the afternoon in his room, went out for a light supper, and turned in early. He set the alarm for one am.

He need not have bothered: he couldn't sleep. He was half dozing when the alarm went off. Minutes later he was behind the wheel of the Audi, driving along the now familiar route to the gold coast. It was a cool, clear night, and the moon and stars were out. He would have good visibility, but so would anyone in the house who happened to look out of a window towards the lake. It was a risky operation. But he knew he had no choice but to go on. In that house might be the key to Carrie's freedom.

Arriving in Herrliberg, he cruised slowly past Seestrasse 7 and was relieved to see no lights in the windows. He checked his watch; it was just after two am.

He parked beyond the house, at the place he had selected that morning. He opened the boot, removed his gear, and made his way through the trees to the lake. The water was shimmering in the moonlight, and it looked cold.

He stripped down to a T-shirt and swimming trunks and got into the black wet suit. It covered him from the neck to the ankles. He slipped the buoyancy compensator over his head and stowed his torch in its pouch. He put on the luminous wrist compass, strapped the knife to his ankle, and buckled six pounds of weights around his waist. He clipped the waterproof pouch containing the dart gun to his belt, along with a smaller pouch that held the skeleton key, the miniature tape recorder, the lockpicks, and the odd-looking sheet of rubber. Carrying the rope ladder and the air tank to the water's edge, he sat down and stretched a pair of skintight rubber boots over his feet. He fitted flippers over the boots, then rubbed blacking on his face and pulled the hood over his head, so that only his darkened eyes, nose and mouth were visible. He adjusted the mask. Then he strapped the tank to his back, picked up the nylon ladder, and slipped silently into the lake.

He dived to twelve feet, just deep enough so that there would be no surface turbulence to mark his progress. Despite the bright moon, it was like swimming in a pool of black ink. He kicked steadily, using his compass to steer a course parallel to shore. When he thought he had swum far enough, he surfaced.

He saw he had misjudged the distance slightly. He dived down, swam another fifty feet, and surfaced again. This time he was directly opposite the house. He worked his way quietly forward to the wooden dock. The house was completely dark, and there was no sign of anyone, nor of the dogs.

200

He came out of the water and tossed the rope ladder onto the grass, then unsealed the pouch containing the dart gun. Even as he reached for the weapon, he could see them coming, three dark shapes racing silently towards him in the moonlight.

There was no time to take off the heavy tank. The dogs were almost upon him, and he could see the gleaming eyes and jagged teeth of the leading Doberman as it leaped for his face. Danner fired; the dart embedded itself noiselessly in the dog's chest. The animal crashed into Danner, slid off the front of his wet suit, and collapsed at his feet.

He was jolted back into the lake by the impact, and the second dog was splashing in after him. Danner reloaded quickly. He darted the attacker a fraction of a second before the dog, its jaws open, would have torn away a large chunk of his leg.

The third Doberman stood on the shore a few feet away, growling menacingly, challenging him to come any closer. Danner reloaded again and edged in nearer to the animal. The dog's eyes were following his movements, and the beast was poised to spring when he fired. The Doberman collapsed like a rag doll.

Danner began to pull out the dog that had fallen in the shallow water. The animal was heavy, and he had trouble getting it up onto the grass. Then, exhausted, he sat down to catch his breath. The Dobermans were breathing normally, fully conscious but paralysed. If all went well, Wellington Lloyd would never know that anyone had paid him a visit in the night.

Danner slipped off his air tank and flippers and left them on the grass. He unstrapped the knife. Then he unbuckled the weights, wriggled out of the wet suit, and picked up the rest of his gear. He reloaded the dart gun and kept it at the ready, in case there was another guard dog somewhere.

Keeping low, he ran towards the north wing of the house, the section with the flat roof. He was an easy target in the moonlight: there was no cover, and he had to cross some fifty yards of lawn. He made it, then looked at his watch. Just after three am. He had a little less than an hour before the dogs shook off the effects of the etorphine.

He untied the rope ladder, stepped back, and swung it. His aim was good; the grappling hooks caught the edge of the roof and held. He tested the ladder gingerly. Then he stashed the dart gun in its pouch and climbed up onto the roof.

Quickly Danner pulled the rope ladder up after him. It was cold in his T-shirt and swimming trunks, and he started to shiver. Directly in front of him, just as they looked in Sam Green's satellite photo, were the skylight and the communications discs. He crept over to the skylight, where the lock should be. Taking out his key, he prayed that OTS had done its work well.

He eased the key into the lock and tried to turn it to the right. It would not budge. He pulled the key back a fraction and tried again. No luck. Danner swore. He jammed it in as far as it would go, and still the lock would not give. He jiggled the key up and down; suddenly it turned.

Gently he lifted the skylight. The hinges creaked noisily. Danner drew in his breath and listened. Only the wind in the trees answered him.

He peered down through the open frame. It was like staring into the Grand Canyon at night; he had no idea how big a drop it was to the floor. He retrieved his ladder, hooked it to the frame of the skylight, and lowered the rungs until he felt the ropes go slack against the bottom. Then he climbed down into the house.

He waited a moment for his eyes to adjust to the dim light. The high-ceilinged room in which he found himself would have been perfect for an artist's studio. There were no easels in the room, however, just a couple of chairs, a desk, and a lot of electronic equipment. The radio gear explained the discs on the roof. Lloyd apparently had his own communications system for contacting his people around the globe.

Danner moved to the door. It was locked. He checked his watch: three fifteen.

He decided to risk the torch, but dimmed it by putting his fingers over the light. Removing his tools from the smaller pouch, he set to work. The lock was well machined and difficult to pick. It took ten minutes before he succeeded. Then, turning off the torch, he eased the door open and stepped onto the landing.

The wooden floor was old and creaky. He moved slowly, stopping often to listen. All he heard was the steady breathing of someone asleep in a bedroom off to the right.

He was almost at the head of the stairs when he bumped into a chair. It scraped hard against the wall. He froze. Whoever was in the bedroom—and Danner assumed it was Lloyd—was coughing and turning in his sleep. After a couple of minutes, the rhythmic breathing resumed. Warily Danner crept downstairs to the first floor.

He moved quietly past the open dining room to the study, and slipped inside. As he had hoped, the moonlight shining through the large windows gave him good visibility. Again he checked his watch: three thirty. He had only half an hour until the dogs recovered—if the paralytic worked exactly as it should.

He looked around for a wall safe but, as he had expected, did not find one. He went over to the Bertoia sculpture in the centre of the room. Opening his pouch, he took out the miniature tape recorder and the circular sheet of rubber with the peculiar pattern of holes cut in it.

He studied the sculpture for a moment. The thin brass rods clustered in their wooden base were almost four feet high. At the top of each rod was a cylinder, much wider than the rod itself and about two and a half inches high, so that the sculpture looked like a cluster of metal bullrushes. The cylinders were almost touching, barely a quarter of an inch apart.

The sculptor, Harry Bertoia, Danner had learned from his research, had been born in Italy but moved to the United States in the 1930s. He became a successful artist known for his "sounding sculpture". Danner knew that if he so much as brushed against the delicately balanced rods, they would go into motion, swaying crazily against each other and chiming loudly enough to wake the household. Wellington Lloyd had chosen an ingenious place to hide his tapes. The Bertoia was an artistic burglar alarm.

Moving with extreme care, Danner held the rubber circle above the sculpture. Gently and slowly he lowered the sheet until it was resting on the flat tops of the metal cylinders. He exhaled. The rods had not touched.

Gingerly he began the delicate task of working the holes over the cylinders. The job took eight minutes. When it was done, Danner stepped back and admired his handiwork. It was probably the first time in history, he reflected, that anyone had used a silencer on a sculpture.

He got down on his knees and checked the wooden base of the Bertoia. It was round and apparently built in smoothly joined panels. There were no knobs or drawers visible. He pushed in on each panel, but none gave way. He ran his fingers underneath the wood, hoping to find a release lever. There was nothing.

Then he had an idea: he began pressing on the panels with both hands, on opposite sides, applying pressure here and there. Suddenly the front section of the base fell open.

He reached inside. There was a single tape cassette in the hollow base. Removing it, he put it in his recorder. He inserted an earphone in the jack and ran the machine forward at high speed, stopping twice to make sure that there was still someone talking on the tape. A little way through the first side, the voice stopped. The rest of the tape was blank. So was the other side.

As Danner had requested, his recorder was designed for duplicating, with two compartments on opposite sides. The side he had just used was for playing only, so a tape could not be erased by mistake. A blank cassette was in place in the recording compartment. He pushed the record button. His watch said three forty-five.

At high speed it took only an instant to copy the tape. When it was done, he rewound the original and returned it to where he had found it. He closed the front section, and the base was sealed.

He stood up and eased the rubber sheet off the sculpture, releasing each cylinder separately. It was excruciatingly slow work, and it took all of his self-discipline not to hurry. Finally he freed the last cylinder. The brass rods were vibrating slightly, but the cylinders did not touch.

He stowed the rubber sheet and the tape recorder back inside the waterproof pouch. He looked at his watch. It was four o'clock. He had run out of time.

Slipping back to the stairs, he moved as quickly as he dared up to the second floor. He crept along the hall to the room with the skylight, stepped inside, and softly closed the door behind him. It clicked shut. He tried it: it was locked. He clambered onto the roof, then pulled up the rope ladder and locked the skylight behind him. He secured the grappling hooks to the edge of the roof and lowered the ladder.

Clouds had completely obscured the moon. Danner peered out towards the lake, but he could not see the dogs in the darkness. He took out the dart gun and checked to make sure it was loaded. Then he climbed down to the lawn. He jiggled the ropes, and the grappling hooks tumbled down. He gathered up the ladder and ran towards the water.

At least he could not be seen from the house now. The problem was the dogs. Where were they?

He reached the lake and was relieved to find the Dobermans just where he had left them. They were beginning to stir. Quickly Danner pulled the darts from the dogs' bodies and dropped them in the pouch.

He guessed he had no more than a minute or two before the drug wore off. He jammed his legs and arms into the wet suit, then strapped the compass to his wrist, the knife to his leg, and the weights around his waist. He clipped the pouches to his belt.

One of the Dobermans was trying to get to its feet. It was growling, enraged at seeing its enemy again, and its powerful jaws were flecked with foam.

Danner sat down at the water's edge and slipped on his flippers. The dog was moving towards him now, stumbling groggily but coming on fast, a lethal dark shadow in the night.

"Good boy," Danner said. "Good boy."

He strapped the air tank on his back, and fell backwards into the frigid water at the same instant that the dog leaped. As he sank to safety, Danner could see the yellow eyes of the Doberman staring down at him from the surface of the Lake of Zurich.

THE LOFT WAS SECLUDED in a three-storey building that in an earlier life had been a paint factory. Pete Vanucci had converted it into a sound studio.

His business seemed creative enough to blend in with the surroundings. The lower Manhattan neighbourhood, once an industrial area, had gradually been taken over by art galleries, restaurants, and little shops that sold antiques and jewellery.

Danner walked up to the top floor and rang the bell. The door was opened by a short man, slender but wiry, with jet-black hair. Vanucci might more easily have been taken for a gangster than for what he was, an expert on tape recordings. He had left the CIA several years ago to set up his own sound lab. The loft was crowded with electronic equipment.

Danner took the cassette out of his jacket pocket and put it down on a table. "This is it."

"I got a question," Vanucci said. "How come you didn't take it to the OTS lab?"

"You're supposed to be the best at voice identification."

Pete grinned in acknowledgment. "I won't say no."

Operating from his modest loft, Vanucci made a lot of money

working for corporations that were trying to protect trade secrets, and for lawyers in domestic cases. He did no wire-tapping or bugging himself. But tapping a line was only the beginning. Often it was essential to pinpoint a voice. Who was buying secrets from the disloyal lab technician in a drug company? Who was calling an adulterous spouse to arrange an assignation? Identification was the key.

"The material on the tape is sensitive," Danner cautioned.

"Man, in my line of work I'd be at the bottom of the river by now if I talked about what I hear."

Vanucci put the cassette in a recorder and pushed the play button. A woman's voice boomed out of two nearby speakers.

"This is your friend again. The information on this tape should be of p-p-p-particular interest to the C C Group. Rome station is r-r-reviving the secret Masonic lodge known as *P-P-Propaganda Due*, or P-2. As you know, the most p-powerful members of the Italian establishment in all walks of life b-b-belonged to P-2. The objective of the f-f-founding of the new lodge will b-be to increase the agency's influence within the Italian government. The officer responsible for creating the lodge is Kendall Cameron. F-F-Funding will be handled via M-M-Milan base."

There was a crackling noise, as though a microphone had been switched off, and then silence. Vanucci turned off the recorder. "I remember that Masonic lodge business. All the Italian generals and bankers and judges and members of parliament belonged to *Propaganda Due*. There was a lot of crooked stuff going on."

Danner nodded. "It brought down the government."

"You don't have any idea whose voice it is?"

"No. Some of her inflections are familiar, but I would remember anyone who stuttered like that. I don't know her."

Vanucci furrowed his brow. "My guess is that the voice on the tape has been altered. It sounds a little mechanical in places."

"Is there any way to recreate the original voice?"

"That depends on how sophisticated the technician was who processed the voice. But, with luck, it might be done."

"Where do we start?"

"With a few basics." Vanucci snapped a cable into the recorder and plugged the other end into a metal box that had a few knobs on the front. "This little gadget is an analogue-to-digital converter," he said. "It takes the sound we hear with our ears and converts it to a series of numbers. What happens is that the converter assigns a number to each bit of electrical voltage as it comes out of the tape recorder. The voltage drops or increases with changes in the voice. The higher the number, the louder the voice."

Danner grunted. "You're a little over my head. But go on."

Vanucci adjusted a knob on the box. "The converter is plugged into this computer," he said, indicating a nearby terminal. He pushed the play button on the tape recorder and waited. In a moment he turned the tape recorder off again. "There. You've only got a minute of speech on that tape. It's all stored in the computer, in the form of six hundred thousand numbers."

He sat down at the terminal. "Now we have the computer do a spectrum analysis." He punched in some instructions on the keyboard, and a bar graph appeared on the screen. "OK, you're looking at a snapshot of a sound one twenty-thousandth of a second in duration." He hit a key. "Here's the next frame."

The computer was flashing a series of graphs on the screen. Vanucci watched them intently. "Wait a minute," he said. "We've come to the part where she's begun to stutter. The spectrums are repeating. Look, here you see the beginning of the word p-p-p-particular. These first three frames are the first *p* sound. The next three are the second *p*."

"They look the same," said Danner.

"That's just the point. They're identical. It might sound that way to your ear when someone stutters. But in actual speech there would be slight variations. You see what it means? The stutter was created by a computer."

Danner stared at the screen. "Incredible!"

Vanucci rolled back to the first letter *p* and punched in more instructions. "I'm telling the computer to remove the stutter." He then rearranged the connections between the computer terminal and the tape recorder, hooking them up to a new component. "This box," he said, "will get us back to sound we can hear."

In a moment he played the tape again. This time the voice sounded the same, but the stutter was gone.

Danner listened carefully. "There's something haunting about that voice. But I still don't know who she is."

"That's because the speed and pitch were manipulated to create a new voice. I may be able to find a pattern of alteration. Let me play around with it a little." Vanucci cycled back to the first frame. He

208

was absorbed in thought, entering numbers on the keyboard, muttering about harmonics and integers.

He lit a cigarette, took a long drag, and exhaled the smoke. "All right. Let's try this."

"This is your friend again," the voice repeated.

"Hey, wait a minute," Danner said. "That's a man!"

Vanucci grinned. "I suspected it from the beginning. Whoever altered the tape kicked up the pitch."

"The voice," Danner said. "It's almost familiar now. But there's still something wrong."

"We'll work with it," Vanucci said. "Like a composite photo drawn by a police artist. You tell me how to change it."

"When he says *Propaganda Due*," said Danner, "try making the voice a little richer. More bass."

"OK, done." Vanucci played it again.

"Keep going. Let me hear the whole thing." Danner listened. "All right," he said quickly. "On the second syllable of 'objective', give the speech pattern more emphasis."

Vanucci cycled back, entered more numbers, and played the tape from the beginning. "What's the matter?" he asked. "You look like you were just run over by a truck."

Danner sat back, the colour drained from his face. He spoke softly. "Record the whole thing for me, will you?"

Vanucci obliged. "You know who it is, huh?"

"Yes," Danner said grimly. "I know."

Vanucci handed over the new cassette along with the original. Danner thanked him and walked down the dingy stairs and out into the street. He needed to think. It was baffling, frightening, like being lost in a forest. What he had learned in the last half hour had turned all of his assumptions upside down.

Chapter 10

Deep in the valley below Grindelwald, skiers were crowding onto the platform of the cable car station. It was late in the afternoon, and they were anxious to get in one or two more runs down the slopes before dark. Above them towered the Eiger, a mountain of snow and ice reaching into the clear Swiss sky. From the valley, tiny gondolas hanging from a moving steel cable climbed to a height of

7,317 feet in thirty minutes. It was the longest uninterrupted cable-car ride in Europe, a fact of particular interest to two men waiting in line.

The taller of the two stood poised on the metal grating, ready to board the bright red gondola that was swinging rapidly towards him. He wore a blue anorak and ski pants, photo-grey goggles, and a red wool cap that did not quite cover all of his white hair.

The empty gondola jolted to a halt, and the automatic doors flew open. The tall man slapped his skis into metal containers on the side of the cabin and stepped quickly on board, carrying his poles. His companion did the same.

The two passengers sat facing each other in the swaying gondola. The shorter man was dressed in bright yellow and wore mirrored goggles that concealed his eyes. He had dark, curly hair and the powerful build of a peasant.

The short man was Aleksandr Sergeyevich Pavlov, chief of the KGB. He broke into a smile, showing several gold teeth. "An unusual meeting place," he said in heavily accented English. "But extremely private. And best of all, free of our respective body-guards."

"It was good of you to meet me on neutral ground," said CIA director Brooks Jordan, returning the Russian's smile.

These were no ordinary two men. Between them they controlled secret power undreamed of by the great conquerors and rulers of the past. And like those predecessors, they wanted more.

At sixty, Brooks Jordan lived for power, totally absorbed by its pursuit and exercise. He was a man made for Washington, which was in a real sense a company town. Politics was its business, and power its product. And within the CIA, as anywhere, survival was the first necessity of power. One could not wield power out of office. In that respect, Jordan's uncertain future in the Forbes administration had an almost exact parallel in the shaky position of Aleksandr Pavlov within the Kremlin walls.

Like Jordan, the Russian had been born in 1924. He had been educated at the Kemerovo Technological Institute, had joined the Komsomol—the Communist youth organization—and eventually become its deputy chief. Pavlov had risen through the party ranks, and by the 1950s he had been selected by the KGB for special training in Moscow.

In 1954 he was posted to Berlin, where he had some minor

brushes with a young CIA agent named Brooks Jordan. After Berlin he worked in New Delhi, Paris and London, where he distinguished himself in agent-spotting, recruitment and operations. By the mid-1970s he was back in Moscow as a senior KGB official, directing the branch that handled covert action and deception. His record was outstanding, and he did not neglect his political ties to the Central Committee. In time he was promoted to the top job in the KGB.

When Yuri Kalin became leader of the Soviet Union, he inherited Pavlov as head of the secret police. By that time Pavlov was too entrenched to be easily dismissed, but their personal relationship was an uneasy one. In much the same way, Lansing Forbes had kept career man Brooks Jordan on at the CIA after his own election as president.

Pavlov took a packet of Russian cigarettes from his pocket and lit one. "My position has greatly improved in recent months," he said. "With your help. Within the Politburo I have been able to claim credit for disrupting your operations. Kalin has the impression that we have the CIA on the run."

Jordan's eyes were expressionless behind his goggles. "Now it's time for you to keep your end of the bargain," he replied.

"I am prepared to do so, my friend." The Russian reached inside his anorak and removed a white envelope. "The drawings for the SS-18, Mod 4 missiles. We have three hundred and eight of them."

Jordan took the envelope and put it in his pocket. "Perhaps this will help to ensure that they are never fired."

The Russian gazed out at the Eiger, where so many men had died trying to climb to the top. "The world has become too dangerous to entrust to political leaders," he said. "And why should there not be discreet cooperation between our agencies?"

"The benefits will be enormous," said Jordan. "Not only for our countries but for us."

Pavlov broke into a huge grin. "With Forbes, in your case."

"Yes." As both men knew, the secrets Jordan was receiving would solidify his position. Jordan was aware that Vice-President Prentiss Brock and Richard Janney, the White House chief of staff, had been using the blown operations to discredit him with the president. It was a risk that Jordan had faced from the start. The documents now in his pocket would more than outweigh any temporary damage that might have been done to him.

"We all have our presidents," Pavlov said, a note of sympathy in his voice. "But by sharing each other's secrets, you and I will become more powerful than they. When we meet next, I may be able to make available the plans of our most closely guarded weapon. The charged-particle beam."

Jordan's grey eyes flickered. The Soviets were far ahead of the United States in development of the beam, which could, if perfected, destroy an incoming missile much more efficiently than any other known weapon. Pavlov's offer was staggering. "You would do this?" Jordan asked.

Pavlov nodded. "Perhaps."

"But you wish to bargain. What are your conditions?"

Pavlov hesitated for a second. Then he said, "The CIA will assassinate Yuri Kalin."

Outside, golden shafts of light from the setting sun were striking the tops of the Eiger and the Jungfrau, leaving dark, cold shadows on the jagged peaks. Inside the cabin, there was no sound except for the wind and the throbbing noise of the cable moving steadily overhead.

Jordan spoke at last. "Your price is too high."

"What I have to offer is worth it. Not only the beam. A continuous flow of the innermost secrets of my government."

The CIA director stared out at the Alps. "If Kalin is a problem," he said, "why can't the KGB terminate him?"

Pavlov grinned, showing his gold teeth. "There is no one I could trust. Kalin's people are everywhere, even inside the KGB. But you, an outside agency, could do it."

"There are limits, Aleksandr Sergeyevich. Even for us."

Pavlov flushed. "The man is unstable. I will tell you something you do not know. A few weeks ago, in Chistopol Prison, six men and two women were shot by a firing squad. They were Kalin's personal chef and the rest of the kitchen staff in the Kremlin."

"What had they done?"

"Nothing. They were completely innocent. But Kalin has decided that people around him are trying to poison him. The man is mad. A danger to our country and to yours."

Jordan nodded. "And you have your own objectives, certainly."

Pavlov shrugged. "With Kalin gone, I can consolidate my power and that of the KGB. Our countries can look forward to a long period of stability."

Although Aleksandr Pavlov did not know it, the operation he was proposing was not an impossible idea to Brooks Jordan. Three months earlier the CIA director had been summoned to the Oval Office by President Forbes. If only Kalin were removed from power, the president had ruminated, it would eliminate a major threat to world peace. Forbes had read the CIA psychiatrists' reports on Kalin's mental condition, and they were disturbing. National security was directly involved, since Kalin had nuclear power at his fingertips.

The departure of Kalin, Forbes had pointed out, would also ease the pressure on Chairman Huang of China, who regarded the Soviet leader as his greatest enemy and who feared the Russian troops massed on his country's border. If the United States could somehow assist in Kalin's removal, it would solidify ties with China, enhance security, and eliminate a major foe.

At no point in the Oval Office meeting did the president actually suggest that Kalin be assassinated. His language was always carefully ambiguous. Jordan had not acted, since he had received no clear instruction. Now the head of the KGB was bluntly asking him to do the very thing the president had hinted at.

It was true that Kalin's behaviour had become alarmingly erratic. Eliminating him might save the world from disaster. But assassination was a dangerous tool. So many things could go wrong. A failed attempt might even trigger a war. Then millions of lives would be lost, not saved. The CIA director hesitated, feeling frozen by the enormous pressure weighing upon him.

Pavlov leaned forward and gripped Jordan's arm. "My friend," he said, "Kalin is a poisonous growth in our midst. He must be uprooted, destroyed. You have the means."

Jordan gazed out at a deep gorge to his left. After a long silence, he turned back to the KGB chief. "Not only the beam weapon, you said. The flow of secret information will continue?"

Pavlov smiled. "*Da*. I have promised it."

"And after Kalin is neutralized," Jordan continued, "you will use your influence to end the pressure on the Chinese border?"

"Your conditions are reasonable. And accepted."

"All right," Jordan said. "It will be done."

"I suggest that we call it Operation Valki," Pavlov said. "For the city in the Ukraine where Yuri Kalin was born."

"Very well, then. Operation Valki."

The gondola was at the top now. It moved into the covered station and settled on the platform. The doors sprang open, and Pavlov jumped out first. The two men recovered their skis from the side of the cabin and pushed through the turnstile.

Jordan stepped into his ski bindings, planted his poles, and pushed off, schussing down the trail towards Grindelwald. Pavlov headed in exactly the opposite direction, skiing towards Wengen in the valley below, where his people were waiting for him.

As soon as he returned to headquarters from New York, Danner rang the office of the CIA director and asked for an appointment. He was told that Jordan was away but was expected back the following morning. The earliest that Danner could be scheduled was eleven am. He said that would be fine.

He telephoned Julie and was told she was still out of the country. He was achingly disappointed, longing to see her.

When the cassettes had been safely tucked away, he dropped a note to Andy in New Brunswick and then went home. He spent the rest of the afternoon in the apartment, reading. He knew what he had to do now. Only Jordan could help him; until he saw the director, he must avoid Dixon Hadley, who might ask questions, and the best place to be was anywhere but headquarters.

The director glanced at his watch, as if to remind Danner that he was a busy man whose time was limited. They sat in armchairs across from the mahogany desk. Jordan looked unruffled, every white hair in place.

"I've done what you wanted," Danner said.

Behind the rimless glasses, the cold grey eyes betrayed nothing. "You've found the mole?"

"Yes."

Jordan, his face expressionless, asked, "And his identity?"

"You know that." Danner's voice was flat, without triumph. "I have one of the tapes. Your voice has been reconstructed."

The director did not reply at first. Then he leaned forward. "Hadley was right," he said at last. "You are a remarkable man. But you're wrong in your basic premise. There is no mole. The whole scenario is an agency operation. Controlled by me."

Danner shook his head. "That's an ingenious defence. But it won't stand up."

214

The director sighed, as though he were a schoolmaster with a slow pupil. "What you've stumbled into is the biggest counter-intelligence operation in the agency's history. I am personally running the most valuable double agent we've ever had. Aleksandr Sergeyevich Pavlov. The head of the KGB."

Danner was stunned.

"I'm getting incredibly sensitive material from him," Jordan went on. "It's going directly to the president, Eyes Only Category One." With some satisfaction, he added, "Even Richard Janney isn't cleared to read it."

A note of doubt crept into Danner's voice. "But you've blown your own operations. You betrayed them to the Group."

"I had to give Pavlov something," Jordan said smoothly.

Danner felt his hands growing cold. The conversation was not going at all the way he had planned. "You've been trading in agency secrets."

"As director I have that authority. None of the blown operations was vital. A third-rate defector in Tokyo. A few names in London. And if you're thinking of Vienna, frankly the Czech traffic is not that important to us. The Soviets don't tell them anything."

"What about MS/Skylark? He was shot."

"Stein was expendable."

Danner remained unconvinced. "If there's no mole, why was I brought in?"

Jordan smiled. "Dixon Hadley saw operations going bad. He picked up traces of the old boys in each instance. Naturally he assumed there was a mole. He insisted on bringing you in. I had to go along, or he would have been suspicious. I never thought you'd get this far. I underestimated you."

Danner weighed Jordan's words. The man was either the most brilliant master spy in CIA history or a traitor. He didn't know which. "Then it was you who told the Soviets about me."

"No," Jordan replied. "I may have mentioned your presence to the old boys. They could have tipped the Russians."

Danner erupted. "What do you mean, *could* have? You know damn well they did. You're the reason they grabbed Carrie!"

Jordan shook his head. "The Soviets acted on their own."

"I want her back, Jordan. You're going to get her for me."

The director licked his lips nervously. "I don't know if I can."

"You don't have a choice. You've betrayed agency operations to

215

the KGB, operations you're sworn to protect. You're in trouble." Danner paused. "But I'm prepared to offer you a way out. My silence in exchange for my daughter."

Jordan drummed his fingers on the arm of his chair. "You've not told Hadley whose voice is on the tape?"

"Not yet. If Carrie is returned unharmed, I'll tell him that the voice couldn't be identified. In the meantime, I'll say that the lab is still working on the tape. Trying to reconstruct the voice."

The director was silent for a long moment. Then he said, "Everything I told you is true. I'm handling Aleks Pavlov. The take is incredible. And to protect the operation, I accept your terms."

To protect yourself is more like it, Danner thought. "All right," he said. "How soon can you get her back?"

"It will take a little time," Jordan replied cautiously. "There are certain matters that have to be brought to a conclusion. Then I can approach the Soviets."

Danner nodded. "The renegade old boys," he said. "They never realized what was going on, did they?"

"Of course not. They thought someone on the inside was trying to help them regain power. That was hardly my purpose, since I would have been the first to go." Jordan smiled again. "They were penetrated from the start."

"Who did you have? Braswell?"

"Oh, we needn't get into that. I had three sources, actually. Old boys who couldn't stop being covert operators, even in retirement. When I learned of the Group's plans to disrupt our operations, I decided to make it easy for them and send the anonymous tapes. It was the sort of clandestine touch that I thought would appeal to them."

"It's all a game with you, isn't it?" Danner said. "National security, the high-sounding foreign policy objectives, they're all justifications for the secret game."

Jordan shrugged. "The game is all there is."

"Secrecy has become the end of espionage," said Danner. "Not the means. It's taken me a long time to understand that."

"Secrecy and power," Jordan corrected him.

"But the power flows from the secrecy," Danner went on. "It's like the games we played as children. With a secret club. The club was not necessarily better than anyone else's, but it excluded other kids. That's what defined it, made it important."

216

The director laughed. "Just so."

"Victory over the Soviets isn't your goal," Danner said slowly. "Playing the game is enough."

"Neither side can achieve a victory," Jordan said. "And if we did, there would be no need for a CIA."

Danner rose. "I've done my job. Now tell your Soviet friends I want my daughter back unharmed. You have one week. In the meantime, I have the tape with your voice on it in a safe place. It'll be made public if anything happens to me."

Chapter 11

It was almost a week later, on a chilly November morning, when Dixon Hadley telephoned Danner's apartment. He sounded agitated. "I need to talk to you," he said. "I'll meet you at the zoo. By the sea lions."

Hadley was waiting for him at the railing when Danner came down the steps from the bear dens. He remembered having taken Carrie there years before, when she was very small. Mark, the giant Kodiak bear, had been her favourite.

"Hello, Dixon. Pretty cold spot you picked."

"But secure. We can talk freely here."

There were very few people in the zoo, and no one in sight. The wind came up, rippling the sea lion pool. Danner shivered despite the heavy car coat he was wearing. "Yes, secure. Unless you've wired the sea lions."

Hadley didn't smile. "Anything new from the sound lab?"

"No," Danner lied. "They're still working on the tape."

Hadley nodded. "I assumed as much." He pulled up his coat collar against the cold. "That's not why I asked you here. I'm worried about Special Operations. There's something going on. I've picked up traces, but I can't figure out what it is."

"What kind of traces?"

"SO is secretly training an agent as a circus clown."

"A what?" Danner wondered if the agency was getting even more bizarre. "Why would they do that?"

"I don't know. That's just it. I haven't been able to find out where it's going on or why." The deputy director shook his head. "I don't know the name of the agent either."

217

"How'd you learn about it?"

"Jellison, the blind man," the DDO replied. "He was brought in by SO to whistle a call. On another matter. But while he was there, he overheard something about a clown. He thought it sufficiently unusual to report it to me."

"So Jellison works for you. A spy among spies."

Hadley nodded. "Over the years he's been quite useful."

Danner shrugged. "Why tell me about this?"

"You're on hold at the moment, waiting to hear from New York. I thought you might have a go at this in the meantime."

"It's not in my contract."

"Then do it as a favour to me." Hadley looked at him anxiously. "It's that important?"

"I think so. You develop an instinct in this job. There are little signs floating around. A lot of meetings on the sixth floor this week between Jordan and some young hotshots from the SO support staff."

At his confrontation with Jordan, Danner had sensed that the director was not telling him everything. He was intrigued by Hadley's information. What was it Jordan had said? There were "certain matters" to be brought to a conclusion before he could approach the Soviets about Carrie. Intuitively Danner felt that her safety might be involved.

"All right," he told Hadley. "I'll see what I can find out."

IN HIS OFFICE after lunch, Danner called the Washington *Post* and asked for Eric Benson in the Metro section. Benson's father, Kit, an old agency hand, had called in to chat several weeks earlier and had mentioned that his son was just starting out as a reporter.

"Eric? Bill Danner. I'm an old friend of your dad's."

"Out at the pickle factory?"

Danner laughed. "That's right. Listen, I was hoping you could do me a small favour. I'd like you to check your library and pull any feature stories on retired clowns in the Washington area."

"No problem. You gonna run away and join the circus?"

"Maybe."

Half an hour later Benson called back. "There wasn't much in the clips. One story from 1950 about a retired clown. And a 1980 interview with "Pops" Henkel of the Washington Clown Alley. It says he lives up near Frederick, and he's in his seventies."

218

Danner checked with information and got a telephone listing for an Otto Henkel in Woodsboro. He wormed the address out of the operator, and soon he was driving north towards Frederick and from there through Maryland farm country.

The house looked almost abandoned. It hadn't been painted for years. Danner parked, got out, and picked his way through the mud to the front door. A dog started barking.

"Be quiet, Lulu." The old man who came slowly to the door was grinning, his square, weather-beaten face crinkling with pleasure at his unexpected visitor. "She gets excited," the man said, "when she sees chickens or people. You're not a chicken, are you?" He broke into uproarious laughter, enjoying his joke.

"Mr. Henkel?" Danner asked. "Otto Henkel?"

"Most people call me Pops. That was my professional name."

"I know. That's why I've come to see you."

"Come in," the old man said. "It's too cold to stand outside." He led the way into a dimly lit room and offered Danner a seat in a bedraggled stuffed chair. Henkel sat opposite him on a couch. The dog followed them in and hopped up next to Henkel.

Danner introduced himself and said, "I wanted to talk to you about clowns. When did you retire?"

"Many years now. Many. But I was good, you know. I had a funny act. I had a very little dog who would jump up into my back pocket, with just his head out. Then I was looking all over, but I never could find him."

"How do you learn to become a clown?" Danner asked.

The old man looked at him through suddenly narrowed eyes. "You have to be eighteen, nineteen. Not a man your age."

Danner smiled. "It's not for me," he said. "It's my son. He has his heart set on joining the circus."

Henkel shook his head. "It's no life for a boy. Riding the trains, sleeping in a little cubbyhole, eating bad food. Do your show, make them laugh, then on to tomorrow's town. Surrounded by freaks." He sighed. "The boy, he really wants to be a clown?"

"Has his heart set on it. So I want him to get the best training. Where did you learn how?"

The leathery face lit up like a candle. "In Germany. I started with a little mud circus—sweeping up, carrying water for the animals. I watched and I learned. But today is different. Now he can go to Clown College."

"There's a college for clowns?"

"Sure. Ringling Brothers and Barnum and Bailey run it. At their winter quarters in Florida. And the Alvarez Brothers, they're Mexicans, they run a fine clown school in the Florida Keys. Those are the best places he can go."

Danner stood up. "I've taken too much of your time," he said. "Thanks."

"Come again," said Henkel. "Me and Lulu, we don't get too many visitors."

As Danner walked to his car, the old clown shouted after him. "Tell the boy you saw me. Tell him you talked to Pops Henkel."

Danner drove back to headquarters, went up to his office, and pulled out a telephone book. He found a Washington listing for Ringling Brothers and dialled the number.

A woman answered. "I'm interested in enrolling in your Clown College," Danner said. "Can you tell me where it's located?"

"Venice, Florida," the woman replied. "But classes ended a few weeks ago. Would you like an application for next year?"

"I'll let you know."

Next he dialled information and got the number for Alvarez Clown Alley on Big Pine Key. He placed the call and spoke to a secretary.

"Classes started a week ago," she told him. "But there'll be another session in January."

Danner thanked her and hung up. Then he looked in the agency directory and dialled Norm Appelman, the CIA's liaison man with the Federal Aviation Agency.

"Norm? Bill Danner. Can you get me a list of all passengers who've flown from Washington to Key West in the past month?"

"I guess so. But it may take a while. Most airlines keep passenger lists in their computers for six months or a year. But they're slow getting the names over to FAA, and FAA is fussy about giving them to us. They always want the reason in writing."

"Tell them we're on the trail of an international terrorist group that's planning to divert Florida flights to Cuba. That should speed things up."

Appelman sounded alarmed. "When do you need the list?"

"This afternoon."

"You've got to be kidding," Appelman said.

"It's up to the FAA," Danner answered nonchalantly. "If all the

220

airlines want to land in Havana, they can wait until next week to deliver the list."

"I'll talk to Buzz Conway. Maybe he can expedite it."

"Thanks, Norm." Danner hung up, then called Hadley and told him his plans. The deputy director sounded worried and warned him to be careful.

Late that afternoon Appelman arrived with the list. He was a serious young man, who wore a perpetually worried expression. "Here it is," he said. "Seventeen hundred names. I really had to scare Conway to get it so fast."

"You're a good man, Norm. I really appreciate it, but our work is just beginning. Now, do me a favour and make copies of this. Get one over to IRS and one over to Social Security. Have them run the names through their computers. Tell them there's no Privacy Act problem. We don't want anything from their files."

Appelman looked puzzled. "Then what do you want?"

"Simply that they indicate anyone on the list who *isn't* in their files.

Appelman nodded slowly. "I don't see why they should object. I can get them going on it tomorrow."

"Terrific. I'll be out of town, but I'll call you for the names. There shouldn't be very many. And one other little thing. Take a copy down to Personnel and have them check to see if any name on the list matches that of any agency employee."

Appelman looked like a man who had stepped into quicksand. "Does that mean the terrorists have someone inside the agency?"

Danner's expression was grave. "Norm, for your own personal safety, after you get the information I need, I'd advise you to forget that we ever talked."

"We haven't," Appelman said, bug-eyed. "Ever." He stood hesitantly for a moment, then opened the door and fled.

THE PHONE BOOTH at Key West International Airport was hot and stuffy. Danner was glad he hadn't worn a tie.

He fished a telephone credit card from his wallet and called Appelman at headquarters. "Any luck?" he asked.

"Some," Appelman replied. "I've got three names that match names on the passenger lists. They don't have social security numbers, and they're not in the IRS computer."

"Good work. Go ahead and give them to me."

"Juan Perez Escobar and Hector Diaz Fernandez, both of Bogotá, Colombia, and Dominique Cobb of New York City."

Danner wrote them down. "Thanks, Norm." He hung up. Following a hunch, he then dialled Danny Keeler, a friend at the Drug Enforcement Administration in Washington with whom he had worked years ago. As he suspected from the Bogotá connection, Juan Perez Escobar and Hector Diaz Fernandez turned out to be big cocaine dealers.

"I mean big," said Keeler. "Clever, too. We haven't been able to bust them."

"Where do they operate?"

"Out of Bogotá and Miami. It's the usual pattern. Most of their stuff is flown to little airstrips in south Florida. But some of it comes by boat to the Keys."

"OK, thanks." Danner left the phone booth, mopping his brow with a handkerchief. Perez and Diaz were out. That left Dominique Cobb.

Danner picked up a hired car and drove northeast on US Highway 1. Traffic was heavy: it took him an hour to drive the thirty miles of narrow causeways from the airport to Big Pine Key. It was one of the larger islands in the string that stretched south and west of the Everglades to within ninety miles of Cuba.

The town of Big Pine was not exactly a metropolis: it consisted of a couple of convenience stores, a restaurant, and a single motel called the Tradewinds. He checked in, and the desk clerk handed him the key to a room.

"Do you have a Dominique Cobb registered?" Danner asked.

"Yes, indeed," the clerk said. "She's one of the students over at the clown school. We have several of them staying with us."

Danner asked how to get to the school, then got in the car and followed the clerk's directions. The land was flat and scrubby, with patches of sand and mangrove swamps. He passed several caravan camps and rows of retirement houses built along a canal. Finally he pulled up in front of a large Spanish-style house on the water. There was no sign on the tile-roofed building, but it was the only place that fitted the motel clerk's description.

The front door was open. Inside, several students, some in clown costumes, were lounging around the big front hall. One or two gave Danner a curious glance, but no one challenged him.

There were classrooms on either side of the hallway, and groups of students were wandering into one of them. Apparently a class was about to begin. Danner slipped in with the stragglers.

He found himself in a large room in which several long tables had been set up with small mirrors spaced at three-foot intervals. About three dozen students sat at the tables. Danner took a seat near the rear.

A fat man in jeans and a white T-shirt did a forward somersault into the room and landed gracefully on his feet. "Ta-da!" he cried, with a flourish of his arms. As the class applauded, Danner asked the student on his right which of the Alvarez brothers it was.

"Chico," she whispered. "Pepe is the short one. He's not here yet."

Danner stuck out his hand. "I'm Bill Morrissey of the Miami *Herald*," he said. "I'm doing a feature on the school."

Chico Alvarez was a big, dark-skinned man of about fifty, with a jet-black moustache. "This afternoon we start off again with make-up," he told the class. "The first two tables will do *auguste*, the rest of you whiteface."

He walked among the students. "Don't get greasepaint in your ears," he said. "And always keep your eyes closed when you powder."

The girl Danner had spoken to used her fingers to paint her cheeks and the end of her nose red, then made blue lines radiating from her eyebrows. Using a matchstick, she drew black eyebrows, and made a face at Danner.

"Not bad," he said. "Pretty good, in fact."

The *auguste* clowns were painting on mouths with grotesque lower lips, some reaching down to their chins. All but a few were putting on red plastic noses. Danner watched the students, wondering which one might be Dominique Cobb.

Chico intervened here and there. "Follow the natural geography of your face," he instructed them. "Take advantage of the lines you already have."

In a few minutes each of the students had on a different face.

"Now," Chico said, "you can't just go out in a clown face and a costume and wave your arms and think people are going to laugh. They won't. Clowns need personality, and they need gags. So we're going to work on gags again with Pepe."

As he spoke, a wiry, muscular man about half his size came quietly into the room and sat down on a stool in the front. Pepe

Alvarez moved like an acrobat. He had a highly mobile face, and Danner imagined he could be very funny.

"OK," Pepe said. "I want to try the cleaning lady and the thieves once more. I wasn't satisfied with it yesterday."

Several students groaned.

"Thieves to the front," Pepe sang out. A blonde woman in whiteface, wearing a bowler hat, got up and was joined by a skinny youth called Larry, who wore pink greasepaint.

"Cleaning lady," Pepe ordered.

A dark-haired, heavy-set student made up as an *auguste* came forward. Chico handed him a mop and a red wig, which he put on. He gave Larry a bundle of sticks painted red and wrapped in wire. "Dynamite," he said. "This chair will be the safe. OK, start the gag."

The charwoman began swabbing the floor with exaggerated gestures. The two thieves stole in and made for the safe. The blonde woman with the bowler played the safecracker. She put her ear to the tumblers, spun an imaginary dial, and listened. She shook her head; no luck. She motioned for the dynamite. Larry brought the bundle of sticks over and placed it next to the safe. Then he lit a match on his rear end and, with an elaborate flourish, lit the fuse. The thieves stole back out of the way.

"C'mon," Pepe said. "Look scared. There's going to be a big bang, right? One of you put your hands over your ears. That's it, Larry. You, Dominique, cover your eyes."

Danner started at the name. Dominique Cobb was the woman in the bowler! The charwoman, mopping closer to the safe, spotted the dynamite, looked around, and seeing the thieves, picked up the bundle and threw it at them. Larry caught it. Dominique motioned frantically to him, and he tossed it to the charwoman. The dynamite went back and forth a few times. Finally the thieves put it down by the safe again and ran.

"Policeman, get ready!" Pepe shouted. A girl wearing a Keystone Kop helmet edged up from the back of the room.

"Boom!" Pepe yelled. "The safe has just exploded, and the smoke is coming out. Cue, policeman."

The Keystone Kop rushed to the front, blowing her whistle and pulling out an imaginary gun as she chased the thieves. The cop took aim and fired. "Boom!" the class shouted. Dominique and Larry reacted as though they had both been nailed in the rear with one shot; everybody laughed, Pepe and Chico included.

224

"Very nice," Chico said. "Everyone's timing was much better. OK, take a break. Five minutes."

About half the students piled out of the classroom, but others, including the blonde clown in the bowler, remained at the tables, working on their make-up. Danner moved to one side, where he could get a better look at the woman called Dominique. Her face was covered with thick greasepaint and she had on a big red nose. Her hair was the wrong colour, but there could be no doubt.

Quietly he slipped into the empty chair next to her. She turned, and her clown face formed a mask of fear and surprise.

Danner smiled. "Hello, Julie."

Julie could only stare at him, her green eyes wide. "We can't talk here," she said finally. "Come outside."

He followed her into the garden. They walked over to the edge of the canal, well away from the other students.

"What are you doing here?" Her voice was low and intense.

"We heard that SO was training a clown. Hadley asked me to look into it."

"*Nobody* is supposed to know about this."

"I'd like to kiss you," Danner said quietly. "But your nose is in the way." It broke the tension. Julie started to laugh, and then they both laughed.

The students were beginning to drift back towards the house. "We'll talk later," she said. "I have to go in."

He followed her into the classroom and took his seat at the rear again.

Chico had begun a lecture on gags. "OK," he said. "Most clown gags are built on three things: surprise; public embarrassment— somebody dropping his pants always gets a laugh; and deflation— having a dignified matron take a pratfall on a banana skin. A lot of gags also involve transformation, like the old Turkish bath gag, where a big clown is steamed into a midget."

Hardly pausing for breath, he launched into a discussion of the history of clowning. He talked about mimes in ancient Greece, court jesters, the harlequins of the Middle Ages. "And you've all heard of Grock, the great Swiss clown. And the three Fratellini brothers."

"What about Soviet clowns?" a student asked. "Aren't some of them pretty good?"

"Oh, yes," Pepe answered. "Russia has a strong tradition of

mimes and troubadours, the *skomorokhi*. And Russia has produced some famous clowns in our own century. Lazarenko led marches on stilts during the Revolution. Popov, the greatest of the Soviet clowns, is a fantastic juggler and slack-wire artist."

It was late afternoon by the time classes were dismissed. Julie went to the dressing rooms to take off her make-up, and Danner waited for her in the car. Then they drove out to Doctor's Point and parked by the water.

Julie touched his hand. "I'm glad to see you," she said.

"You were gone too long. I missed you."

She brushed her hair back. "I felt the same way. But you've put me in a very tight spot by coming here. If I say anything, I may be placing you in jeopardy. The SO security hoods are wild men. I can't predict what they might do."

Danner shrugged. "Then don't say anything."

"By the rules, I should inform SO we've been damaged." She bit her lip. "Except I just can't."

"I'm sorry. I didn't know it was you."

She was silent, staring straight ahead at the water.

"Why clown school?" he asked gently. "What's going on?"

"I don't know yet. I won't be briefed until the training is over."

"Oh."

"You sound as though you don't believe me."

"I think I do." It would be normal procedure on a high-security operation to train an agent before revealing the mission.

She looked at him. "Then what's the problem?"

Danner sighed. "You said once that I've held back with you. I guess the reason is that I haven't trusted you completely."

"But why?" She searched his face.

"Partly because you work for SO. But mostly because of Vienna."

"What about Vienna? I don't understand."

"That night in your apartment, you knew I was going there. You said what a beautiful city it was. Your favourite."

"But you *said* you were going there."

"I didn't. I never mentioned Vienna."

She avoided his eyes. "Let's get some air," she said.

They got out of the car. The sun was setting over the Gulf of Mexico, turning the palm trees gold. They walked along the water's edge. "All right," she said at last, "I made a mistake. A slip. SO has been tracking you from the beginning."

Danner tried to control his anger. "*Even you.*"

"You don't understand." She stopped and faced him. "The director asked us to. I suppose he was checking up to make sure you did your job."

"And our meeting, your giving me the matchbook, our love for each other, was all of that because the director asked you to?"

Her eyes flashed. "Of course not. How could you even think that?"

She put her arms round him and burrowed her head into his shoulder. He hesitated, then put his hand on her cheek and felt tears rolling down her face.

"I'm sorry," he said. "It's the agency. It's created suspicion even between us. I'm sorry."

"You mustn't blame everything on the agency. You've been doing that number for years. The agency isn't evil; it's the world we're trying to cope with. Blame human beings, blame Adam and Eve, but don't blame the agency."

Danner laughed. "I'm not holding it responsible for original sin. But we've corrupted the ideals we were set up to defend. Like a serpent eating its tail. You're still loyal. I know better."

"I'm just trying to do my job."

"So am I."

"And have you? Have you found the mole?"

It was Danner's turn for silence.

"You see?" Julie said. "I'm not the only one who isn't telling everything. You do the same."

"All right. You've got a point. But Julie—" He broke off.

"Yes?"

"Through all this double-dealing and secrecy and concealment we're drowning in, we have to find something we can hold on to, and believe in. To keep from going under. I thought once that could be each other. Maybe it still could."

Julie looked up at him. "Yes," she said. "Maybe it could. But love isn't just reaching out to someone to keep from drowning. Love is caring about the other person, caring whether he's happy and fulfilled."

"I care about you that way," Danner said. "That's why I wish you didn't work for the agency."

"It's my choice. You did, after all, for twenty years."

"I know. And the truth is that part of me is still drawn to it, even

227

now. I never faced that before. It's seductive. That's why you should get out. Before it's too late."

The tropical breeze caught her hair, ruffling it gently. Then she held him tightly and gave him a kiss that neither of them wanted to end.

Chapter 12

The next day, back in his office at headquarters, Danner dialled Violet Lemley in Personnel.

"This is William Danner," he said. "Code 3941. Level one clearance. I want to see your file on Julie Nichols. N-i-c-h-o-l-s." He gave her his room number, and she promised to have the file sent up at once.

He called to schedule an appointment to see Dixon Hadley. Then he pulled a picture of Carrie from his wallet and looked at it for a long time.

When the messenger arrived from Personnel, Danner signed for the envelope and opened it. He felt uncomfortable, knowing he was violating Julie's privacy. But there was no alternative.

The file was in reverse chronological order, and he began at the back. The first document was a basic biographical sheet. Julie Lanier Nichols had been born on May 6, 1956, in Philadelphia, the daughter of Sinclair and Katherine Nichols. Because her father was a foreign service officer, she had lived abroad with her parents in France, Austria, Italy, Belgium, and—here Danner was startled— the Soviet Union. Julie had never mentioned living there.

He read on. There was a potential recruitment report from a professor at Bryn Mawr College, dated March 1976, suggesting that Miss Nichols, because of her fluency in several languages, her international background, and her father's government service, would be an excellent candidate for agency recruitment. The PRR was stamped APPROVED by Personnel. It was followed by Julie's application form, an extensive background check, and a copy of the secrecy agreement she had signed upon joining the agency in 1977.

The file showed that after her training, Julie had been assigned to the Central Cover staff of the Clandestine Services. Periodic evaluation reports from supervisors gave her high ratings. She was fluent in English, French, German, Italian and Russian. One other item caught Danner's eye. During her training weeks on the Farm, at Camp Peary, she had distinguished herself on the rifle range. In the box that evaluated her ability with firearms, Julie Nichols was listed as a sharpshooter.

He checked his watch. It was time for his meeting with Hadley.

When Danner arrived, the DDO waved him to a chair. "Well," Hadley asked, "did you find him?"

"Her."

Hadley looked surprised. "Who is she?"

"Julie Nichols. I know her. She's enrolled as a student at a clown school in Florida."

"What's she learning?"

"Make-up, gags, slaps and falls, acrobatics, you name it."

"But what can her objective be?" Hadley asked.

"My guess is it's to provide access to the target. I read her personnel file this morning, and I learned two important things. She's fluent in Russian and she's a sharpshooter."

"So the target is in the Soviet Union."

"Probably. The Russians are big on circuses, you know. You remember their famous clown Popov? They also have bears that do things like roller-skate and ride motorcycles."

"Bears that ride motorcycles?" Hadley looked distressed. "It's just one more example of an area where they've pulled ahead of us." He got up and began pacing the room. "Do you have any clues about the target?"

"I'm working on it. I suppose what we should do is access the SO computer to find out the details of the operation."

"That will be very difficult. There are only a few terminals, and they're kept in a high-security area. The SO system is completely separate from ours."

"I know that. But shall I talk to Roudebush in Lockpicking?" Danner said, getting up to go.

Hadley hesitated. "Well, I don't see why not. Provided you don't tell him what you really have in mind."

Danner returned to the fifth floor. Across the hall from his office he found a free terminal for the Clandestine Services computer, and logged on. He asked the computer to tell him what foreign government officials had circus interests or backgrounds.

After a few moments he got three readouts. Ian Blackwood, the minister of defence of New Zealand, had once been a circus acrobat.

Esmeralda Gonzales Ortega, the wife of the president of Bolivia, was an ex-trapeze artist. And Yuri Vladimirovich Kalin, president of the Soviet Union, was a circus buff who attended performances whenever his duties permitted.

Everything fitted. Now it was clear what Jordan had meant by "certain matters" to be resolved. Julie spoke Russian, she was a crack shot, and her target was Yuri Kalin. Her mission was to kill him at the circus. Danner felt numb at the enormity of the plot. And if Julie succeeded, he knew instinctively, he would never get his daughter back. Julie herself would not get out of Moscow alive, he was sure of it. She was expendable. Like Max Stein.

Danner quickly returned to his office and dialled the Soviet Russia division. He tried to keep from betraying the urgency he felt. "I need to know the performance dates of the Moscow Circus," he told the voice on the other end of the line.

"Which one? There's the old circus, or *stariy cirk*. It's very small and traditional. The big, glamorous one is the new circus, or *novyi cirk*, out in the Lenin Hills area, near the university."

"And the dates each one performs?"

"Well, this time of year both troupes are in Moscow, not on tour. They perform some afternoons and almost every night."

"You certainly have everything at your fingertips."

"Normally I wouldn't," the voice said. "But it's funny the way things run in cycles. About a week ago I was asked for the same information. By somebody in SO."

THE FIRST THING that struck one about Roudebush was that he was extraordinarily fat. His stomach rolled over his belt, and his jowls and double chin almost hid his collar. But he was the best lockpicker in the CIA, a man whose pudgy fingers could perform miracles with pin tumblers, wafer discs and combination locks.

He sat now in his office, hands clasped across his belly, blinking at Danner through thick spectacles. It was Roudebush who had provided the key to the skylight on Wellington Lloyd's roof, and Danner began by thanking him.

"I knew it would work OK," Roudebush replied in a gravelly voice, "once you showed us the picture."

"I have a new requirement," Danner said. "I have to get through a high-security lock, almost certainly pin tumbler. I can try it with picks, but I wondered if you had something more sophisticated."

230

"Why don't you take one of our people with you?" Roudebush asked. "Let us handle it."

"Can't," Danner said.

Roudebush nodded. "We do have something. A gadget called a valentine. It's practically foolproof. But you have to have access to the target twice."

"I can do that."

Roudebush got up and moved, surprisingly nimbly, to a wall safe. He spun the dial and removed a device with a thin metal rod on one end and wires leading to what looked like a meter or dial. "The rod vibrates electronically when you push this button. You insert the rod in the keyhole, and the vibrations read the length of the tumblers. That's translated into numbers that show up on this dial. Just write the numbers down, and we'll machine the key. The numbers will tell us how to make the cuts."

"Thanks," Danner said, taking the device. "I'll be back."

Returning to his office, Danner dropped off the valentine. Then he went downstairs to Data Processing and asked for Tom Sandifer.

In a moment Sandifer came out and escorted his visitor back to his office. He was a man in his late twenties, with a dark beard and moustache and a self-assured manner.

"Hadley's office said to give you whatever you need," he told Danner. "What's up?"

"I have to penetrate a high-security computer and get into the data base. I need you to tell me how."

Sandifer whistled. "That's going to be tough. How well is it protected?"

"It's in a well-guarded installation"—Danner saw no reason to tell Sandifer he meant the building they were sitting in—"but I can gain access to a terminal." He remembered Julie explaining the SO computer to him, that day when they flew her kite in the monument grounds. "And I know a password I can use to log on. It belongs to someone else."

Sandifer smiled broadly. "Excellent. The problem is that there will be multilevels of security. The minute you seek access to specific files, the computer will ask you for other passwords."

"That's where I need your help."

Sandifer thought for a moment. "We'll have to use brute force. Attack the computer with a program that will try thousands of possible passwords until it hits on the right one."

"Won't that take a lot of time?"

"Yes. But there are short cuts. Most passwords are simple, because people have to remember them. Our own computers are programmed to take long, complex passwords, and what do people use? Boxcar or puppy. We see it all the time."

"So you try all possible combinations of something short, say five letters?"

Sandifer shook his head. "No, we use a dictionary. Most computers have them now. You can run a dictionary through the system to see if there are any misspelled words in a manuscript, for example. We can use the same principle here."

"How would it work?"

"Most dictionaries are eighty or a hundred thousand words. We don't have to go that high. The vocabulary of an educated adult might be, oh, thirty thousand words. We'll fit you out with a microcomputer, one you can put in an attaché case. We'll program it with thirty thousand words ordered sequentially according to frequency of use. Then we'll add in a thousand of the most commonly used proper nouns. If you have to run the whole program, it might take two hours. But there's a chance you'll hit on the right password in half that time."

Danner rose. "Thanks a million. I really appreciate it."

"No problem. Come back tomorrow and I'll have your micro, with the program all ready to roll, on a floppy disc."

Danner returned to his office. At six o'clock he went down to the cafeteria and had dinner. Afterwards he dropped in at the employees' lounge and watched the evening news on television. Around nine o'clock he wandered back up to the fourth floor. The building was mostly empty now, except for the watch officers and a few employees working late. Guards in blue uniforms patrolled the corridors.

Danner waited at his desk impatiently as the hours ticked by. Shortly after midnight he took the valentine device up the staircase to the fifth floor and stepped out into the hall. There was no one in sight.

He made his way to a door marked SPECIAL OPERATIONS—RESTRICTED AREA. Taking the valentine from its case, he inserted the thin metal rod into the lock and pushed a button. He could feel the rod vibrating, and a series of red numbers was flashing on the dial. He wrote them down, removed the rod, put the valentine back

232

in its case, and started for the stairwell. A guard, a tall, alert-looking black man, rounded the corner. "Good evening, sir," the guard said. "May I see your badge?"

Danner looked sheepish. "After twenty years, I still forget." He grinned, dug into his pocket, and produced the badge.

The guard inspected it carefully, making sure Danner's face matched the photograph. "Thank you, sir," he said, handing it back. "Please remember to display it."

"Sorry about that."

Danner continued walking, to the lifts this time. When he reached his office, his heart was pounding. The people in Lockpicking, he decided, earned their money.

THE SPECIAL OPERATIONS offices were darkened and deserted the next night when Danner let himself in. Roudebush had cut the key himself, and it worked smoothly on the first try.

It was one am. Danner reckoned he would have five hours, maximum, before the early shift reported in. He took off his jacket and laid it along the bottom of the door so no light would show in the outer corridor. Using a pencil torch, he moved past a row of silent offices. Halfway along an inner corridor, on the left, the beam of his torch picked up what he was looking for.

The computer terminal stood in a square room with no windows. He stepped inside, closed the door, and turned on the light switch. He blinked as his eyes adjusted to the fluorescent glow, and then he looked around. Aside from the terminal, there was nothing much in the room—a small conference table with blue chairs round it, and a single filing cabinet.

He snapped open his attaché case, took out the microcomputer, and put it aside for the moment. He sat down and switched on the terminal of the SO computer. The words PLEASE LOG ON appeared in orange letters on the black screen.

He typed in "Log on".

The computer responded: ENTER USER ID.

"Nichols", he replied.

The computer answered: ENTER PASSWORD. He entered "8L6D4Z", Julie's alpha-numeric password.

The terminal hummed obediently and flashed: COMMAND.

Danner took a deep breath and typed in "List directory". He was asking what files were stored in the data base. The computer responded: USERS. OPERATIONS. RESEARCH. COVER. WEAPONS. SUPPORT.

So far so good, Danner said to himself. Then he entered "List operations". Perhaps the computer would tell him the subheadings under that entry.

The machine printed out: CATEGORY. CODE WORD. START DATE. BUDGET. OP OBJECTIVE. DESCRIPTION.

He typed in "List category". The computer obeyed, answering with: HOMETOWN. STRANGER. BOTH.

Danner smiled. Just as Julie had told him, the computer broke down operations into domestic and foreign. "Retrieve category stranger", he typed in.

FOUND, the computer replied.

"List code word", Danner commanded.

In a moment the computer began to spew out code names: BANJO. MANTIS. VALKI. CLOVER.

He stared at the screen. One of those operations must be Julie's. But which one? Names often gave no hints. He might as well try them in order. He typed in "Retrieve code word banjo".

FOUND, the computer responded.

Tense now, Danner typed in "List op objective".

ENTER PASSWORD, the computer demanded.

Danner reached behind the terminal and unplugged the RS232C twenty-five-pin connector. He took a Y-adapter out of his attaché case. To it, he connected the leads running from the main frame computer, the SO terminal, and the microcomputer.

He moved over to the keyboard of the micro, and as Sandifer had instructed, typed in three words: "Run brute force". Like David and Goliath, the tiny micro was now attacking the much bigger main computer. Its thousands of circuits were systematically searching the thirty-thousand-word dictionary for the correct password. The words it tried were not echoing on the terminals. All Danner could see on both screens was INVALID PASSWORD. Each time the micro tried three wrong passwords, the terminal automatically disconnected, but Sandifer, anticipating that, had programmed it to log again, cycle back, and try the next three words. All of this was taking place in milliseconds. Still, it was a time-consuming process.

Danner's watch said two thirty-four when the password PICNIC came up on the screens of both terminals. The brute force program had worked. Picnic was the key to Operation Banjo. Words

234

appeared quickly: OP OBJECTIVE: TO WEAKEN REGIME OF CUBAN PREMIER CASTRO BY RELEASING DISEASE-BEARING MOSQUITOES ON ISLAND.

One down. Using the micro as a terminal, Danner typed in "Retrieve code word mantis". When he commanded "Run brute force", again the micro attacked the larger computer, systematically searching the dictionary for the password. Danner checked his watch. Less than three hours left. He had to be out before six am.

It was four fifteen when the password OXBOW appeared. The computer obeyed: OP OBJECTIVE: TO DESTABILIZE UNFRIENDLY GOVERNMENTS IN CENTRAL AMERICA BY COVERT FUNDING OF OPPONENTS IN POLITICAL PARTIES, LABOUR UNIONS, BUSINESS, AND NEWS MEDIA.

Danner cursed his luck. He was learning everything except what he wanted. "Retrieve code word valki", he ordered.

At five ten am the micro came up with CRYSTAL, the correct password. The computer complied: OP OBJECTIVE: TO BRING ABOUT A CHANGE IN LEADERSHIP OF SOVIET UNION THROUGH NEUTRALIZATION OF YURI KALIN.

Danner literally felt his hair stand on end. This was it! Quickly he typed in "Dump valki". If it worked, he would get the full text of the operation now.

Both terminals responded. Danner moved over to read it on the larger screen.

OPERATIONS CATEGORY STRANGER VALKI. START DATE 4/12. BUDGET: OPEN. DESCRIPTION: PLANNING GROUP D HAS DETERMINED THAT KALIN IS CIRCUS BUFF WHO REGULARLY ATTENDS MOSCOW NEW CIRCUS AFTERNOON PERFORMANCE ON THIRD WEDNESDAY EACH MONTH. DIRECTOR HAS APPROVED APPROACH TO TARGET AT MOSCOW CIRCUS 19/12.

"Good Lord!" Danner spoke aloud in the empty room. The nineteenth was less than a week away. He read on.

SPECIAL OPERATIONS OFFICER J. NICHOLS HAS BEEN SELECTED FOR PRIORITY ONE ASSIGNMENT. NICHOLS UNDER PSEUDONYM DOMINIQUE COBB CURRENTLY UNDERGOING CLOWN TRAINING. SHE WILL ENTER SOVUNION WITH TOURIST VISA VIA HELSINKI UNDER PSEUDONYM SISTER MARY WALSH ART HISTORIAN CATHOLIC UNIVERSITY. STATED PURPOSE WILL BE TO STUDY RUSSIAN RELIGIOUS ART.

The screen was scrolling rapidly. Danner looked at his watch nervously. It was getting late.

IN MOSCOW, NICHOLS WILL SHED IDENT SISTER MARY WALSH. UNDER PSEUDONYM LUDMILLA PETROV SHE WILL BE INSERTED AS CLOWN IN MOSCOW NEW CIRCUS WITH COOPERATION OPPOSITION SERVICE.

PLAN CALLS FOR NICHOLS AS PETROV TO APPROACH TARGET DURING PERFORMANCE ON ABOVE-MENTIONED DATE AT 3:42 PM MOSCOW TIME. CLOWNS MAKE ENTRANCE IN CLOWN CAR 3:30 PM. NICHOLS/PETROV WILL PLAY ROLE OF AMERICAN COWBOY CLOWN IN WESTERN SALOON. AS OTHER CLOWNS APPROACH BAR, SHE WILL DISPATCH THEM WITH BLANK-FIRING BLUNDERBUSS PROP. AS LAST CLOWN FALLS, SHE WILL SWITCH TO A TOKAREV 7.62-MM AUTOMATIC LOADED WITH REAL BULLETS AND PROVIDED BY OPPOSITION SERVICE. PLAN CALLS FOR NICHOLS/PETROV TO FIRE AT TARGET AND ESCAPE IN CONFUSION IN CLOWN CAR, WHICH SHE WILL DRIVE FROM ARENA THROUGH UNLOCKED GATE INTO N. KOPERNIKA STREET BEHIND PERFORMERS' ENTRANCE, WHERE CAR AND DRIVER PROVIDED BY OPPOSITION SERVICE WILL BE WAITING.

CAR WILL RETURN NICHOLS TO HER HOTEL. SHE WILL CHANGE INTO CIVILIAN CLOTHES EN ROUTE, RESUME IDENT SISTER MARY WALSH, AND LEAVE MOSCOW ABOARD SAS FLIGHT 731 TO STOCKHOLM 6:45 PM. IF AIRPORT CLOSED DUE TO SUCCESSFUL TERMINATION OF TARGET, NICHOLS/WALSH WILL DEPART NEXT AVAILABLE FLIGHT.

OPERATION VALKI WILL BE CARRIED OUT ENTIRELY BY SO STAFF.

Danner checked his watch. It was five forty-seven. He logged off, disconnected the microcomputer, and reattached the RS232C twenty-five-pin connector to the main terminal, which he then switched off.

He put the micro in the attaché case, turned off the lights, and felt his way towards the front door, not daring now to use his pencil torch. He picked his jacket up off the floor. Taking a deep breath, he opened the door.

Two cleaning ladies were mopping the corridor. They paid no attention to him. He closed the door behind him and strode down the hall as though he belonged there. He returned to his office, where he flopped into his chair and leaned back, exhausted.

He was chilled by what he had read, and knew that he would have to try to stop it. Operation Valki carried the risk of nuclear war. With each side poised to annihilate the other in minutes, it was insane for an intelligence service to liquidate a Soviet or American president, no matter what the rationale.

Once again he thought through his compelling personal reasons to act. Julie was risking her life, probably in the mistaken belief that the operation had been ordered by the president. An escape route had been included in the plan, but she would never make it back.

Danner felt sick. He pulled up the blinds and watched the winter sky turning pink in the east. Above all, he knew he would have to act for Carrie's sake. Once Kalin was dead, Aleksandr Pavlov would in all probability become the new leader of the Soviet Union. And when he did, he would have no further need to intrigue with Brooks Jordan. Or to send Carrie home.

Danner leaned back in his chair and shut his eyes. He stayed that way for two hours. At eight thirty he shook himself awake and dialled Dixon Hadley's secretary.

The DDO came on the line immediately. "Yes Bill?"

Danner's voice was tired. "It's worse than you can imagine," he said. "And we don't have much time."

Chapter 13

Austrian Airlines flight 601 from Vienna to Moscow had fewer than a dozen passengers. Seated towards the rear of the plane, Danner was deeply absorbed in a catalogue illustrated with pipes and flues. In his pocket were a US passport and a Soviet visa made out in the name of Richard Culver. He was a representative of a heating supply company in Indiana that was seeking to expand its markets into the Soviet Union.

His dark hair was now crew-cut and dyed brown; all traces of grey had been removed. He had on a pair of glasses with thick lenses, which did not, in fact, affect his vision. In his wallet were business and credit cards, an Indiana driver's licence, and a colour snapshot of a woman sitting in front of a fireplace with a teenage boy and girl. The back of the snapshot was inscribed, "Love, Jennifer, Susan and Jack."

The pilot announced that the aircraft was over Soviet territory and that it was forbidden to take photographs. A flight attendant served a light lunch. Danner ate mechanically and thought back over his battle with Dixon Hadley.

The DDO had agreed that Operation Valki must be stopped at all costs. It had been more difficult persuading him to send Danner in alone. At first Hadley had wanted to use Moscow station. Danner had argued that the station's loyalties would be divided. Jordan had ordered the operation, Hadley was countermanding it. Chaos would result if the station were brought in. Danner had to do it on his own.

The seat-belt sign flashed on, and the jet swung into its final approach to Sheremetyevo Airport. It was after four pm, Moscow time, when they touched down in the rain.

Inside the terminal, the first thing Danner noticed was the armed, uniformed militiamen. They seemed to be everywhere. He lined up with the other arriving passengers to go through passport control, where two grim-faced officers sat behind safety glass in a booth.

When he got to the window, he shoved his passport and visa through a narrow opening at the bottom. The young guard on the left examined the documents for a long time. Danner wasn't worried. The visa was real, routinely issued by the Soviet embassy in Washington. The passport was indistinguishable from any other US passport.

The guard tore off one half of the visa. He slid the other half and the passport back under the window.

Danner moved on, claimed his bag from a conveyer belt, and prepared to go through customs. Two blue-uniformed officials sat behind a high yellow counter that housed a bank of X-ray machines. He chose the official he thought looked friendlier and placed his bag in front of the man. The X-ray device closed over it. Danner held his breath. The radio in his suitcase was the one piece of equipment that might get him into trouble, because of the weapon concealed inside a thin lead lining. But the official, who must have seen the radio on his screen, did not ask to examine it. The machine slid open, and Danner picked up his bag.

In another few steps he passed into the main terminal. There was a foreign-exchange window to the left, and he bought a hundred dollars in roubles.

It was a long walk to the taxis. Danner took the first one in line. "Hotel National," he said to the driver, a young blond man who spoke a few words of English.

It was very cold out and completely dark. The rain was sluicing off the windscreen in sheets as the cab hurtled towards the city. When it reached the National, Danner paid the fare, took his bag, and went inside.

The eighty-year-old hotel, where Lenin had lived for a time, was across the street from the Kremlin and Red Square. Danner's room was on the top floor, and the view was spectacular. Just in front of him two huge red stars atop the towers of the Kremlin glowed brightly against the black December sky. The rain had stopped, and a light snow was falling.

He opened the French windows and stepped out onto the balcony in the biting cold. He felt exhilarated, an enemy agent standing at the very centre of Soviet power. Somewhere in the same city, Julie was preparing to alter the nature of that power, only two days from now. Unless he could stop her.

IN THE MORNING Danner went down to the dining room and had a breakfast of ham and eggs, toast, and coffee. Afterwards he bought four copies of *Pravda* at a news kiosk, then went back up to his room to spend some time pretending to be Richard Culver. He had with him the name and telephone number of Nicolai Tolichev, an official of the Ministry of Foreign Trade.

He was not able to reach Tolichev but talked with an assistant, a Miss Kisalova. "You cannot meet with Mr. Tolichev," she said. "This is not possible."

Danner tried to sound disappointed. "I've come all the way from Indianapolis, Indiana, to meet with Mr. Tolichev. I was told he was the right official to see."

"Is not possible. He is very busy, is Mr. Tolichev."

"Well, is there someone else I can see?"

"Yes, certainly. You must find out the proper official."

"How do I do that?"

Miss Kisalova was beginning to lose patience. "There is no one at the Ministry of Foreign Trade who can see you. You must call the Ministry of Light Industry. Comrade Tarasov. But he will not speak to you. He is the minister."

"Thank you very much." Danner hung up. He suppressed a

strong desire to laugh. He knew he had better not. His room, like all hotel rooms in Moscow in which foreigners were put, was undoubtedly bugged.

He phoned the Ministry of Light Industry and was transferred to five different extensions and then cut off. He called again and finally reached a low-level official in the division of heating and energy supplies, one Viktor Chudin, who gave him an appointment for Thursday at eleven.

The timing was perfect. This was Tuesday. The final act of Operation Valki was to take place tomorrow, Wednesday. He now had an official reason for waiting around in Moscow.

He picked up the phone again, dialled the American embassy, and asked for the commercial attaché. "I think I'm getting a run-around from the Russians, ma'am," he told a secretary. "I'd like to see if I can get any help from the embassy. They do business here different from back home."

"Certainly, sir," she said. "If you'll come to the embassy, I'm sure that someone will see you."

Taking out his flight bag, Danner crumpled and stuffed in the copies of *Pravda* so that it looked full. Then he put the bag over his shoulder, went down to the street, and hailed a taxi. *"Amerikanskoye posol'stvo,"* he told the driver.

When the taxi swung into Tchaikovsky Street, they pulled up in front of an ancient orange-yellow building that looked like an apartment house. Two militiamen in thick grey double-breasted coats and bluish fur hats guarded the entrance. Danner had no trouble getting past them once he produced his passport. There was no gate. It occurred to him that the Soviet Union was probably the only place in the world where the US embassy did not need a gate to protect it. In a police state no one would dare to attack it unless ordered.

Inside, a sign instructed visitors to go to the eighth floor. When he got out of the lift, he was in a small reception area. A uniformed marine guard, blond and crew-cut, sat behind a counter. "My name's Culver," Danner told him. "I'd like to see the commercial attaché. I called a little while ago."

The marine checked his phone directory. "That would be in the economic section, sir. Mr. Merrill." He dialled an extension and spoke briefly to someone. "He'll be right out, Mr. Culver, sir."

In a moment a grey-haired, handsome man of about forty-five

strode into the reception area. "Mr. Culver? Charley Merrill. My secretary says you've been learning about the Moscow bureaucracy. Come on back, and let's see if we can be of any help."

"I surely do appreciate it," Danner said. He followed Merrill down the hallway to an office, and then into a conference room that looked as though it had been built inside another room, with double walls. They sat down at a table that was bare except for two packages wrapped in brown paper and sealed with tape.

"We can talk here," Merrill said. "The walls are metal-lined and the room is swept twice a day. Your trip OK?"

"No problems," Danner said.

"The packages arrived by pouch this morning from Helsinki."

"Good." Danner unzipped his airline bag and took out the crumpled copies of *Pravda*. In their place he put the larger of the two parcels. It just fitted into the bag. He stuck the smaller parcel in the pocket of his coat.

"We got a top secret message from headquarters saying you were coming," Merrill said, "but that Moscow station was to have no contact, except for this meeting. Whatever it is, it must be pretty important."

"I guess so." Danner picked up the bag and got to his feet.

Merrill cleared his throat. "Well, I'll escort you out."

At the lift, he said, "Sorry we couldn't help, Mr. Culver. But there's really not a lot the embassy can do."

"Well, thanks for seeing me, anyway. It feels real nice to have a little bit of the USA under my feet."

Outside the embassy, Danner found a taxi and had himself driven to the Alexander Gardens. He strolled along the paths beneath the Kremlin walls and sat down on one of the yellow benches. He looked around. There did not seem to be anyone following him. People streamed by, Slavic-looking men in leather jackets and wool caps, an occasional self-important bureaucrat carrying a briefcase, mothers with small children in brightly coloured snowsuits.

It started to drizzle. He got up and strolled again. When he came to Red Square, he walked across the rough cobblestones towards St. Basil's Cathedral, with its striped onion domes and brick mosaic. Before reaching the cathedral, he turned and headed for GUM, Moscow's largest department store. In the crush of people pushing through the double doors he was shouldered and buffeted by stocky peasant women.

241

The store was swirling with shoppers. Danner fought his way to the first floor, where word had obviously spread that a shipment of boots had arrived. Three hundred people were crammed in front of the boot counter. Another swirl of people moved towards a counter selling pots and pans; by some mysterious means, the shoppers, like swarming bees, had learned that desirable merchandise was being sold. Apparently one went to GUM not to buy a particular item but to see what was being offered today.

Danner snaked his way among the crowds until he reached a little snack bar at the far end of the second floor. He ordered a sandwich and a glass of hot tea. While he ate, he glanced around occasionally. He could see no one watching him, but it would have taken Houdini to stay on his tail in GUM. He finished his tea, went downstairs, and found an exit.

Outside, Danner walked a block, then took a taxi to the Yaroslavsky train station, where he mingled with the crowds. He found a left luggage office in a corner of the station. A wrinkled crone took the airline bag and handed him a metal claim tag. There was some risk in leaving the parcel there, but he could not take it to the hotel. If his room were searched and the parcel found and opened, he would be in trouble.

He spent the rest of the day as Richard Culver might, visiting Lenin's tomb and St. Basil's Cathedral, walking around Moscow. That night he had dinner at the Uzbekistan Restaurant.

On the way back to the hotel, Danner thought about Julie. She had left the clown school without a trace. He wanted desperately to find her, to stop her. But how could he reach her? The chances were that even if he did, she would be under Pavlov's close surveillance. No, it would be too dangerous. He had to stick to his plan. The attempt against Kalin was planned for tomorrow afternoon. Until then he would have to be patient and live his cover.

DANNER SLEPT LATE and awoke refreshed. He felt good, and not really nervous, except for a little tightness in his stomach muscles. He had breakfast brought to the room, and while he ate, he reviewed the plan of Operation Valki in his mind. He wanted to be sure he had not forgotten anything.

When it was time to get ready, he took the parcel from the pocket of his coat and carefully undid the brown paper. The clown costume inside was lightweight nylon and had been prepared by the Physical

242

Disguises branch of OTS. It consisted of purple trousers, a loose-fitting red-and-white-striped shirt with socks to match, and a rubber mask of a smiling face with a red nose.

He picked up the radio from the night table, released a small lever on the back, and slid out the inside of the case. Using a screwdriver attached to his pocketknife, he removed six screws from the thin lead lining. It fell apart, revealing the Taser.

The battery-powered electronic stun gun was not much bigger than two packs of cigarettes and looked like an ordinary camping torch. But it could fire two small barbed darts up to a range of fourteen feet. Very thin wires attached to the darts sent a high-voltage, low-amperage electrical pulse into the target. The first jolt from the Taser would knock down a two-hundred-and-fifty-pound man. The target could be kept immobilized by pressing the trigger and sending continuing pulses of electricity along the wires for a few seconds. The Taser left no harmful aftereffects.

Danner dressed in a pair of dark, heavy slacks, a T-shirt, and over that, a blue sweatshirt with two large side pockets. Into the pockets he slipped the stun gun, his wallet, and the metal claim tag. After that he put on the clown costume and tried on the mask. Richard Culver, businessman, was transformed into a grinning clown.

He took off the mask and put on his overcoat. Buttoned, it completely hid his costume. He rolled the mask into a ball and shoved it in his coat pocket. He put the radio back together, then checked the room. Everything looked normal. He left Richard Culver's passport and thick glasses on the night table, a present for the KGB.

He glanced at his watch: one thirty pm. Time to go. He walked along the hall and took the lift downstairs. Outside, he hailed a taxi and told the driver to take him to the *novyi cirk*.

They took off, driving southwest, away from the centre of the city. Soon they crossed the Moscow River by the Metro bridge, and they were in the Lenin Hills. In another few moments the driver pulled over. "*Novyi cirk*," he said.

There it was—the Moscow Circus. A round and attractive modern building with a domed metal roof and glass walls, it was set back from the street on a broad paved plaza. As Danner joined the crowds streaming towards the arena, he was suddenly aware of excitement and tension rising within him.

He walked as far as the entrance but did not go in. Through the glass walls he could see snack bars and cloakrooms. He continued round to the rear of the arena, where he came to a square two-storey administration building. He went down the nearby steps leading to a lower level of the plaza and came out on N. Kopernika Street.

From his vantage point Danner could see that the administration building was connected to the arena on the ground level. The performers' entrance was set back about twenty-five feet from the street. There were two driveways wide enough for trucks to bring in the animals. Closing off the driveways were gates of lightweight aluminium, obviously meant more for show than for security. He noted with alarm, however, that both gates were locked, although only with small padlocks. According to the op plan in the SO computer, the gates were to have been open.

It was two thirty, and performers and workmen were crowding into the back entrance. Danner took out a laminated pass that identified him as Mikhail Osipov, an employee of the *novyi cirk*. Entering the drab lobby, he was surprised and relieved that there were no armed guards, only performers and employees hurrying to and fro. Those just ahead of him were moving towards a wide concrete ramp that led down to the floor of the arena. At the head of the ramp a grey-haired woman sat eyeing those who streamed past. A few employees flashed their identity cards at her, but most didn't bother. Danner held his card casually but made no effort to display it.

At the bottom of the ramp he stepped into a scene of noisy confusion. To his left was a labyrinth of dressing rooms and offices. On the right the animals were pacing in their cages—bears, leopards, monkeys. Scantily clad women in miniskirts were lining up for the opening production number.

There wasn't much time. Danner ducked down a corridor and found an empty dressing room. He went in, took off his coat, and hung it behind the door. On the floor lay a pair of floppy slippers; he slid them on over his shoes. He checked his costume in the mirror and decided it looked good. He put on the clown face, then cautiously stepped out again. Walking towards the ramp, he heard the band strike up as the audience broke into loud applause. That would be Kalin, arriving for his ringside seat.

Danner mingled with a group of performers alongside the main entrance. Precisely at three the curtain opened and the orchestra struck up a fast Russian folk tune. As the miniskirted dancers pranced down the passage, Danner got a good look into the arena.

In the style of most European circuses, there was only a single ring. It had four entrances leading into it, and the surrounding seats sloped steeply upwards. Yuri Kalin, grinning and gesturing to his blonde daughter, sat directly across from the main entrance. Two men in dark raincoats flanked the Soviet leader and his daughter, and two more occupied seats behind them. Other than that, there appeared to be no security. Danner was amazed. In a similar setting an American president would have been protected by swarms of secret service agents.

The dancing girls made their exit, and a whip-cracking, bare-chested man came in from another entrance with a leopard act. At its climax, one of the leopards jumped up on a horse and rode it round the ring. The audience clapped rhythmically to show its approval.

Danner checked his watch. It was three ten. Operation Valki was planned for three forty-two. His timing would have to be perfect. He touched the Taser in his pocket.

A female aerialist in red tights performed under the domed ceiling. The pace picked up. An elephant lumbered down the passage past Danner and stood on one foot in the centre of the ring. Two monkeys dressed as little girls cavorted about, and a juggler balanced on a high wire. A nearly naked woman with a python came out and danced in a single spotlight.

She was followed by performing bears. Dressed as musicians, with their trainer conducting, they began to play the accordion, cymbals, balalaika and tambourine. A bear on roller skates glided by Danner, followed by another on a bicycle. Then two bears came roaring into the ring driving motorcycles. Danner looked at his watch. It was three thirty, time for the clowns.

They made their entrance from the opposite side, in a yellow car painted all over with flowers. The car came in tooting its horn, and screeched to a stop in the centre of the arena. Out tumbled about ten clowns. The audience laughed and cheered.

Danner's heart leaped as he saw Julie. She was dressed in a Russian version of an American cowboy costume, wearing oversize shoes and carrying a blunderbuss. The Soviets had mixed up the Wild West with the Pilgrims, Danner thought.

With an exaggerated gunslinger's strut, she flapped over to a bar that had been set up in the ring and ordered a drink. The clown bartender poured beer into a huge glass in which the head rose up about a foot and overflowed. A rival clown in a cowboy hat and spurs bellied up to the bar and drew his six-shooter. Julie shouted and pointed to the ceiling. When the cowboy, distracted, looked up, she shot him with the blunderbuss. The blank cartridge made a loud bang, and smoke poured from the muzzle.

One by one the other clowns challenged Julie to a shoot-out, but she mowed each one down. Pudkov, a dwarf clown, was the last challenger. As he approached the bar, twirling a six-shooter, Danner began moving down the passage into the arena.

Julie dropped the blunderbuss and drew the Tokarev automatic from the holster on her belt. She was standing less than thirty feet from Kalin, and there was no one in the line of fire.

Danner broke into a run, reaching for the Taser as he did. Julie turned slightly and took deliberate aim at Kalin. Approaching at full tilt from her right, Danner fired the Taser.

Julie never saw him coming. The darts caught her in the thigh, and she fell hard, dropping the gun. Danner picked her up, carried her to the clown car, and put her in. The dwarf tried to stop him, but Danner kicked him; the dwarf fell over backwards, howling. The audience, confused at first, started to laugh, thinking this was all part of the act. Out of the corner of his eye Danner saw Kalin's bodyguards hustling him up the aisle towards the exit.

The orchestra struck up a brassy tune as Danner turned on the ignition. The car responded and shot out of the ring. No one tried to stop him. At the end of the main passage, he turned and headed towards the locked gate on the south side. He hit it at thirty miles an hour and it flew open. Danner kept going along the driveway straight into the street. There was a black Volga waiting at the kerb, engine running, just the way it was supposed to be.

Julie was sitting up groggily as Danner brought the clown car to a sudden stop and tore off his mask. She stared at him. "You?"

There was no time to reply. He jumped out of the car and pulled her after him as half a dozen tough-looking acrobats came running down the driveway. Julie got in the back seat of the Volga, and Danner tumbled in beside her.

The driver turned and looked at him questioningly. "Tell him there's been a change of plan," Danner said tersely. "I'm coming along for the ride."

Julie exchanged a few quick words in Russian with the KGB man, who shrugged and hit the accelerator. Two of the acrobats were almost at the car, and one of them managed to jump up on the bonnet. But as the car picked up speed, the man thought better of it and rolled off unhurt.

The driver wheeled the car round, heading for the river.

"Why did you do it?" Julie demanded. "Valki wasn't just our operation. The president ordered it."

"Did Jordan say that?"

"No. But they never would have sent me in otherwise."

Danner looked at her. "Your faith is charming. But it doesn't work that way."

He began ripping off his clown costume. Julie took off hers as well, then wriggled into the clothes that the driver had brought for her.

"We can't go to your hotel," Danner said.

"Why not? That's where he's supposed to take us. I turn back into a nun and get out tonight on an SAS flight."

"Not any more. The KGB is looking for you now. Pavlov will have to tell Kalin he has a dragnet out all over Moscow."

The driver was crossing the Metro bridge at a fast clip, leaving the Lenin Hills behind. Then, swerving suddenly left, he pulled up on a deserted service lane near the Central Stadium.

Slipping from behind the wheel, he came round to the side of the Volga. He held a gun equipped with a silencer, and he pointed it at them through the window.

Danner opened the door fast, catching the driver in the groin and knocking him off balance. Vaulting out of the car, Danner hit the man with a hard right to the jaw. The driver fell, and the gun went skittering along the pavement. The KGB man wasn't moving.

Danner jumped into the driver's seat, and Julie moved up beside him. He took off swiftly, heading back across the river. "We'll circle the city on the outer ring," he said. "They won't expect us to come this way."

"The driver," Julie said after a moment. "He was outside the circus the whole time. He had no way of knowing I didn't shoot Kalin. He was going to kill us."

"They never planned to let you out of Moscow alive," Danner said. "If you succeeded, the KGB had to kill you."

"And Jordan knew that?"

248

"He could have guessed." Danner gave her a handkerchief. "Better get off as much of your clown face as you can."

She worked on the greasepaint while he manoeuvred through traffic. "Where are we heading?" she asked.

"To the Yaroslavsky station. I have to pick up a package. And we'll get rid of the car."

Julie looked at him. "Are we going to make it?"

His eyes met hers. "I don't know. We're going to try."

From the ring road, Danner swung right and drove past a cluster of three railway stations. He turned into a side street beyond them and parked. "We'll split up for a while," he said. "Start walking back towards the ring road. I'll duck into the station, then catch up with you around the Hotel Leningradskaya."

"All right." She touched his hand for a moment, then got out of the car and began walking. He watched her go with a tenderness that seemed incongruous in the midst of their danger.

The station was crowded, for which Danner was grateful. There was a queue at the left luggage office. When he finally reached the counter, he handed the metal claim tag to the woman attendant. After what seemed an interminable wait, she came shuffling back with his flight bag, and he sauntered out by the front exit.

Danner walked along the street as fast as he dared. About a block past the hotel he saw Julie. He hurried to catch up, and fell into step beside her.

She looked enormously relieved to see him. "I thought something might have happened to you," she said.

"There was a queue." He looked around, spotted a taxi, and flagged it down. "The Kremlin," he told the driver. "The Troitskaya Gate."

Julie gave him a questioning look but said nothing.

As they approached the Kremlin, Danner was struck by the size of the fortress of the czars when seen close up. It was a mile and a half around, with walls twenty feet thick and sixty-five feet high. He paid the taxi driver, then led Julie across a bridge and through the entrance at the Troitskaya Gate.

Inside the walls, they joined the flow of tourists crossing a wide, cobblestoned plaza outside the Council of Ministers building. Danner looked at his watch. "There's a British Airways flight out of Moscow two hours from now," he said quietly. "We're going to be on it."

"They'll be watching the airport," Julie said.

"I know. Trust me."

He led the way towards the Kremlin's Cathedral Square. A busload of Italian tourists had assembled on the steps of the Cathedral of the Annunciation. As the Italians surged inside, Danner and Julie fell in with them. They followed the group into a small chapel filled with icons and murals, an astonishing display of artistic riches. "I remember visiting here as a child," Julie whispered. "We're in the private chapel of the czars."

"The Cathedral of the Annunciation was built in the fifteenth century," a guide was saying in Italian. "It was destroyed in 1547 during the reign of Ivan the Terrible."

Danner nodded to Julie, and they slipped towards the back of the cathedral, where they found the cloakrooms. There was no one around. Danner opened the flight bag, untied the parcel, and handed Julie some clothes. "Go inside and change," he said. "I'll be doing the same. Leave your other clothes behind."

She emerged five minutes later in the blouse, navy-blue skirt and blazer of a British Airways flight attendant. She had tied a red, white and blue silk scarf round her neck and wore a dark blue cloche with a downswept brim. Danner was waiting for her, smiling broadly, in the dark blue, gold-braided uniform and crushed cap of a pilot.

"You look terrific," Julie said. "Who are we?"

"Stewardess Flora Begg, of Chippenham, Wiltshire," he said, "and Senior Captain Alan Fraser, of Plaxtol, Kent." He handed her a British passport and an ID card. Both contained her photograph and her name. The card proclaimed in bold letters FLYING STAFF BRITISH AIRWAYS.

"We're members of the crew of flight 711, leaving Moscow for London in two hours," Danner said.

"What about the real crew?"

"They're expecting us. Hadley arranged it with MI6."

They left the cathedral and turned right, past the Grand Kremlin Palace, once the home of the czars. They walked along the river side of the Kremlin, heading for the Borovitsky Gate. Suddenly Danner grabbed Julie's arm. Julie saw them at the same instant—four men in civilian clothes who had blocked off the exit. They were stopping people and asking for identity papers.

"We're going to turn towards the embankment, stop there a

minute, and stroll back the way we came," Danner said quietly. He pointed across the river as though he were explaining the sights of Moscow. Then they turned and headed back through Cathedral Square, walking until they were close to the gate where they had entered. It was blocked as well. "They've sealed off the Kremlin," Danner said. "We're trapped."

"We've got our British Airways IDs," Julie said. "We could try to get through."

Danner shook his head. "Not yet. I don't like it. We wait."

They walked back into the centre of the Kremlin, where dozens of tourists were gathered around the huge Czar Cannon, taking photographs. Mingling with the crowd, Danner had an idea. A large cream-coloured bus was parked nearby, and the tour guide was nowhere to be seen. Danner and Julie got on and took seats near the rear. In about ten minutes other passengers began climbing aboard.

When the bus was full, a guide and a driver climbed in. The guide, a middle-aged woman with a schoolteacher's manner, picked up her microphone as the bus started to roll. "The first walls of the Kremlin were built in 1156, the present walls in 1492," she said. "The Ivan the Great Bell Tower on your right is one of the tallest in the Kremlin."

The bus was easing towards the motor exit from the Kremlin at the Spasskaya Gate. Julie squeezed Danner's arm. A wooden barrier and armed guards blocked the way. To the side of the barrier a black Chaika was parked with its motor running. One of the guards motioned the bus to stop.

While Danner and Julie watched, a short, stocky man in a dark suit got out of the limousine. "It's Pavlov," Danner whispered.

The KGB chief boarded the bus, followed by a thin-faced younger man. Danner felt his hands grow cold. It was the driver of the car they had ditched.

Pavlov and the driver walked slowly down the aisle, scanning the faces of the passengers. They stopped when they came to Danner and Julie. Danner saw the younger man nod.

"I regret the delay," the KGB chief said politely. "May I see your identity papers?"

They handed over their British documents, and Pavlov studied them. "Captain Fraser, Miss Begg, please step outside."

There was nothing to do but obey. They were caught. Pavlov must have been tracking them all along, Danner realized.

Pavlov dismissed the driver and walked with them away from the bus. The armed guards were close by, watching carefully.

"Mr. Danner," Pavlov said, "I have several options. The most attractive would be to have you and Miss Nichols executed."

Danner waited, his breath visible in the intense cold.

"But," Pavlov continued, "the usual procedure would be to interrogate you first. And what you say might be inconvenient for me. I will therefore exercise my second option and let you go." He handed them their documents. "I should warn you, however, that my plainclothesmen have orders to find you. I cannot change those orders. You are, in short, on your own."

"The driver?" Danner said.

"You should have killed him, Mr. Danner. Now we will have to remedy your oversight."

Pavlov escorted them back to the bus. "I apologize for the inconvenience," he called out as they got aboard. "Goodbye, Captain Fraser, Miss Begg. Have a safe journey home."

Danner and Julie edged back to their seats. The soldiers pulled aside the barrier, and the bus started through the gate.

At the next stop, across the river from the Kremlin, everyone got off the bus. While the tour guide was pointing out the sights, Danner and Julie drifted away and rounded a corner.

Julie leaned against the wall of a building to recover. "I thought it was all over," she said.

"So did I. But we have just enough time to get to the airport." He flagged down a taxi and they got in. "Sheremetyevo," he told the driver.

It had started to rain and Danner was worried. The wet roads might slow the traffic.

"As members of a flight crew," Julie asked quietly, "do we go through a special entrance at the airport?"

Danner shook his head. "We have to go through the whole drill, like the passengers."

"But we have no visas," Julie said. "They'll know something is wrong."

"No. Flight crews have permanent visas on file, since they go in and out so often. We'll just have to show our passports and ID cards."

"Suppose they check the visa file. They'll realize we don't exist."

Danner smiled. "But we do. Flora Begg and Alan Fraser are real employees of British Airways. Their visas are on file with the Soviets. Their names were chosen because they're approximately the same physical types as we are. In our uniforms we should pass muster."

They were at the airport. As Danner paid the driver, he noticed three men standing just inside the terminal, looking over the departing travellers. Two wore dark blue raincoats, and the third had on a heavy grey overcoat.

"KGB," Danner said to Julie when they were out of earshot. "Just keep smiling. You're a stewardess."

"Flight attendant," she insisted as they walked through the long terminal. "Stewardess is sexist."

"The British still say stewardess. Don't blow it now by using the wrong title."

They were approaching the customs barrier. There was an opening at the centre, and they fell in behind a group of passengers. On either side of them more plainclothesmen were scanning faces. Danner prayed they would not look too hard at the British Airways pilot and the smiling stewardess.

He and Julie showed their passports and cards. The documents were examined briefly by customs officials. A severe-looking woman behind the counter asked, "Do you have anything to declare, Captain Fraser?"

Using his best British accent, Danner replied, "No. We just did a bit of window shopping this time, I'm afraid."

"Very well," the woman said. "You may pass through."

The real test still lay ahead, Danner knew. Passport control. He led Julie towards the glass booth. "There's an overhead mirror," he warned. "They'll be watching your hands. Try not to show any nervousness."

Julie took a deep breath. There were two more men in dark coats standing near passport control. Danner went first. Both of the guards behind the glass examined the passport and studied Danner's face, comparing it to the picture. His ID card received the same scrutiny. The documents were then returned through the little opening at the bottom of the window. Danner was motioned along, but he hung back to stay near Julie.

She showed her passport and card through the opening. The younger of the guards inspected the passport, turned to the colour photograph, and eyed Julie. He handed it to the other guard, who studied the photograph grimly. "Get the visa file, Sergei," Julie heard him say in Russian.

The younger guard swivelled in his chair and dug through a stack of papers. "Why are they taking special precautions today?" he grumbled. "It makes more work for us."

The other guard shrugged. "There was some trouble at the *novyi cirk*. They are looking for a girl. Maybe it's this one. Her height, age and hair colour are about right."

Sergei removed a paper from the stack. He studied the visa photograph and compared it to the passport picture, looked at Julie, and back at the visa. "Her hair is longer in the visa picture," he said doubtfully.

Julie smiled, pretending she understood nothing. Beside her, Danner looked at his watch and said, "They're taking a bit of time tonight, aren't they? We're going to be late."

The young guard contemplated Julie for another minute while Danner said a silent prayer. Then the guard slowly closed the passport and pushed it and the card back through the opening. Julie, breathing easier, gathered them up.

They came to a doorframe that was a metal detector, and walked through without setting off the buzzer. At the gate, the final barrier, they flashed their British Airways cards. An armed militiaman was watching them.

They walked up the closed ramp into the plane. The senior steward, a thin blond man, greeted them with a smile. "Captain Fraser, Miss Begg, good to have you aboard." They took seats near the rear of the cabin.

There were a few Russian passengers on the plane, so Julie and Danner said little to each other. Danner stared out at the rain. Julie closed her eyes and put her head back. In a few moments the jet surged down the runway and they were airborne.

Julie took his hand and smiled. "We're safe," she said.

"Don't celebrate yet. Until we're out of Soviet airspace, the plane can be recalled."

Alarm crossed her face. "How long will that be?"

"I'd say about an hour and a half."

"I think I need a drink."

"So do I." He buzzed for the steward and gave their order.

When their drinks were brought, Danner drummed his fingers on the arm of his seat and looked out into the blackness.

"Cheer up," Julie said. "We're going to make it."

"Viktor Chudin will be annoyed."

"Who's he?"

"An official of the Ministry of Light Industry. I have an appointment with him tomorrow."

Julie laughed. "To missing your appointment." She touched her glass to his.

The time seemed to pass quickly. They were both beginning to unwind when the captain came back and stood by their seats. His expression was grave. "Captain Fraser, Miss Begg, I'm sorry to have to tell you this. The Soviets have recalled flight 711 to Moscow."

The younger passport guard, Danner thought. He had finally put it together. "Where are we?"

"Over Latvia. Our airspeed is more than nine miles a minute, but we're still about thirty-five miles inside Soviet territory."

"What are you going to do?" Julie asked.

"Well, the rules require us to fly back. But if we never received the message . . . that's another story, then, isn't it?"

Julie smiled. "Thank you, Captain. Thank you very much."

Chapter 14

By the flickering firelight Brooks Jordan's face was half obscured in shadow. He sat by the hearth, sipping brandy, listening but saying little. Danner had insisted on meeting the director at his house. Outside, the winter night was cold and crisp, and the capital was covered with fresh snow.

"You should not have meddled," Jordan said finally. "The president ordered the operation."

"I doubt you can prove that," Danner said. "Targeting Kalin could have triggered a nuclear war. You put the world at risk."

Jordan's eyebrows arched. "Kalin alive may be the greater risk. The man is unstable. His finger's on the button—"

Danner cut him off. "I don't think that's why you did it at all. I think you did a deal with Pavlov."

Jordan sighed. "Like so many people, you long for an orderly world. It isn't like that. The world is an uncivilized place."

"Yes. But our only chance for survival is to pretend it's civilized. There have to be limits. Rules of the game. Even for the agency."

"The normal rules don't apply to us," Jordan replied. "We were set up to break the rules."

"Not when millions of lives are at stake."

The director shrugged. "It doesn't matter now. It's over."

"I want to be sure of that. The terms I offered you at our last meeting still stand: my silence for my daughter."

"I don't know whether the Soviets will return your daughter now. Pavlov may be rather cross with you."

"Within forty-eight hours," Danner said, "either Carrie is freed or I go public with the whole lousy story. The renegade old boys, the tapes, the Moscow Circus. Everything."

Jordan coughed slightly. "I wouldn't do that."

"There's something more. I want your personal guarantee that there will be no more trading secrets with the KGB. I'm ready to talk to the Senate Intelligence Committee and the television networks. If I do, you and Pavlov will both be finished. He'll be shot. You may end up in prison."

The director glowered at him, his face contorted with anger.

"And in case you get any other ideas, remember, I have the tape with your voice on it. I also have the full text of Operation Valki on a floppy disc. I've arranged to have both of them made public if anything happens to me."

Jordan seemed to sag into his chair. He ran his fingers through his snow-white hair in an uncharacteristic nervous gesture. "All right," he said in a hoarse whisper. "I agree."

TWELVE HOURS LATER the telephone rang in Danner's apartment. He groped for the receiver by the bedside.

The voice was heavily accented. Slavic, Danner guessed. "You must go to California today," the man said. "Be on the beach at Carpinteria at sunset. Begin walking south. Come alone." There was a click as the man hung up.

This was it. Danner phoned and got a seat on the midday flight to Los Angeles. He thought of ringing Francesca, but there was no point in getting her hopes up. And the voice had said to come alone. He didn't want his ex-wife, the county sheriff, and the Santa Barbara *News-Press* turning up on the beach.

He dialled Sam Green and caught him before he left for the agency. "Sam? Bill. Take a walk at ten o'clock. I'll meet you by the north car park."

"Hey. Real spy stuff. OK."

Sam was waiting, bundled up against the cold, when Danner drove into the north car park a few minutes after ten.

"I don't have a lot of time to explain," Danner said. "I'm on my way to the airport. I want you to have this key. If anything happens to me, call Andy, my head guide. He'll tell you the name of a bank and the number of a safe-deposit box. There are certain materials in there. See that they get to the Senate Intelligence Committee."

"Oh, man!" Sam said.

Danner handed him the key. "Hang on to it, ole buddy." With a wave to Sam, he turned and drove out through the gate and across the barren winter landscape towards National Airport.

He checked in, got his boarding pass, and found a window seat near the rear of the jet. He was too keyed up to read and passed the time half watching the movie. It was after three by the time his flight landed in Los Angeles. He hired a car and drove north up the coast on Route 1.

The traffic thinned out after he passed Malibu. There were patches of fog on the highway, but in between, the view of the Pacific from the craggy cliffs was spectacular. He glanced at his watch. He would be there in plenty of time.

At Carpinteria he swung off the highway, zigzagged slowly through quiet back streets, and parked near the water. It was a little before five pm, and the sun was low over the Pacific. The beach was deserted and getting chilly.

He got out and walked over a dune. He could be stepping into a trap, he knew. The KGB might take its revenge, even here. But as the sun slipped into the water, Danner started south along the shore. There was no one in sight; only the sounds of the wind and the gentle surf broke the stillness.

He had walked for perhaps ten minutes in the fading light when he saw a tiny speck moving along the beach towards him. He realized in a moment that it was a child. His child. Carrie.

She saw him now and they were running towards each other, both laughing and crying, and then she was in his arms, and they were hugging each other, tears streaming down their faces.

"Carrie," he said softly, over and over again. "Carrie, darling. Are you all right?"

She was clinging to him, holding on tight. "Yes," she said at last. "I'm all right. They didn't hurt me. Oh, Daddy."

Gently he brushed her tears away. "Thank God," he said. "Thank God."

She looked up at him. "Is Mom all right?"

"Yes, she's fine."

"And Mr. O'Malley?"

"He's great. Andy's taking good care of him."

They began walking back up the beach. He reached into his pocket and took something out of an envelope. It was brittle and dried out, and he knelt to wet it at the edge of the sea.

"What's that?" Carrie asked.

He answered by reaching over and gently putting the winged maple seed on her nose. She laughed, remembering. "That day on the river. You said it would bring you luck."

He put his arm around her and drew her close. "It did."

FRANCESCA WAS SO HAPPY to have Carrie back that she did not cross-examine Danner. Her daughter was home; for the moment that was all that mattered.

Danner took care of telephoning Detective Walker of the sheriff's department. "She's back," he told him. "Turned up at her aunt's in Milwaukee."

"It's usually that way, sir," Walker said. "Like I tried to tell you. I'm glad everything turned out OK."

Danner checked into a motel and spent several days in Santa Barbara visiting Carrie. She had come through her ordeal remarkably well. She was having trouble sleeping at night, but apart from some loss of weight the doctors found no serious damage.

Danner tried to make their time together as relaxed as possible. They visited familiar places. They went riding and hiking together in the hills. One afternoon they bought chocolate milk shakes and took them down to the beach.

As they sat on the rocks drinking the shakes, Carrie looked out at the Santa Barbara Islands. "The people who kidnapped me," she said. "Why did they do it? For money?"

"No. They were Russians. They wanted to stop me from doing something."

"Did they?"

"No, but I worked things out so they would let you go."

Carrie was silent for a while. Then she asked, "Are you through being a spy again?"

258

"Yes."

"What will you do now?"

"Go home, I guess. Back to the river."

She smiled. "I'll come and see you and Mr. O'Malley in June. We'll go fishing. And *this* time you better not go away."

Danner gave her a hug. "I promise."

THE HUGE RED, blue and black Calder mobile was slowly rotating over their heads in the light and airy east wing of the National Gallery in Washington. Sunshine was streaming through the glass walls. Danner and Julie stood at the balcony railing for a long time, watching the bright shapes turn.

"You're sure, then?" Julie said. "You're leaving?"

Danner shrugged. "My work is over."

"I'll miss you."

He hesitated. "I've been thinking," he said. "While I was untangling the mess at the agency, I found out some things about myself. I've begun to care about life again. And about you. I've discovered a lot of feelings I didn't know I had."

"So maybe it was for the best that you came back for a while."

"I don't know," he said. "I've led a very warped existence. Twenty years in the agency is bound to make you different from other people. It's so far removed from ordinary experience, how could it be otherwise?"

"I guess it can't. It's part of what happens to us."

He touched her hand. "Julie. Will you come with me?"

They looked at each other, and he could see tears in her green eyes. And love. "Don't ask me to choose," she said. "Please."

"I am asking."

She looked away for a long moment before she answered. "My work is here. I want to continue my career. At the agency."

"Even though we love each other?"

She nodded. There were still tears in her eyes.

"All right," he said. "Thanks for the dance."

She tried to smile. "Thanks for coming to the party."

THERE WAS A LOT OF WORK to do to get the camp ready for the first guests in the spring, and on Danner's return he and the guides were kept busy. Danner threw himself into his work and tried not to think about Julie.

Soon geese were honking over the Miramichi, returning home from their winter journeys. The sun warmed the river, and the ice finally broke with a great roar. Pale green leaves appeared on the white pines, the maples and the poplars. And in mid-April the season opened for the early fish, the dark salmon that had spent·the winter under the ice.

On a morning late in April, Danner rose early to fish the home pool. It was a clear, sunny day, and there was the smell of spring in the breeze. He was standing near the shore in his waders and casting with a white Butterfly when he heard the drone of an aeroplane in the distance.

He looked up and was surprised to see a seaplane following the river from the south. The aircraft turned, headed into the wind, and landed on the water in front of the camp. It taxied over towards Danner. He wondered if it was a guest, but he was not expecting anyone for two more days.

The plane was only thirty feet away when the pilot cut the engines. An attractive woman in blue jeans and a bright red sweater stepped out onto the pontoon. "Mr. Danner," she called.

"Miss Nichols?"

"I was wondering if you could use an extra hand at your fishing camp?"

"What kind of experience do you have?"

"Well, I used to work for the government. But I quit. There was someone I missed too much."

The seaplane was drifting close to shore. Julie was only a few feet away now. She was smiling broadly.

"If you quit your job," Danner asked, "what are you doing?"

"Not much. I guess you could say I'm an unemployed clown."

Danner thought about that for a moment. "Well," he said finally, "in a way, so am I. I guess I'll take a chance."

He waded over and lifted her off the pontoon. And then, carrying her in his arms, he came ashore.

David Wise

David Wise gives the impression of being a man who enjoys secrecy. During a recent interview he mentioned that while in Moscow researching *The Children's Game* he had used a CIA street map to find his way around. "It's more complete than anything the Russians have to offer," he confided. And how did he obtain the map? Wise smiled mysteriously. "I'm not going to tell you." Is his novel's main character, William Danner, based on anyone real? Again that evasive smile. "I'd rather not say."

Like his fictional hero, Wise has made a career of espionage. He was first an investigative reporter for the New York *Herald Tribune*, then a writer of books about the CIA, the KGB, and our own MI6. His book *The Invisible Government* was about the danger posed to a free society by a secret intelligence organization. Applying that same concern in a fictional format, he produced his first thriller, *Spectrum*.

The idea for *The Children's Game*, Wise says, sprang from an actual event—the Hallowe'en Massacre of October 1977, when hundreds of high-level agents were dismissed from the CIA. "I asked myself what might happen if some of them struck back at the Agency." Then, researching the book, Wise attended the Moscow Circus, spent a week salmon fishing on the Miramichi River in Canada, and even managed to interview CIA Director William Casey at the Agency's headquarters in Langley, Virginia.

Back home in Washington, where he lives with his wife, Joan, and their two teenage sons, Wise is keeping his ears open for new ideas, new secrets. At the moment he has no plans for future books. But maybe he's just not saying.

A KIND _of_ MAGIC

A condensation of the book by

MOLLIE HARRIS

With line drawings by John Ward
Published by Oxford University Press

*When I look back, the days of my childhood
seem to have had a kind of magic about them.*

So begins Mollie Harris's charming account of
growing up in a small Oxfordshire village in
the twenties. Life as one of seven children in a
poor, hardworking family was often far from
easy, but the warmth and happiness of those
days shine out from the pages of this
delightful autobiography.
Going to the village feast, searching for the
first wild flowers of the season, helping her
mother make the Christmas puddings—all
these colourful events in the country calendar
are described in a delightfully natural style,
ensuring that the magic of those days is never
forgotten. *A Kind of Magic* paints a
remarkable picture of rural life sixty years ago.

St. Bartholomew's, Ducklington

THE VILLAGE

When I look back, the days of my childhood seem to have had a kind of magic about them. They were colourful, exciting, demanding—full of discovery, joy and adventure.

There was a sense of wonderment about our everyday lives—searching for the first wild flowers of the season; sliding on a frozen pond at night in the crisp, frosty air; luscious, country, stuffingy, Christmas smells; homemade jam boiling on an open fire; the magic of firelight and stories at bedtime; the closeness of a big family in an overcrowded but happy home; our mother's indestructible gaiety, some of which, thankfully, rubbed off on her children.

The village where we lived was set in the low-lying valley of the Windrush—it was long and straggly, stretching a mile and a half from the milkman's in Little Ducklington to the flour-mill cottages in Ducklington proper. It seemed always to smell of cows—a sweet, grassy, pungent smell, a mixture of milk, warm animals and manure.

Apart from the ordinary cottages there were several farms dotted about—Pudney Wilsdon's, Hoppy Druce's (Hoppy because of his bad foot), Holtoms' and Stranges'. Good-living and hardworking, they employed a number of local men, who mostly lived with their families in tied cottages near the farms. Men who were known by their calling—Carter Temple, Shepherd Spindlow, Cowman Godfrey.

Men who didn't work on the farms in Ducklington puffed up to Witney on their bicycles to the blanket mills. Most of the ordinary girls worked on the looms at one or other of the blanket factories

265

too, often walking over "The Moors", a short cut to town; few could afford a pushbike. The more genteel girls served in the shops and in-betweens worked in the big steam laundry. But a few still went away to domestic service.

Most of the cottages in the village were built of Cotswold stone, roofed with grey slate quarried at Stonesfield nearby. Others were thatched in thick yellow straw that seemed to touch the ground. And the long gardens at the back were filled with cabbages, potatoes, rabbit hutches, pigsties and earth closets.

A few houses of red brick were dotted about. The flour mill, too, was red brick, and its continuously throbbing engine, chunk, chunk, chunk, could be heard at the other end of the village.

The heart of our small community was the wide square, dotted with cottages, near the protecting church. Over the road was the school and the pond.

There was a chapel up the other end of the village, as well as two pubs and two small shops—these were in front rooms of cottages, their tiny windows bursting with glass jars of brightly coloured sweets, sherbet dabs, liquorice pipes and aniseed balls—a haven for a child with a penny to spend. There was Baker Collis to bake our bread, and the milkman who came clanking up the path in his hobnailed boots to dole out milk from a shiny can.

We had travelling men who came puffing down the dusty road. One weekly visitor was Hog Puddin' Walker, a giant of a man who peddled his hog puddings and beautifully plaited chitterlings (the pigs' smaller intestines), in a yellow wicker basket fixed on the front of his huge black bicycle. His wares were kept covered with a whiter-than-white cloth, and there was always fresh green parsley dotted about among the puddings.

Saturday was something of a field day for us—that was when Benny Clements, the oil and rag-and-bone man, paid us a visit. He was small and ragged and wore a long overcoat winter and summer; it reached nearly down to the ground, almost covering his boots.

He brought paraffin oil right up to the doors of the cottages. Amongst his rags and rabbit skins were tall shiny tins of sweets, which we called "Benny's Black'uns", and for a handful of rags the old man would dole out a few of these black peppermints, although the flavour was often lost because Benny handled them with black-grimed, paraffin-soaked hands.

Many a duster or house flannel found its way to Benny's cart.

"Yes, you little hounds," Mother would shout, "no wonder I can't find a duster anywhere—halfway to Witney on Benny's cart, I'll be bound!"

We called another tradesman "Spetter" King because he spat on his hands a lot, although some people said he was called this because he stuttered. Whatever the reason was it didn't matter. All we were interested in were his sweets. In his shop in the town nearby he made a wonderful assortment of boiled sweets: clove, lemon, aniseed and cinnamon, acid drops and peppermints. And once a week he would cycle out to the village to try and sell some. We would hang round him, a dozen or more of us.

"Giss one, giss one," a big boy would say.

"Du—du you want to to buy any?" Spetter would splutter.

"How du we know if we shall like 'um? We ain't tried 'um yet," another would say.

And we would nudge each other, pressing forward till we nearly knocked Spetter over, and his bike and his wares as well. Then he would give us each a sweet to taste, popping them into our open pink mouths like a parent bird feeding a brood of young fledglings.

Perhaps one of the boys would buy a hap'orth; then he would slink off with half a dozen more kids following him saying, "Giss a lick, giss a lick," knowing they would never be given a whole sweet.

Packmen called too; sometimes our mother bought thick, warm, twill sheets and boots for us all, paying perhaps a shilling a week onto the dog-eared card until the debt was cleared. By then the boots were worn out, so more were ordered. With seven growing children skipping and scauting about it must have been boots, boots, nothing but boots to pay for on that dog-eared card.

Tramps and gypsies were other visitors; tramps always called on us, the middle cottage in a row of three. It was funny they never called at the others, that stood either side of us. Our mother said that the tramps left signs for their fellow travellers by scratching marks on the wall with bits of stone. We would search the walls for signs but never found any. Our mother never turned a tramp away with an empty billycan. Gypsies she wasn't too fond of—they used to cadge water from our well, dipping their dirty buckets into the cool water, sometimes breaking the well hook into the bargain.

The close-knit village enveloped us every day. We youngsters and our mothers were a little community on our own; only the men and girls who worked in the town knew a different sort of life. We knew everything that was going on. Always somebody's mother was having a baby—we saw birth and death in the farmyards and fields—but we didn't probe, or bother to find out why or where; many of us were thirteen and fourteen before we started to pick up the facts of life, and then these were whispered and giggled to us by older girls, who had picked up snatches of conversations at work.

I must have been nearly fourteen when a gang of us stumbled across a village girl and boy lying close in the thick-standing grass. "I'll bet he's giving her a french letter," a fifteen-year-old girl whispered. But I wondered what this youth could be doing with a french letter—he had only attended the village school. It was as much as any of us could do to master English, let alone read a french letter lying down in a grass field.

Then two of the older girls that I was with started singing and catcalling to the courting couple. The young man in the grass half rose and shouted, "Shut up that singing or I'll clout your ears." We all ran off squealing and laughing.

The pond was just opposite the church, and in January, when the surface froze solid, it became a meeting place for every able-bodied person. In the evenings men, women, boys and girls would congregate down there—someone might bring a lantern if there was no moon—and we would cut great glassy slides from one side of the pond to the other.

When the thaw set in we were lost for a while—then it was back to the fireside and our stepfather trying hard to tune in to 2LO on our crystal set. "Be quiet or you'll go to bed," he would shout. "And take that dratted kettle off the fire, I don't know whether it's that or London I can hear."

On Saturday nights poor people walked up to Witney. After eight o'clock you could buy "bits": oddments of meat and bones. A shilling's worth would make a lovely meat pudding or pie, enough for the biggest family. Many of the villagers kept a couple of pigs, and everybody had big allotments as well as their gardens, growing enough potatoes and other vegetables to last all the year round. Nobody could afford "boughten" vegetables or fruit.

This then was how most folk managed. "Rough and enough" the women called the heavy meals they dished up for their families. Some did not have enough to eat, and pale, skinny children either grew up as weaklings or died. But most of us thrived on stews and suet puddings, bread and dripping, jam and fat bacon.

MY FIRST AND MOST lasting memory of my mother is of a tall, majestic person. She was five feet ten, well-built and with fine features. She had a mop of thick black wavy hair coiled on top of her head and laughing, sparkling eyes, and she was as strong as an ox. Of course, over the years she became grey and bent but the sparkle in her eyes was always there.

She had started her working life at thirteen when she was packed off to service, never earning more than £8 a year. Of course she had good food in the gentry's houses, and uniforms were found. Then she met and married my father, a mail-van driver. When they set up house their furniture was not the ordinary cottage type, but upholstered chairs and a good sideboard and a really nice bedroom suite. For he was a hardworking, steady fellow and did not squander his money.

Then just two months before I was born my father died. Our mother already had three children, my two elder brothers, Bern and Bunt, and my sister Betty, and they were all under five years old. Apparently our father, normally a very fit man, had been taken to Oxford Infirmary with acute appendicitis. Within a week it had turned to peritonitis, and he died.

Then the long struggle began for our mother. Her parents begged her to go back to their quiet village in the Cotswolds, but she refused, thinking that we would stand a much better chance to get on in life if we stayed where we were. "A little bit nearer civilization," as she put it. So, with the help of neighbours and friends lending a hand or keeping an eye on us, she took a job in the town at the local cinema, The People's Palace.

Her job was to take the money and show customers to their seats, but her generosity was her undoing. She would let old Susie go in free. Susie was a dirty woman who picked up dog-ends and sorted over people's dustbins. She did not want to look at the pictures but just to sleep in the warm cinema. Our mother used to say: "You go down and sit in the front row, Susie, you'll be all right." The front seats were the very cheap, hard ones, and Susie, looking for comfort, used to sneak up to the more expensive red-plush seats at the back. One night the house lights went up and there, between a colonel and a major, sat Susie, snoozing. Susie was banned from The People's Palace and our mother got the sack.

She did other jobs—one was gloving at home. Quite a number of the village women did this hand-stitching of gloves for a local factory. The work was tedious and very poorly paid and our mother, who always hated sewing, did not do this for long.

At this time we were living in a tiny low-windowed cottage down Hell Corner, near the church. One day we children were all crammed by the bedroom window while our mother dusted and changed the bed. Suddenly there was a knock on the door and four small faces surged forward to see who the caller was. I was first to meet him—straight through the glass panes onto the dirt path below, suffering no more than a badly cut leg! The caller was our future stepfather and he was tall and good-looking, with a mop of curls and bright blue eyes. He was dressed in his army clothes and I could feel the prickly material stinging my legs as I sat on his lap to be comforted. He became a regular visitor, and looked at our mother as I had never seen anyone look at her before.

He was a dispatch rider and told us tales about the countries he had been to, places with strange names—Mesopotamia, Dardanelles. He brought us presents and sang cheeky army songs to us—and we loved him.

270

After he married our mother we moved from Hell Corner to a bigger cottage in Little Ducklington, a small community of thirteen houses separated from Ducklington by the village green. Here, three more children were born, my stepsister Mick, and brothers Ben and Denis. Our cottage, called "Wayside", was a two-up-and-two-down affair with a large landing that served as a third bedroom, and it was to be our home until the older ones began to leave and marry. With our parents and seven growing children it must have been crammed, to say the least, but we didn't notice it.

The meals were all cooked and eaten in the living room, but the washing-up was done in the back kitchen where there was a small larder and a place we called the dungeon. It was really a cupboard under the stairs, where we kept the brooms and brushes, and sacks of potatoes in wintertime.

Somehow on a great black grate our mother concocted wonderful meals—tasty and filling. In a great oval pot that was suspended over a good fire she cooked hunks of fat bacon along with potatoes and cabbage. The vegetables were put into string nets to keep them separate. When they were cooked she would fish them out with the aid of a fork. Then into the same water, along with the bacon, she would drop a suet roly-poly or a currant "spotted dick".

Occasionally an uncle and aunt who lived in the Cotswolds would send us a couple of rabbits by post. They usually came at a particularly hard-up period. "If the Lord don't come, He sends," our mother would shout gleefully, holding up the furry objects. In no time at all the skins were pulled off. Sometimes we would get sixpence for these from Benny, the old rag-and-bone man. Into the oven went the jointed rabbit covered with thickly sliced onions and halved potatoes covered in dripping. And later we would all sit down and have a meal fit for a king.

In our house jam was made from anything that was going, and during one bad period of about three years we almost lived on blackberry and apple jam. It came out of the jars in great solid lumps—we had it on porridge, boiled rice, suet puddings, toast—three times a day sometimes, till we were all sick of the sight of it. But at least it was wholesome and nourishing. Blackberries were ours for the picking, everybody had an apple tree in the garden, and sugar was no more than 2d a pound.

Once when dried apricots were cheap our mother bought some—soaked them in water till they "plimmed up" and then set about making jam. It only cost about 3d a pound to make, but she made one mistake—she cooked it in an iron saucepan. This killed all the apricot flavour, but we had to eat it. It was much too precious to give to the pigs. We waded through about fourteen pounds of the stuff, and after all these years I still expect apricot jam to taste of iron. But except for an occasional slip-up our mother's cooking, although slapdash, was the best I've ever tasted.

Sometimes she would buy three penn'orth of bones, set them in water in the oval pot, throw in every sort of vegetable and herb that was available, and top it all up with suet dumplings as big as tennis balls. "That'll put a good lining in your insides," she'd say to us as she ladled out the thick, warming stew.

When it began to get dimpsy in the evenings the paraffin lamp was lit and carefully stood in the centre of the table where it cast a soft, gentle light over the room. Through the years, in spite of crowded families in the village, I never did hear of a lamp being knocked over. Candles were used to light the rest of the house.

The only fire scares we ever had were when our mother, perhaps late back from shopping in the town, would fling paraffin onto the fire to "jostle it up" ready for cooking. Then there would be a minor explosion and flames and wood ash would shoot out into the living room, covering everything, sometimes setting the chimney on fire as well. "Quick!" she would shout to one of us. "Fetch me a sack." She would plunge the sack into a bucket of water and stuff it up the chimney with the end of the broom handle, and quell the fire. When the danger had passed she would fetch the sack down, bringing with it great lumps of black smelly soot. "Never mind," she'd cry, "that'll save me having it swept."

Washing day, always on a Monday, began before we left for school. First, every drop of water had to be drawn from the well out in the yard. Our mother hooked the bucket onto the well hook, plunging it down into the cool depths, bending and pulling up the dripping bucket time after time, until she had filled the old copper in the corner of the washhouse which stood away from the cottage. When the copper was full she would light a fire underneath to get the water good and hot. All day long she would be washing, blueing and drawing more water. The only aids she used to get the clothes clean were a big bar of yellow washing soap, and soda. A few years later, when Hudson's Washing Powder was put on the market, housewives thought they were really in clover.

272

In summer our mother would drag a heavy table out from the washhouse and do her work in the sun. Some women in the village had huge wooden roller mangles. Not us though, and our mother, the world's worst wringer, often slapped her washing over the line dripping wet. The copper was still hot at the end of the day, so she would fill it up again and the next morning the water was quite warm, for Tuesday was the day when the bedroom floors were scrubbed in a mixture of soda, water and paraffin. This was done to make sure that there were no fleas hiding in the floorboards, for fleas, like headlice, were easily picked up.

There were no mats or lino in the bedrooms—such luxury was kept for the living room only. This was warm and cosy: the stone floor was covered in fawn coconut matting, but in front of the fire stretched a lovely rag rug, one our parents had made and the sort of thing to be found in most of the cottages. They were made from old coats and dresses. We children used to help cut up the cloth into strips about six inches long and an inch wide. From somewhere our stepfather would get a good big strong hessian sack, which was washed and opened out flat to form the base of the rug.

It was quite simple to do: you just made two small holes in the

hessian with a wooden meat skewer and poked a strip of material through, and each time you did this it made a double tuft. You just kept doing row after row until the hessian was covered. The colours used would be mostly browns and black but people usually managed to find a bit of bright material—blue, green or red—to make a little pattern in the centre and the corners.

In the summertime the living room got very hot, because the fire had to be lit in the afternoons for cooking. If on a Sunday we had a joint or a tin of potatoes or a rabbit to be baked, we would take them down to Baker Collis's. In his bread oven he would cook any of the villagers' dinners for a penny.

On one day each week in the summer the fire had to be lit specially, so that our mother could do the weekly ironing. As soon as the fire was nice and red she would hang a metal stand onto the fire bars, and the irons were stood on it—the fronts against the fire.

Two irons were necessary, one heating while the other was being used. She used to test the hot irons either by holding them up near her face or by spitting on them—then the little balls of bubbling spit galloped down the iron onto the hearthmat.

Such a lot of ironing there was too: knickers and nightgowns, pinnies and petticoats, working shirts and overalls, as well as bed linen. Then the freshly ironed clothes were hung on the fireguard to air. The guard was always kept round the fire when it was alight, so that the little 'uns were safe from it. But when we children had gone to bed our mother used to take it away so that they might get more comfort from the fire.

DOWN THE GARDEN, quite a walk from the house, were our and Missus-next-door's lavatories, side by side. These, when we first lived there, were "privies", or vault-type, a huge deep hole in the ground that was emptied about twice a year. Over the top of this hole was built a box-like contraption with two places to sit. This was a "two-holer", the kind that most villagers had, although some had three- and four-holers. In ours there was one large hole for grown-ups and a smaller one for children. These really should have had wooden lids on when not in use, but not ours.

After we had been living at "Wayside" for about seven years these awful vaults were replaced by bucket lavatories, but not before an incident occurred that could have easily been a tragedy in our family. I must have been about nine at the time and young Ben, one of my stepbrothers, about four. He had got into the habit of wanting to answer nature's call in the evening, just as he and Denis were undressed and ready for bed. He would say, "Mum, I want to go to the lavatory," and our mother would say, "Mollie, take him down," and I, no bigger than two penn'orth of 'apence, would stagger down the dirt path with Ben on my back, our light a candle that often blew out on the way down.

Ben was a cheeky, spoiled show-off and each night as I carried him down he would jog about on my back and whine, "I wants tu go on the big seat, I wants tu go on the big seat." I suppose he thought he was old enough, but of course he was much too small.

As the weeks went by I got fed up with this nightly ritual, and suddenly, one night, I didn't bother to sit him carefully over the small hole but backed straight onto the big one and let him go. He folded up just like a shut-knife and went down the hole backside first, leaving only his head, hands and feet showing. He let out a bloodcurdling scream and I yelled at the top of my voice—the noise brought the whole family running pell-mell down the garden path. They hauled Ben out, smelly and frightened. I got a darned good hiding and Ben a good hot bath. But that "larned" him. He answered nature's call earlier in the day after that.

OUR STEPFATHER, after working for a couple of years on a farm, got a job as a lorry driver for the brewery in the town. He liked this varied job; it took him to many of the towns and villages within a radius of fifty miles, where he delivered great barrels of beer and bottled stout to the firm's pubs and sampled the beer at each one.

At weekends he was glad to do a bit of seasonal work for the farmer who had previously employed him. I've known him take on the job of cutting and laying a hedge just for the privilege of taking the wood home, which was mostly blackthorn that burned like coal. We kids would help by dragging the piled-up truck home time after time, with the smaller children carrying the chips.

He kept many of the habits he had acquired in the army and he was very strict. No going out in the morning without a clean pair of boots and no talking at mealtimes. If we were disobedient it was "quick march" up to bed whatever the time of the day. He kept himself as smart as it was possible to do with such a big family, and his military moustache was kept clipped and twirled.

Often on a winter's night we would sit at home in the dimpsy light, gazing into the glowing embers and playing a game called "pictures in the fire". Usually it was just the four of us younger ones, Mick, Ben, Denis and myself, curled up on the warm hearthrug.

"Look," Mick would shout, "look, there's a fairy castle like the one in my Christmas picture book."

"No, it isn't," Ben would butt in, "it's an army fort with turrets and guns coming out of it."

"It's not either, it's just like Windsor Castle where our King and Queen live," I told them seriously.

While we were arguing, the picture would change. Now the castle became a man's bearded face, now it was a dog, and for a moment a dog's head, his mouth open as if barking, would glow clearly in the fire. Now it became a bird—then suddenly the door was flung open and a wave of cold air would sweep round the room as Bern, Bunt and our stepfather came in from work, cold and hungry. Our mother would jump up. "Time I lit the lamp," she'd say. "Didn't realize the time had got on so, listening to you kids." And in a moment the warm glow of the oil lamp filled the room.

"Come on," my brothers would say, "move back a bit, you kids, we bin out at work all day." Stiff, hard boots would be taken off and stood in the fender so that they might be dry by morning.

Our mother would dish up the meal, serving the menfolk first; then we children had ours, dipping chunks of bread into the gravy or thick stew. "Jam roly-poly for pudding," she would cry, brandishing a great knife. "Whose turn is it for the end bit?"

"Our Mollie's," came a chorus.

"No, it isn't, it's our Bern's," I would protest. Nobody wanted the end bit, there was never any jam in that piece.

"You can wash up in here tonight, you girls," our mother would say if the weather was cold. I would fetch the enamelled bowl from the freezing back kitchen and an old tin tray to turn the crocks on to drain. Mick was supposed to dry up, but she often invented a surprise trip to the lavatory or a bad hand or headache.

I would try to slip the kettle back empty on the hob. Someone would notice. "Come off it, Mollie, go and fill it up." Nine times out of ten the bucket was empty, so it was out into the ice-covered yard to the well, thrusting the well hook, slippery with ice, down into the depths. The stars in the clear sky were sparkling in the frosty air as I drew up the heavy, full bucket.

Then it was off to bed for all of us children, so that the grown-ups might have a little warmth and comfort. We went to bed much earlier than lots of the village children. Our mother said it was good for us and that we grew while we were sleeping anyhow.

Sometimes when she was feeling sentimental she would tell us stories of the past. Of how, when she was a schoolgirl, she used to go up to the big house every night during the wintertime to get jugs of rabbit soup. This was during the late 1800s, when times were very hard and people were starving. Not in their village though. Thousands of rabbits were shot on the estate and made into stew in the big house, and anyone from the village could go and get some daily.

"That stew," our mother would say, with a faraway look in her eyes, "was the best I've ever tasted. It was supposed to be for my dad's tea, but walking back across the park with that lovely smell wafting round my nostrils was too much. I kept having a swig and it was nearly always half gone by the time I got home."

Feeding the hens in winter

THERE WAS A TIME

My idea of heaven was to go and stay at the home of my grandparents who lived in the gate lodge of a country estate in the little village of Sherborne in Gloucestershire. My grandfather was shepherd for the lord of the manor and my grandmother was gate-opener, for the lodge where they lived was at the main gate to

277

the great house that had as many windows as days in the year.

The lodge was a sort of bungalow with one large living room, kitchen, back scullery and two bedrooms. The one that I slept in was filled with the smell of ripe apples and lavender. Under the bed were boxes and boxes of apples carefully packed away for winter use, and the cool clean sheets that I slept in always seemed filled with the scent of a summer garden.

They were great gardeners, both of them: more than half their living came from the well-kept plot. All summer long we picked and potted, pickled and chutneyed anything that it was possible to preserve for the coming winter. Such crops they grew! Giant cabbages and potatoes, row upon row of broad beans and peas, such as I have never seen since. My grandfather liked to eat his broad beans old: "pitch-eyed" he called them. "As big as a baby's ear, six on a fork, that's how I like 'um," he would say, "an' boiled in a drop of bacon water too."

Still, they had most everything to their advantage to grow good stuff: a couple of pigs in the sty and the midden—the countryman's useful compost heap where both kitchen and garden waste was thrown—gave them a good supply of manure.

As well as this there were the yearly "sheep dags" that formed part of my grandfather's perks. About a month before the sheep shearing, the flock had to be tidied up a bit, because mucky fleeces were not accepted at the wool staplers. So on a mild spring day my gramp would drive a few sheep at a time into a smaller pen, where he would hand shear wool from the animal's rear end.

Sheep's wool is impregnated with lanolin and this, along with the clinging manure, makes a wonderful base in which to plant beans, and the wool holds the moisture in the roots. It was a job to keep insects off the growing beans and gramp believed that soot was the best deterrent. But soot is harmful unless it is at least a year old, so it was carefully left to mature before they sprinkled it liberally over the young plants. When the beans were fully grown, my gran and I would sit for hours, stringing and salting them for winter use, packing them tightly into fat yellow stone jars.

Another thing my grandfather believed in was " 'tater 'awks" as he called them. Living on the edge of a great park, their garden was at the mercy of hordes of woodland birds, and the only thing that scared them away was " 'tater 'awks". Each spring he would say, "I shall have to get old Nathan (the head keeper on the estate) to shoot

278

I a sparrow'awk or two." Then he would get several nobbly potatoes—nobbly so that he could tie a piece of string round them—and he'd stick the largest feathers from the sparrowhawks into the potatoes. These feathered contraptions were hung on a piece of string about a yard long and tied onto a stick which was then pushed into the soil at a slight angle, leaving the "'tater 'awk" swinging and twirling in the breeze. The finest bird scarer I've ever seen.

Any vegetables and fruit that were not wanted for immediate use, or for pickling and jam, were used to make wine. Both my gran and gramp made all sorts, which they imagined cured any complaint. The gallons of agrimony that my grandfather consumed! He really believed that this wine kept him free from rheumatism—most likely it did, for he was out on the Cotswold hills for the best part of sixty years in all winds and weathers, with never a day off for illness. Each wine, they believed, had its own medicinal properties: clover for bronchitis, parsley for clearing the blood, beetroot for anaemia, mulled elderberry to sweat out a cold, dandelion for a sluggish liver and metheglin, made from honey and sweet herbs, for a real good pick-me-up.

In the back scullery there was always wine of some sort or another fermenting. Gran never hurried her wines: after boiling they were allowed to settle in a big red earthenware pan. Then she would place a slice of barm-covered toast on top, leaving the concoction to ferment before straining it off into bottles and casks.

Several journeys I made during the summer to Northleach—three miles there and three back—to get a penn'orth of barm, the froth that forms on top of fermenting beer, from the local brewery. I was given a two-pound stone jam jar to collect it in, and on the way back I often poked my fingers into the barm, sniffing and savouring the sharp beery taste.

We drank wine after the midday meal and again before going to bed and if anyone called they were always asked, "Will you have a glass of wine?" At seven years old I was quite a confirmed wine drinker!

My grandparents' flower garden was a riot of colour whenever I saw it, full of pansies and pinks, stocks and hollyhocks. Old-fashioned sweetbrier roses and phlox tumbled and bloomed everywhere. Seeds were carefully gathered and saved each year and cuttings and slips swapped with other villagers.

Visitors never went away unless they were armed with some of my gran's best blooms. She would scratch and bob about amongst the greenery like an old hen selecting the choicest flowers for them. "Never give a bunch of flowers away unless you slips a sprig of rosemary in, my dear," she once told me. "It'll bring the receiver good luck, and bad to you if you forgets."

SUCH EXCITEMENT there was in our house one Christmas—well, at least for me—I was seven then—for I was getting ready to go and stay with my beloved gran and gramp for the festive season. I must have been a favourite grandchild because I was the only one of our family that was allowed to stay with them for any length of time.

At six o'clock in the morning I'd got my flannel nightgown and my pinny packed, and all the little presents we had been busy making for me to take to the grandparents. Our mother bundled the two youngest, Ben and Denis, into the pram and we set off for Witney, where I was to be put in the capable hands of Mr. Groves, the carrier. I was wearing one of my sister's coats that was miles too long and it flapped round my legs as I skipped alongside my mother. She had knitted me an emerald green tammy with a fluffy bobble on, and my stepfather had made me a muff from a rabbit's skin that he had cured. It was cold and frosty and I snuggled my hands deep inside the warm muff, my new shiny boots squeaking in rhythm as we hurried along.

I'd been to Sherborne by carrier cart several times before, but never had it been so crowded as it was on this day. The inside was stacked high with boxes and bundles and sacks of apples, and there

were hares and rabbits hung on the sides, and some chickens in a crate at the back.

It took the carrier ages to get to Burford because he had to call at several of the cottages in the villages that lay along the valley of the Windrush, delivering boxes of groceries. When he went into the cottages to deliver things I could hear squealing and laughing and he would come out red-faced and beaming. Then I noticed that he'd got a piece of mistletoe tucked into the peak of his cap. "What have you got that in there for?" I asked him, and he threw back his head and laughed a big, throaty, hearty laugh. "Comes in very 'andy, do that bit of mistletoe," he replied. But it was years before I realized how handy it must have been.

When we got nearer to Burford Mr. Groves said that I could come and sit out front with him. It was freezing cold and getting dimpsy. He flung a smelly horse-rug over my legs. The lamps and candles had been lit in the cottages and Mr. Groves kept banging his hands across his chest to warm them. Then he lit the lamps on the cart and they glowed warm and bright, and as the pony's feet hit the stony road they sent out a shower of sparks like the sparklers did on bonfire night.

We dropped down the last hill into Burford, the lights of the town winking and blinking in the gathering gloom. Mr. Groves pulled up outside the house where he lived and lifted me from the cart—I could hardly walk, my feet and legs were so cold. We went into the hot, welcoming kitchen where his wife sat by the roaring fire making toast for our tea. They had four or five children: merry curly-headed kids they were too. After tea we sat up at the table and made paperchains to decorate the room with. We cut strips of paper from brightly coloured tea packets, sticking the ends together with homemade flour paste.

About six o'clock Mr. Greig, the baker, called for me. He was to take me the last few miles to Sherborne. He lifted me onto the front of his cart and wrapped me in a couple of coarse sacks. He had to deliver bread at three more villages before we got to my gran's. I was so tired: I'd been travelling since twelve o'clock, and I kept dropping off to sleep, but woke with a start every time the baker shouted, "Whoa there, Jinny!" to his pony.

Then he brought me out a cup of hot, homemade wine from one of the cottages; it smelled sweet and strong. I took a sip. "Go on," he said, "open your shoulders and let it down, it'll do you good. It just bin hotted with a hot poker." I could feel the red liquid dropping into my stomach and soon a muzzy feeling crept over me; it was much stronger wine than my gran's.

Next thing I knew, my gramp was carrying me into the warm kitchen. My gran took off my shiny new boots, and my long black stockings, and I cried as the life gradually came back into my frozen limbs. "'Ere Harry," my gramp said to the baker, "'ave a jackety 'tater, warms yer 'ands an' fills yer belly." My gran cut open a steaming potato for me and spread it with lard. After a bit the baker got up to leave and my gran handed him a bottle of "me matheglum wine" as she called it, and my gramp gave him a hen pheasant, one of a pair that his employer had given him for Christmas.

Presently my gran said, "Come on, my little maid, you must be tired out—time you went to bed."

My gramp swung me up in his great arms. "Have you put that hot brick in the bed, Mother?" he called. And I was slipped into the lavender-smelling sheets. The heat from the brick that had been in the oven all day warmed me through and I was soon asleep.

Next morning when I woke, the pale sun was shining on the window. There had been a sharp frost overnight and the panes were covered with frosty forests of Christmas trees, that seemed to glisten with a million fairy lights. I sat up in bed and scratched the frost with my fingernail, then huffed on the pane, making a small clearing.

This was the day before Christmas and my gran had lots to do. I knelt up in a chair by the big white scrubbed table and helped her to prepare the herbs for the stuffing—parsley and thyme and sage. Gleanings from a summer garden they were. After picking and carefully drying the sage, parsley and thyme, she had rubbed the fine leaves from the stalks, afterwards storing the leaves in jam jars tied down with brown paper. The onions for the stuffing came from a big thick rope that hung out in the back kitchen. Roping them had been gramp's job after he had harvested them the previous autumn, and as we chopped and mixed the herbs and onions the kitchen was filled with lovely, country, stuffingy smells.

We were going to have such a dinner on Christmas Day—that's all we talked about as we plucked the feathers from the bright cock pheasant. I'd never tasted pheasant before—not that my gran and gramp had it often, only when his employer, the old squire, presented his workmen with a brace each at Christmastime.

My gran showed me what she had had from her ladyship. "Look, my dear," she said, holding up yards of red flannel. "Make me some good warm petticoats—needs a bit of wool round yer bones in this climate." There was a pound of tea, too.

Every housewife whose husband worked on the estate had had a present of some red flannel and tea, as well as boots for the children who were still at home.

Every now and then, my gran had to go and open the park gate to let people through. "Drat the visitors," she'd say after several interruptions. "Don't give a body time to settle at nothing."

My gramp came home from work about five o'clock. He was a giant of a man and he wore trousers that squeaked as he walked. He had leather straps round his legs, just below the knees. They were used to hitch the trousers up so that the bottoms would not get wet and muddy. All farm workers seemed to wear them. His face was the colour of a russet apple and he had a mop of black curly hair which he washed every day, and screwed-up, bright blue eyes. I asked why he screwed his eyes up and he said, "Ah! against that pesky old wind out there," nodding in the direction of the hills.

There was no trouble getting me off to bed that night. My gramp said that he would be sure to see that the fire was out before he came to bed so that Father Christmas wouldn't burn himself when he came down the chimney. Hopefully I hung one of gran's black stockings on the brass bed knob. Yet I wondered how Father Christmas would know that I was not still at Ducklington.

Next morning, almost before it was light, I crawled to the bottom of the bed. He had been. I could feel the nobbly, filled stocking. It was packed with things—sugar mice, a liquorice pipe, nuts, an orange and a rosy apple, a painting book, a chocolate watch like my gramp wore in his wesket pocket and, best of all, a beautiful little doll dressed in pink.

I squealed with delight—I had never had a real doll before, only black ones our mother used to make from old stockings. My gran found one of her crocheted shawls and I sat by the roaring fire nursing my lovely doll while she got on with the cooking.

Into the oven went the pheasant and potatoes while on the hob a monstrous Christmas pudding bubbled and boiled in the great saucepan. Up to her elbows in flour, my gran made pastry for mince pies. Her face was red and shiny where she kept bending and peering into the oven as each batch was drawn out.

For the hundredth time I peeped at my doll, then I let out a loud scream. "Whatever is the matter, my little maid?" my gran said, rushing over to my side.

"Look, Granny, look," I cried, my cheeks streaming with tears, "my doll's face, it's gone." The heat from the fire had melted the pretty wax face; now all that was left was a shapeless lump. I cried for the rest of the day. I couldn't even eat. I never did taste the pheasant we had prepared so excitedly the day before.

As my gramp ate his Christmas pudding he kept finding shiny threepenny bits. "Come on, my little maid," he said, "you might find a florin in yours." But it was no use—nothing comforted me.

We went to church the next evening, walking down the beech-lined drive to the village. As we went up the church path a horrid boy snatched my green tammy off by the bobble and I punched him so hard he soon dropped it. "Proper little spitfire, en't you?" he said, but he didn't try it again. My grandparents were slightly ahead of me, chattering, otherwise they would have chastised me for such unseemly behaviour so near the church.

As the lord and lady of the manor took their seats in the cold, grey, candlelit church, the women all curtsied. Her ladyship was dressed in deep purple and sat stiff-backed and regal. The brilliant feathers round her turban-shaped hat fluttered at the slightest movement. She showed up like a jewel against the sea of Sunday-best black of the village.

Out in the cold moonlight night once more; goodnights and "'appy New Year if I dun't see 'ee agen" echoed again and again. Then back through the park, quiet now, save for the hooting owls and scurryings across the leaf-strewn path of things I couldn't see; and I held my gramp's hand tight for fear of being whisked away by witches and hobbly-goblins into the trees.

The next day one of the footmen from the big house knocked at the door of the lodge. He handed a big brown paper parcel to my gran. "It's for the little girl," he said. We stood there for a moment, speechless. "Whatever is it, Mr. Carter?" my gran asked.

"Well, Mrs. Broad, her ladyship heard that your little grandchild had had a most unfortunate accident with her doll. There's a note inside," he said, and was gone.

Still bewildered, we went back into the house and I snatched at the wrappings, tearing the paper with excited fingers. "Careful, child," my gran warned, "it might be something breakable." She read the note pinned on the top of the box: "For the pretty little girl in the gay green tammy." Inside was the biggest, most beautiful doll I have ever seen. My gran said that it must have belonged to one of her ladyship's children when they were small. It was dressed in fur-trimmed satin and all the clothes could be taken off, and I dressed and undressed that doll a hundred times or more that day I'm sure. Excitedly I told gramp about the doll when he came home from work. He lifted me on his lap and said, "It's worth all the tea in China to see you laughing again."

A few days later the baker picked me up. I was to travel back home as I had come, and although I'd got my lovely doll and a parcel of things for the rest of the family I cried when I left my grandparents. "Come again soon, little maid," they said, but I never did, because during the next year my gran died and my gramp went to live with my uncle and aunt at a nearby farm.

Sometimes I pass the lodge where my grandparents lived for so long and where I spent such happy times. The last occasion was on a cold November day. The place was empty and deserted, the curtainless windows had a ghostly air about them, the Cotswold mist hanging thick in the beech-lined drive. I had a great urge to stop and peer in at the windows. Never go back they say, so I turned away, leaving undisturbed all the lovely memories of the past.

Mollie (top left) and her class

SCHOOL DAYS

The village school, like others of that time, was small and over-crowded. How teachers managed to cram anything into the heads of a bunch of rough country children was a miracle. But with the exception of a few that even a genius could not have taught, we did not turn out too badly.

286

Like most of the children, I started school at the tender age of three. Five was the proper age but my mother, like others with large families, was only too glad to get another child off her hands.

Those first early days proved to be quite disastrous. It happened that Bern and Bunt, my elder brothers, had taught me a jingle. They seemed to find it very funny and on our way to school kept saying it to me: "You wants to ask if you can say it to Sir," Sir being our one-eyed schoolmaster, quite kind and very clever.

All that first week we infants played with sand and beads and listened to the frizzy-haired girl who was in charge telling stories and nursery rhymes. But I liked the one my brothers had taught me better. I kept asking "Miss" if I could tell it to the headmaster.

The first morning of the second week I was called out in front, "We are all going up to the top class, Mollie. Mr. Westwell wants to hear your poem," Miss said. We traipsed up; I walked boldly, swaggeringly, showing off. I was to say my piece in front of the whole school! The headmaster lifted me up and stood me on his desk. "Silence!" he said. "Let the youngest pupil recite."

Beaming boldly I began:

> *Nipple, Nipple with one eye—*

From the back of the room I could see my brothers waving to me. I waved back and went on,

> *Went to Church on Sundays*
> *Prayed to God to give him strength*
> *To whack the kids on Mondays.*

There was a deadly hush and then suddenly the air was rent with the loud whacking of Mr. Westwell's cane as it came down on the desk, and I nearly fell off with fright. I noticed he had turned the colour of my mother's geraniums. Something was wrong—no clapping from the class, just silence. Suddenly I was seized, turned over and tanned on the backside several times. Bawling and screaming I ran out of the room, round by the pond and the church and home. And my first public appearance was ended.

Because of this incident our mother took us away from the village school and we all trailed up to Witney for a short while. When the old master retired, however, we returned. By then, fortunately for us, a Mr. and Mrs. Preston had been appointed. He was headmaster, teaching standards 4, 5, 6 and 7, and his wife taught the lower classes. They were a marvellous pair, kind and understanding and just what we needed in the village. They were fresh and young and loved by all.

At school, boys and girls played together in a small playground where there were four bucket lavatories for the girls and four for the boys, separated by sheets of corrugated iron. The boys used to try and frighten the girls in all sorts of ways, and once one of them put a great hedgehog in a newly emptied bucket. Then they waited for the first girl to go in.

It happened to be a timid girl who was fairly new to the school. She saw the animal just as she was about to sit down and came rushing out, screaming, with her lace-edged drawers hanging round her knees. Then they fell to her ankles and she went headlong, full length onto the hard playground. The screaming and shouting brought out Mr. Preston, and all the boys got six of the best.

At school you could catch headlice quicker than measles, and our mother dreaded the time when we might be sent home by "Nitty Norah", as some of us called the health nurse who came to our school about once a month to examine our heads. As soon as she walked in our teacher would say, "Heads down, children," and we all folded our arms across the desks and rested our heads on them. Before this public examination the teacher would have a whispered conversation with the nurse, probably about those children who were known always to be cooty. These were sent out to wait in the porch, and told not to come back to school until their mothers had got their heads clean.

During the very cold weather we used to take our dinner to school. Our mother would pack up great hunks of bread and dripping or lumps of bread pudding, and give us each a screw of paper that contained a spoonful of sugar and cocoa. Our teacher would put a kettle of water on the tortoise stove so that we might make a hot drink—that is if we hadn't eaten the mixture beforehand.

After a couple of years Mr. Preston fell ill and he and his wife left. A Miss Spencer became headmistress, and the younger children were taught by shy, kindly, plump Miss Evans. She was young and pretty and I worshipped her. She did her hair up in a knot and wore crocheted jumpers that I could see through and she had dimples just above her elbows. Her voice was quiet but firm and when she read poetry to us it used to make me cry.

288

One Christmas she gave me a present of a lovely handkerchief. Stamped on it was a figure of a Spanish lady, dressed in red. It was the first handkerchief I had ever possessed—bits of old sheeting were doled out to our family for nose-blowing, and always pinned on the jersey or frock so as not to get lost. I could do nothing wrong while I was in Miss Evans's class. "Teacher's pet" they called me, for I was always top, except for sums.

Too soon it was time to move up to Miss Spencer's. She came from somewhere in Lincolnshire and pronounced her words in a different way from us in our small Oxfordshire village. Whereas Miss Evans brought out the best in us, Miss Spencer seemed to do just the opposite—at least for me.

I don't think she was used to country children. She was small and pinched-looking with soft white hands, and catching hold of them in country dancing was like holding a sponge. She wasn't used to our rough ways and would squirm when we brought in frogs and frog-spawn, and fat-backed toads. We had no respect for her at all.

Then suddenly one Monday morning she was not there. She had gone back to Lincolnshire. Stories flashed round the village like wildfire—she was supposed to have been secretly in love with a confirmed bachelor. The poor fellow would have nothing to do with her and, filled with frustration, she packed her bags and left.

That summer our school lessons were continued by a Miss Seed who came pedalling over the Aston hills to fill in. She arrived on an old upright bicycle—"Seedie's bedstead" we called it. But she was jolly and understanding, and above all fair. In the past there had been too much discrimination between the very poor kids and the better-off ones.

It was while she was in charge of us that I won "The Bishop's Prize" for scripture. As my hand shot up to answer the examiner's questions I could see her encouraging smile time and time again almost saying, that's it, my girl, you can do it. I still have the prize, the only thing I have ever won. Inside the worn, red-covered prayer book is written: "Presented to Mollie Woodley, Ducklington School, after an examination held on the 17th of June 1927. Signed: William Preedy, Assistant Diocesan Inspector."

As it was a church school we often attended services during weekdays—Ascension Day, saints' days and Empire Day, and once a year we all solemnly took an egg to a church service, carefully laying our small offering in a wicker washing basket placed near the altar. The eggs were afterwards packed up and taken to Oxford on the train, and then on to the Radcliffe Infirmary.

On Empire Day we all got up early to go into the meadows to pick daisies, which we made into daisy chains to drape on our dresses and garlands for our heads and waists, wrists and ankles. Then after a short church service we would all troop out to the green by the school and march round saluting the Union Jack.

On 29th May, Restoration Day, bedecked with sprigs of oak apple, we linked arms on our way to school and chanted:

> *Shick Shack day,*
> *Twenty-ninth of May,*
> *If we don't have a holiday*
> *We'll all run away.*

And woe betide any child not wearing a sprig of oak. Gangs of us set on such offenders, stinging them all over with nettles.

There were no facilities for anything other than just ordinary lessons at our small school. It was a three-roomed building with part of one room screened off for the infants. When we reached the age of thirteen we girls walked up to Witney once a week to attend cookery and housewifery lessons and the boys went on a different day to learn woodwork.

Some of the town kids looked upon us as a bunch of hobbledehoys: they called us names and teased us about our rough clothes. "You be one o' they dungle-bred 'oodleys from Duckleton," a pale-faced, runny-nosed girl said to me one day, and I set about her and we fought like a couple of cats—nobody called me "dungle-bred" after that.

Sitting in school on hot summer days we could hear the cows going by, to and from milking, with Mr. Druce calling them, "Cup, cup, cup," and occasionally shouting at Blossom or Jenny for stopping to pull grass from the churchyard. The village pond was just outside the classroom and we could hear the cows splash into the green slimy water, where they would stand like statues, cooling their great hot bodies; then we would hear the slosh-slosh as their long pink tongues picked up the water.

Some of the carters were very kind and would give us a ride up to the village, or from Witney if we had been on an errand. I loved to ride on Holtoms' flour carts. Carter Porter used to sit up front, covered in a fine white dust of flour; even his eyelashes were powdered with the stuff. Sometimes he would have three, other times four, great carthorses in the shafts, depending on the weight of the load. The great sacks of flour were stacked in the long Oxfordshire wagon, and in the summertime the horses wore little white caps with blue and red bobbles on over their ears, to keep the flies from worrying them. And always the horses wore harness brasses that winked and shone in the sunshine.

At harvest time we used to go out into the fields where the men were busy loading the sheaves and cadge a ride on the leading horse. Up and down all day from the farm to the fields I've ridden, on the fat brown rump of old Turpin; so big he was he filled the shafts of the yellow farm wagon.

Then one day on our way home from school we came across a little knot of people, so we joined them, pushing forward to see what had happened. Turpin lay helpless in the roadway, his huge brown eyes rolling, his once active body now still and useless. "Dun 'is bit, no good to nobody now," one of the old men said. Someone sent for the knacker man, and crying bitterly we watched them drag the heavy animal, now dead, onto the floor of the cart. Then, roped and chained, he was taken away.

The incident worried me for days, until our mother took me quietly on her lap and explained that Turpin's soul had gone to where the fields were always filled with sweet grass and scented clover. There would be no more hard work—no more clouts on his brown rump for not going fast enough, nothing to do all day but roam about in those ever-green glades with other animals. A little while later Clarke's horse fell down and died, and I didn't feel too bad at all.

THERE WAS NO SPECIAL time to start certain games. For weeks we all might be skipping madly, then one day someone would come to school with a bag of marbles or a whip and top, and suddenly all the other children did the same.

Probably many of the games had been handed down from earlier generations—ring games and ball games with singing and rhymes to accompany them. Some needed more than one child to play them, but it was nothing to see a small solitary figure, pigtailed and pinafored, bouncing a ball against a wall while counting, reciting, chanting or singing. The idea was to keep the ball in play through an ever-changing, intricate sequence of movements. The first dozen

292

times it was simply thrown against the wall and caught, then bounced under the right leg, then under the left leg and finally bounced onto the wall again while the player spun round and caught it in midair.

Skipping was often done by solitary children. Our mother disliked the skipping craze because we wore out so much boot leather, but skip we would. Some of the children possessed proper ropes with nicely shaped wooden handles all painted red and blue. Poorer children had to be contented with any old bit of thick string they could get hold of. Skipping games usually started with a slowly spoken jingle. "Salt, mustard, vinegar, pepper," we would chant, then speed up the rope to finish with an exultant "one hundred."

As we progressed we could skip backwards—at least the rope was twirled backwards—or with the arms across the chest. And if you could jump in the air while the rope was twirled twice under your feet then you were really happy.

Whips and tops were most popular in the spring when the roads began to be dry and clean from mud and muck. You could buy a top for a ha'penny. There were different sorts, and we had a special name for each: carrot, granny, window breaker or spinny jinny. They were usually made of plain white wood but we would crayon the tops so that when they spun round they looked quite pretty.

The shortage of string for the whips presented problems. Who could afford to buy string? If we could get one of the older boys or girls who worked in the blanket mills at Witney to bring us a bit of "mill bonding", a thickish, strong white string only used in the mills, then we were well away.

There was an art in keeping a top going by just thrashing it with a whip. The trouble with the "window breakers"—sleek, slim tops they were—was the fact that they flew in the air as you whacked them, and if your aim was bad they often smashed straight through somebody's front window. Then there was hell to pay—at least the offender's parents were expected to buy new window glass. In the meantime the precious top and whip were flung on the fire.

Hoops was another game that was hard on boot leather. Some of the boys had large iron hoops which they skilfully steered for miles and miles with an iron hook. Girls, if they were lucky, had smaller wooden ones which they tapped gently with a stick—mostly we used old bicycle wheels and had just as much fun.

Marbles was a summer craze, a slower, quieter game, and if you had a penny you could buy twenty chalk marbles. A tally, which was the one you scattered the smaller ones with, usually cost a farthing and was often made of clear glass with bright multi-coloured wavy threads in. If you were lucky enough to find an empty lemonade bottle that had been thrown away, a sharp crack on a stone broke the bottle and released a super glass tally for nothing. Boys *and* girls played the game, but it was really considered more of a boy's game. The marbles were carried around in flannel bags secured tightly at the top with a thread of tape.

During the dry weather we girls played hopscotch—we would mark out the "beds" with a bit of chalk. Sometimes the "bed" would be six large squares joined together and in each square a number was written. The art of the game was to slide a small, flattish stone from one square to the next. This was done by hopping on one foot and gently kicking the stone along with the other so that it landed on the number. If the stone slid too far or landed on a line, then the player had to start again. The winner was the one who could complete the game without any faults.

There was little or no traffic on the roads and so we played games on the way to school. Six or seven of us would link arms—right across the narrow road we would stretch—singing:

> *Queen, Queen Caroline,*
> *Dipped her hair in the turpentine.*
> *The turpentine made it shine,*
> *Queen, Queen Caroline*

or

> *Here we go gathering nuts in May*
> *On a cold and frosty morning,*

fitting other words to this tune as we rushed along:

> *This is the way we run to school*

or

> *Jump in the air and clap our hands,*

and before we knew where we were we'd walked the mile and a half, and were boiling into the bargain.

The most popular game for boys was "Fox and Hounds". On clear frosty winter evenings they would run for miles and miles. The lad chosen for the fox had to be a pretty good runner. He would dash off into the night and a little later the hounds would follow, shouting as they ran, "Come out wherever you are, the dogs are on your tracks." Often, after hours of chasing and running, the "dogs" failed to catch their man and the game would be continued the next night, until the fox was caught.

ABOUT THE MIDDLE of the twenties a travelling concert party settled on the outskirts of the town nearby. They had a huge tent with wooden forms stacked in tiers. There were thre'ponny and sixpenny seats down front. The ha'penny seats, very high, were just rows of boards set almost underneath the tent top. "Going to the ha'penny leg dangle?" we'd say. And halfway through the "Death of Little Willy" like as not you were all suffering from acute pins and needles. But they were exciting nights.

There was a picture house in the town but the cheapest seats were three ha'pence for the Saturday afternoon matinée. Most of the children went then. They were all silent films, of course, with Mr. Lewis playing the piano down front. Many of the children could not read and bigger brothers or sisters read the captions out loud— when half the audience was reading out loud there was a tidy din.

But it wasn't all games—there were errands to be run, often up to the town after school, or kindling wood to be gathered from the nearest hedge. And younger brothers and sisters always needed to be taken for walks while our mothers were cooking the evening meal. As we walked between the thick, berried hedgerows we gorged ourselves with wild berries, fruits and leaves, suffering no more than severe stomachache. "Bread and cheese", the new leaves of the May bush, were eaten as fast as they grew. Even to this day, when the warm spring sun opens those tender green leaves, I still greedily gather some, savouring those halcyon days.

Somehow we all knew what not to eat when it came to poisonous berries and things. I suppose it was something that was automatically handed down from one generation to another, for I never ever remember anyone being poisoned. But we did have a pet jackdaw who, attracted by some poisonous berries that we had picked to decorate our home with, decided to sample them. We found him dead on the sideboard. Everybody cried and we buried him in the garden, and for a few days placed flowers on the tiny mound.

We knew where the first dewy mushrooms grew, and the fattest blackberries, and called every field around by a special name: "the Devil's nutting ground", "Stranges' lucerne", the "flower field", "Parker's forty acres", "Clarke's moon-daisy ground".

There were green lanes between some of the fields and these provided short cuts to the next hamlet or village. And double hedges where we would find our "first of the year" primroses and violets or where we'd play for hours in bramble caves.

There was great competition in our house as to who found the first flowers as they started to bloom. We had no other reward than a good warm hug from our mother and a little praise because we had been more observant than the others. But this made us sharp-sighted and keen, a gentle way of instilling in our minds knowledge that we were to find useful for the rest of our lives.

Witney Feast Fair

LOTIONS AND POTIONS

Our childhood illnesses were either cured or treated by our mothers: having a doctor was almost unheard of, for it cost money. Our mother had some magical home cures handed down to her from her mother—hot, spicy and almost medieval they were; a pinch of this and a sprinkling of that, and taken so hot they nearly seared your throat.

I can see her now, bending over us, in one hand a tablespoonful of one of her special concoctions, and in the other a spoonful of jam—the offending medicine was pushed into our unwilling mouths, our

296

eyes shut tight so as not to see. Then immediately afterwards, the jam was thrust down our throats in an effort to camouflage the horrible taste. Mind you, if you could keep the concoction down, the cure of whatever you had was certain.

Our winter salvation, apart from the great suet puddings we ate, was surely our "possibles", a name we christened the flannel weskits we younger ones were annually sewn up in. At the beginning of the cold weather our mother slapped goosegrease thickly on our backs and chests, then sewed us up in a piece of flannel—next to the skin. This was kept on till spring! No proper baths were taken during the winter; we were merely topped and tailed—washed up as far as possible and down as far as possible; "possible" being that smelly greasy flannel weskit, which was in such a state at the end of the winter that it was simply cut off our bodies and flung in the fire.

When we were small the only thing we were ever given to cure a bad head cold was a steaming hot basin of bread and milk. But when we got older, homemade wine was the answer, heated with a red-hot poker. We would stagger upstairs after a hot toddy of elderberry wine and fling ourselves sweating into bed—then get up the next morning as fit as a fiddle. Other people swore by blackcurrant tea for colds and coughs. This was just a good spoonful of homemade blackcurrant jam in a cup of boiling water.

Some of the villagers had originated from different parts of the country, bringing with them their own special potions and beliefs. Our next-door neighbour's daughter was supposed to be "weak in the chest", and she was never seen without her "velvety band" as her mother called it. It was a narrow, black velvet band fastened round her neck, and was only taken off when she washed.

Some of the older men and women carried either a potato or a nutmeg about with them, believing that this warded off "the rheumatics", the symptoms being any ache or pain they had anywhere in their body.

Others walked around with a number of little leather bags hung round their waists next to the skin; this was really a secret way of believing, and what was in the bags was anybody's guess. Once our mother, very unwillingly, was forced to help lay an old man out ("get him ready to meet his Maker" was the expression often used). He had a number of these little leather bags tied round his waist; how long they had been there remained a mystery. They opened some of the bags and whatever had been in them had disappeared.

There was never any need to put up with warts for long. One old lady could charm them away simply by rubbing them with the inside of a broad-bean pod or, when broad beans were not in season, with a huge black slug. Always in the winter we would rub our chilblained feet with raw onions to ease the itching, and a small piece of silk was carefully hoarded away by most families to be used if anyone had a stye on the eye: first the silk had to be drawn through a gold wedding ring and then the stye was stroked with the silk twelve times night and morning. A general relief for earache and toothache was a small flannel bag filled with common salt. The salt-filled bag would be put in the oven to get it well and truly hot and this would be held against the pain.

My elder sister used to get up very early on summer mornings and go out to Pudney's field and bathe her face in the morning dew, in an effort to get rid of her freckles. Some cottagers swore by nettle beer for clearing the blood, others made a concoction of pearl barley, liquorice, figs and raisins. And one old lady used to make buttercup ointment by boiling up flowers and vaseline, and her almost wrinkle-free face was a proof of its worth.

One of my gran's special herb salves—used for any sores, or to bring a bruise out—was made simply with home-cured lard and freshly gathered groundsel, elderflower and wormwood all boiled together. Our mother was a great believer in bread poultices to bring a boil to a head or to slap red-hot onto any gathering or festered place, but a farm labourer who lived nearby swore by hot cow dung.

Friday night was "jollop night" in our house, whether you needed it or not: either the juice from soaked senna pods or brimstone and treacle was the order of the day. Later on, when we had Beecham's Pills, I remember reading on the wooden lid the words "worth a guinea a box", and wondered how on earth our mother could afford these.

298

Ducklington Post Office

VILLAGE LIFE

In spring, when it was warm enough, we all took a weekly bath in the old washhouse. The copper would be well stoked up with hedge-wood and filled with water from the well. Then we would take it in turns to sit in our mother's zinc washing bath, adding a drop more hot water as each of us stepped in.

In summer there was no need for baths: dozens of us would go down to the River Windrush, bathing and teaching ourselves to swim. Every now and then we would take a bit of soap and have a good wash in the river and this saved our mother the job of filling up the old copper.

Older men who didn't go swimming had what was called "a swabble down" during hot weather. I've seen my stepfather stripped to the waist, sloshing water over his arms and shoulders. This was always done outside in the garden and the soapy water left in the bowl was usually tipped over plants—nothing was wasted.

One of the villagers, Mrs. Pye, used to make a song and dance about their washing habits. She'd say to our mother on a warm day: "Ah, Missus, I be goin' tu light a fire in the hovel (washhouse) an' when that water's good an' hot I be goin' tu wash my fit an' legs, an' ower gel, 'er's a goin' tu wash 'er fit an' legs, and then George (her husband) he's goin' tu rurely wash 'is fit an' legs"—so we always thought of George as a person with much dirtier feet and legs than his wife or daughter.

They came from a remote village north of the county and pronounced their words differently from most of us, and had the most peculiar expressions, too. When Mrs. Pye was hungry she'd say, "My back varnear touches my belly I be that lear, proper famaled I be." When she did her housework she always wore a coarse apron made from a clean washed sack—and a man's cap perched on top of her bun of hair. A hatpin kept the cap firmly in place, and her skirts were long and black.

When Mrs. Pye's daughter and her young man decided that they would be married, Mrs. Pye, eager to show the fellow what a good steady thrifty girl he'd got, suggested that he should be invited to see what the girl had saved up in her bottom drawer. It was rather cold weather just then, so she said to our mother, "Ah, I be going tu light a fire in the bedroom and ower gel's going tu show 'er young man all 'er got."

Since a visit from the doctor was so rare, if anyone had to call him in they would remember for years what he had said, although sometimes the words got a bit mixed—"The doctor says thur's no-thin' 'e can do for I, its summat *eternal*, but 'e wouldn't say more"— a story one woman was very fond of telling.

Villagers didn't just greet each other with a simple "Good morning," but would probably follow it up with "How bist this morning then, George?" "Ah," the other would reply, "I be rough 'an ready like a rat catcher's dog;" or "None the better for your askin'." Typical Oxfordshire expressions were heard every day. Left-handed folk were called "keky-handed", thin folk "herrin'-gutted", and loudmouthed people "chopsey". A person who talked a lot was called a "chattermag" and an awkward one was "tiziky" or "cussed". And the times, when I was small, I've asked grown-ups where they were going, only to be put off by them answering, "Thur and back to see how far 'tis"!

Superstitions ran riot in the village especially with the older folk, although we children believed in them too. There were old ladies who always curtsied to the new moon, or turned their money at the first sight of one, and thought that bad luck would surely befall the person who saw a new moon through a window—unless the viewer went straight out and flung salt over their left shoulder. Speaking and bowing to magpies was quite a common thing, and to this day I still nod my head and politely say, "Good morning, sir," when I catch sight of one.

May blossom was never taken indoors, and holly never before Christmas Eve. And some people still think that having lilac, or white flowers of any sort, indoors will bring bad luck. Once I took a posy of spring flowers to a woman who was ill and her husband refused to take them in until I had removed the snowdrops.

Village funerals were very simple affairs. The undertaker had a

300

motor hearse that conveyed the coffin to church but the few mourners would walk, all wearing deep black. When our gran died our mother had to borrow a bicycle to get to the funeral. It was sixteen miles each way through hilly Cotswold country. I remember her sending my elder sister down to the village to Mrs. Fisher to ask if she could borrow her best black coat and hat to go in.

Villagers were like that. If they had anything to lend anybody worse off than themselves they would do so without any second bidding. When my young stepbrothers had to go to the Radcliffe Infirmary to have their tonsils out, Mrs. Townsend lent them a nice white shirt each to go in.

Some of the older people had what they referred to as "Me best black". The men's were often their wedding suits, green with age and smelling of mothballs. These would be kept for what were called "High days and holidays and bonfire nights", but were really for weddings and funerals, christenings, and church on a Sunday.

Some of the women, like Mrs. Fisher, had their best black; not our mother though. She borrowed again when our gramp died a few years later. In fact, the first new coat that she had during her married life was one I bought her during the last war. But not having new clothes never bothered her; hers, like most of ours, came from jumble sales—"better quality than I could afford to buy new," she'd say, after picking up a worn Harris tweed coat for 2s 6d.

Thursday was market day in Witney, though the locals called it "Hurdle Thursday" because of the hurdles that were set up to make pens in the marketplace. It was a meeting place where whiskered, gaitered farmers prodded the animals for sale and chattered over prices with friends or met in the local for a hard-earned pint.

Living down the bottom end of the village was a deaf and dumb woman called Sally Castle, and for a few shillings Sally would unpick a faded second-hand coat, and then make it up again on the wrong side to fit one of us. Our mother managed to make all sorts of things on her hand-turned sewing machine, but coats were a little beyond her. Our stepfather used to make us things on the machine too, and once, as a special treat, he bought some cheap red velveteen and made us three girls a dress each for Christmas.

WE AT DUCKLINGTON were pretty well catered for one way and another. There were two tiny village shops and the milkman's, the church and the school, Baker Collis's and the travelling men.

We also had Snobby Castle to mend the boots of those who were not clever enough to mend their own, and Brummy Edwards to cut our hair. Once, and once only, Mother sent Bern and Bunt down to him to have a penny haircut.

Brummy sat them on an old box out in the garden and went over their heads with a pair of mule shears, the same pair that he clipped his old mule and donkey with. I think Brummy must have been the originator of the crew cut. When the boys got back home our mother burst out crying. Their hair was cut so short they looked almost bald.

She gathered them into her arms saying, "If I have to gnaw it off myself you'll never go down there again. Look at them," she said to one of the neighbours, "they look like a couple of old men, all their lovely curls blowing about in Brummy's garden."

"Missus," Brummy said when she went at him about it, "thas what folks comes to I for, to have thur hair cut, and I likes to give full value. Anyhow," he added, "it'll grow thick and strong now—a head of hair's like a grass field: cut it off short an' it'll grow all the better." Brummy went on bragging a little. "I got what the papers calls 'the monopoly', thur yent nobody else in the village what can manage the job besides I."

But when our stepfather came on the scene he cut all our hair. We had to kneel up in a chair while he snipped away at our locks—"Keep your blessed head still, young Mollie," he'd say to me, "or we shall be having pickled ear for tea tonight."

A very handy man our stepfather was: night after night he used to sit up mending our boots, tacking leather onto the soles to keep our feet warm and dry. He used to say that his iron foot, that was the thing he slipped the boot onto so that he could mend it easily, was worth a pot of gold to him. It really must have saved us pounds and pounds during the years when we were all at home; one or other of us always needed our boots mended.

He was something of an inventor too. He could make a mincing machine out of a worn-out grandfather clock's insides, or a lathe from an old treadle sewing machine.

His one luxury when we were all small was a melodeon, which he could play beautifully. Sometimes on summer nights we would sit outside the house and go through all the tunes that he knew—the wartime songs, the up-to-date ones, and the dirge-like ones. But from this happy-go-lucky singing man he changed over the years, becoming moody, staying out late and drinking. His pals thought he was a marvellous fellow, yet he had rows with us all and kept my mother short of money. For years I wondered why the rot had set in, but not until after he died did I know. Apparently, our mother found out that he was more than friendly with a young widow at one of the pubs he called at. And that was that: she just never forgave him. Slowly, through the years, she grew further and further away from him and so did we children, not really knowing why.

THE FIELDS AROUND the village were our playground. In spring, the flat green meadows that lay either side of the banks of the Windrush were filled with fat yellow kingcups; water bubbles or water buttercups were local names for them. And in two or three special places we searched for the rare fritillary, a lovely snake-like flower. Sometimes we would find a few white ones, but mostly they were speckled, pinky purple, and for a few weeks our schoolroom windowsills were lined with tightly packed jam jars of them.

When spring had really come and the warm sun had brought out more meadow flowers, we would pick baskets of cowslips so that our mother might brew some homemade wine. We used to keep some of the best blooms ourselves to make what we called "a tisty tosty ball". Taking off the main stalk we would bunch up the thick flowerheads together, tying them in the middle with wool, and this made a lovely soft sweet-smelling ball. Then for hours we would play a game called "Tell me true", each girl tossing a ball in the air, keeping in time with this jingle:

> *Tisty Tosty, tell me true,*
> *Who shall I be married to?*
> *Tisty tosty, cowslip ball,*
> *At my sweetheart's name you'll fall.*

Each of us had our favourites where the boys were concerned and we'd chant their names—Percy, Charlie, Jimmy and Bert. Strange as it seemed, the ball always managed to fall at the name we wanted it to.

A little later on in the year we gathered armfuls of moon-daisies, ragged robin, bloody butchers (purple orchid), meadowsweet and bright yellow flags—always there were plenty of wild flowers for the picking.

Each summer when Pudney Wilsdon cut the grass in the field just over the road from where we lived, we knew it was time to take our tea outdoors. We would arrive home from school to find a mountain of bread and jam cut and stacked on a plate, and a great big white jug filled with hot, strong tea. "Go on, off you go, the lot of you," Mother would say, "and stay out and play in Pudney's field till I call you."

Carefully carrying the precious food, we would file over to the hayfield and make ourselves a house by scooping up armfuls of sweet-smelling hay, piling it up to make it look like a room. Then we would pick some thickish grasses and make ourselves drinking straws. When all the food and drink had gone we would dismantle the house and throw the hay over each other.

"Let's make peashooters," someone would say, and we'd all make a dive for "The Mound", a thick double hedge where the biggest, strongest pigweed grew. These hollow stalks made super pea-shooters, but we didn't use peas. No—haws, or "azzies" as we called them, were our gun fodder. We'd grab handfuls of the berries, not yet ripe, from the may bushes, and fill our mouths with them, and holding the peashooter to our lips we'd blow the berries through, hitting anything and everything. I remember getting a clip round the ear for taking a potshot at old Mr. Judd, stinging him in the face with a volley of azzies. "You be too cheeky by half," Mr. Judd said. "All you Woodleys be the same."

Long days were spent just sitting and playing in the fields, making buttercup and daisy chains, or making hideous noises by holding a blade of strong grass between the thumbs, pressing it to the mouth, and blowing hard. The result was earsplitting, and heard a mile away.

We would pluck poppies from the growing corn and make poppy dolls by turning back the petals, tying them down with a piece of grass, making a red-skirted dolly with one green leg. The boys made whistles from thin sticks cut from the elder trees. First they would scoop out the white pith, then cut holes along the wood, which gave

them a few notes. Ben could play anything you would like to name on one, for it was as good as any tin whistle.

And where birds had at one time dropped the seed of black-currants or gooseberries into the forks of the gnarled old willow trees that stood drunkenly along the river banks, fruit would grow. Perching precariously on a branch, we would gorge on the berries, often before they were properly ripe, while below in the rushes we would find wild ducks' and moorhens' eggs that we took home by the dozen. Our mother always cracked these into a basin first in case they were addled. They were strong and rich, with bright orange yolks. Nine or ten of these completely filled the frying pan and made us a nice nourishing tea.

Other days we pinched swedes and turnips from Parker's fields, and sat down in the middle of a field to have a good feed. Once Mr. Parker, for whom my stepfather occasionally did weekend work, caught me. Our mother had always drummed into us that if we were caught doing anything we shouldn't, we were not to run away, but stand our ground. So I just stood there, watching Mr. Parker getting nearer and nearer, his face purple with rage. "What du think you're doing then?" he bellowed.

"Just eating a turnip," I answered timidly.

"Well," he said, "you tell your stepfather I want to see him. And if you don't tell him I want to see him I shall let him know that I caught you pinching me turnips."

But I never did tell my stepfather—I knew that I would have got a hiding for pinching and I don't think Mr. Parker, for all his faults, ever split on me either.

SO MANY THINGS that were part of our quiet life still remain in the mind. Once a year, always during the summertime, we paid a visit to Yelford. Our mother usually took Kitty Moore with us. Kitty was a cripple girl who lived up the back, and the only way she could get about was if someone took her out in her bath chair.

It was one of those two-wheeled wicker chairs with a small extra wheel in front, attached to a long handle which was held by the passenger, who guided the chair—it just needed someone to push. Kitty would have my young brother Denis on her lap, with Ben riding at the bottom by her poor misshapen feet. We others trotted alongside, holding onto the bath chair when we got a bit tired.

The object of going to Yelford each summer was that, in a

disused garden, there were several gooseberry bushes. The trip took nearly all day—it was over four miles each way. Several times on the journey we sat by the side of the road to rest on the cool grass. One trip I remember vividly.

We passed a few cottages on the way—two after we left Ducklington, and we called at both of them for a drink, greedily gulping the ice-cold well water. When we reached the garden at Yelford we fell upon the gooseberry bushes like a swarm of locusts, stripping off all the fruit, filling our baskets, bags and stomachs, pricking ourselves to death with the sharp thorns.

That morning on our way through the village we had called at Baker Collis's and bought a crisp new cottage loaf. "Come on, grub up," Mother cried, pulling the bread apart with her fingers. Then she spread dripping on it, giving us each a chunk. Like manna from heaven it tasted, as we lay sweating in the overgrown garden, gnawing at our food.

I never taste dripping without remembering that day. There were clumps of columbines and rambler roses, and a rosemary bush and lots of weeds and birds everywhere, and the hot sun bored down from a cloudless blue sky.

We played for a while in the ruins of the burned-out cottage, pulling a few stones from the walls, dropping them into the garden. Then it was time to start for home and the long walk back.

When we reached "The Plantations" our mother cried, "Look at all this rotten wood lying about!" So we rushed around picking up the chunky bits, piling them onto Kitty's lap, squeezing lumps between her and Ben. Suddenly we were all tired. "Let's have a bit of a singsong," Kitty said. "We'll sing everybody's favourite in turn," and for a while our steps were light as we strode along, piping out, "It's a Long Way to Tipperary," and our mother's special, "Keep Right On to the End of the Road".

We reached the village. In the twilight the gardens looked luminous and beautiful, and the night smells rose up from them as we passed—damp grass and middens, stocks and roses. As we trailed along the last half mile, quietly tired, the evening star winked from a westerly sky: it was the end of a lovely day.

THE GREAT EVENT of making the Christmas puddings each year is another memory that is particularly vivid. Try as she would, our mother never managed to get all the ingredients together by the allotted time—Stir-up Sunday, the first Sunday in Advent, in late November. No, more often than not ours were cooked about two weeks before Christmas and were the loveliest I've ever tasted. The preparation often took days. Suddenly the great red earthenware pan was set on the table and little by little the ingredients were thrown in. There was no weighing or measuring, it was all just guesswork. One messy job we children had to do was to stone the raisins. We would sit up at the table with a basin of water near at hand so that our sticky fingers could be dipped in now and then.

Our stepfather always bought a quart of old beer with which to mix the puddings. The mixture was never put into the basins until we had all had a stir and a wish. Then we all had to have a taste of the uncooked mixture just to see if anything had been left out. "Something's missing," our mother would say, and we'd poke our fingers into the raw pudding and taste, gazing heavenwards, trying to decide what it was. One year it was nutmeg, another spice, and another time it was sugar. Then one of us would be sent rushing up to town to get whatever was missing.

The next day the copper in the old washhouse was filled up and the fire lit, and there the puddings would bubble and boil all day long, our mother continually having to make up the fire and add more water as it boiled away.

THE EXCITEMENT OF PANCAKE Day in our house had to be seen to be believed, for on no other day in the year could we afford such luxuries. The fun began as soon as our mother brought her big washstand jug from the bedroom and set it on the kitchen table. Into it went a quart of skimmed milk that one of us had fetched from Sarah Clarke's, and several eggs from our own hens, all whipped up together with plenty of plain flour into a creamy, frothy mixture.

A new frying pan—another annual event for the great day—and a pound of best lard to cook the pancakes in, and we were all set to begin. Our mother's face was flushed and happy, her hair untidily wispy as she bent over her task. The fire burned fiercely, so that she had to hold the pan above the flames. As each pancake was cooked it was doled out to each member of the family in turn, according to age, the eldest first.

The room was filled with squealing and laughing as our mother skilfully tossed each pancake high in the air. Blue smoke rose from the boiling fat and there was a strong smell of lemon as she slipped the long-awaited treat onto each plate. At last it was Ben's turn, he was last but one on the list. He had waited patiently for almost an hour, and as she tossed the pancake Mother cried, "Whose turn is it this time?"

"Mine, mine," Ben shouted excitedly, and he rushed forward, plate in hand, and tried to catch it as it came down—our mother tried to do the same thing. She gave him a quick shove and he went backside first into a bucket of water and she herself, slightly off balance, stumbled a couple of steps sideways onto the sleeping cat. The hot pancake landed right on top of the squealing animal, which made a beeline for the door. Someone rushed to open it and the cat streaked out, completely enveloped in the cooked batter.

"That's yours, boy, go and get it," Mother yelled to him above the din as Ben heaved himself up from the bucket. With water dripping from his trousers he rushed out into the garden. Minutes later he came back, stuffing lumps of fluff-covered pancake into his mouth, having cornered his quarry in the washhouse.

The incident only lasted a few moments but the memory of that particular night will never be forgotten by the family.

OUR PARENTS, like many of the village folk, kept a couple of pigs— "ran a couple of pigs" was the expression. Much of the food they ate was "come by", apart from the toppings (pig meal). After school in summertime we would go off with hessian sacks and fill them with sow thistles, dandelion leaves, keck (cow parsley) and waywind. The pigs loved this fresh-picked food.

Little pig 'taters were boiled up in an old saucepan over the living-room fire every day. These were mixed with a little toppings to make a good evening meal for the animals. Keeping pigs meant there was no waste at all, for they cleared up cabbage leaves, rotten apples and garden weeds, and provided a good supply of manure for gardens and allotments.

In the autumn we paid a visit, each year, to the field called "the Devil's nutting ground", where there were several giant oak trees. Here we collected acorns by the peck. When these were fed to the pigs it was almost guaranteed to put a couple of extra inches of fat on their backs before it was time to kill them.

Then, about the middle of October when the weather had turned colder, our stepfather would go down to the village and ask Piggy Humphries to come and kill them. One we would have indoors for eating, the other Mr. Humphries would buy, and the money we got for it paid Baker Collis what we owed him for toppings and bought us a few warm clothes for the coming winter.

Looking back on it, the pig killing seems to have been a gory affair, but it was such a common occurrence in the village that we took no notice at all at the time.

Mr. Humphries would arrive on his bicycle with his tools carefully wrapped in a sack: a pigsticker, a very long knife, and a sharpening stone. The poor animals seemed to sense that something was wrong: while the men struggled to slip a noose over each snout to help drag them out of the sty ready for the killing, they would set up such a squealing that it could be heard all over the top end of the village.

Once the animal was outside, the men would lift it onto the rough bench; then Mr. Humphries would plunge his pigsticker down the animal's throat, cutting an artery; the blood used to ooze out. Some people made a point of catching the blood in a basin. This, mixed with other ingredients, makes very good black puddings.

Once the pig was dead the carcass was placed on a pile of smouldering straw to burn off the bristles. Then, re-sharpening his already sharp knife, Mr. Humphries skilfully cut up the carcass. Our mother would be standing close by with a couple of dishes and a clean bucket for the chitterlings. Onto the dishes went the heart, liver, kidney and head. And my elder brothers waited patiently for the bladder which they used for ages afterwards as a football—the only sort they ever possessed.

Then the flear—that's the piece from which the lard is produced—was hung up in the washhouse along with the lights. Then the spareribs, hams and backbones were cut out, leaving two sides. After treatment these sides would be our winter's bacon.

The first night's supper after a pig had been killed was the best treat in the world. That was when we had the pig's fry: the liver and fat fried in plenty of lard. Two loaves of bread we would eat with this, wiping our plates round so as not to leave a morsel.

All the offal and the spareribs had to be eaten quickly in case they went off. Sometimes the weather would suddenly turn very mild, and then we had to gorge like mad so as not to waste a thing. For about a week we lived like fighting cocks, stuffing ourselves with great boiled heart and kidney puddings and wonderful faggots that our mother made from the lights, tongue and sweet herbs.

310

Another thing we would have was "Boney pie", made from the backbones that Piggy Humphries cut out when he carved up the carcass. The spareribs we always had on pig-killing Sunday, baked in the coal oven along with huge, crisp, fatty potatoes.

After soaking the head and trotters in salt water, for a couple of days our mother would set about making the most wonderful tasty brawn. "Collared head" is the real country name for brawn. She would boil the head and trotters in fresh water, along with half a dozen good-sized onions, a few peppercorns and a blade of mace, until the meat fell off the bone. The meat was then put onto a large dish and chopped very finely. To this was added a cup of chopped sage, pepper to taste, a teaspoon of nutmeg, and some of the liquor which the meat had been boiled in, making the mixture quite wet and sloppy. While it was still warm it was put into greased basins with a plate on the top and something heavy on the plate to press the brawn well down. When it was cold and turned out it was all set firm and could be cut into slices.

The day after the pig killing we kids would sit round the table and help to cut up the flear into pieces about as big as a meat cube. This was put into saucepans over a gentle heat. As soon as the fat started to run it had to be poured into basins so as not to let it boil away; you had to keep at it all the while. "Pop out and pick me a sprig of rosemary," our mother would say to one of us. This gave the lard a wonderful flavour. (She always put rosemary in milk puddings too.) After melting down all the flear we would have four or five basins of snow-white lard. This would last us on our bread for weeks and weeks.

Another job that had to be done quickly was the salting and pickling of the sides and the hams. Out in the back kitchen where it was cool our stepfather would set up his salting trough on a couple of trestles. He would place the sides in the trough and rub salt and saltpetre well into the meat, turning it over in the brine every day so that it was all well salted. After several days of this treatment the bacon was taken out of the brine and hung up to dry off, either on racks near the ceiling or behind a door, carefully covered with a bit of butter muslin.

Sometimes our stepfather would salt the hams like the bacon, but at other times he pickled them in a mixture of old beer, brown sugar, juniper berries and salt. He would boil these up together and rub the mixture into the hams every day for a month. Then the

312

hams, like the bacon, were hung up. "Best pictures we got in the house," Mother would say to visitors.

The flavour of ham pickled like this was wonderful and something I have never tasted since. While it lasted we used to have a slice each on Saturday nights for supper, cut thick and fried in plenty of lard. They were such great slices that one filled a good-sized dinner plate.

A miller's wagon

NEIGHBOURS AND ACTIVITIES

Filled with untold energy we threw ourselves into the few village activities. We romped along from the fair to Harvest Festival, from Christmas to the Parish Tea, and so on through the year. There was little or no money to spend, yet the joy of those simple, unforgettable affairs remains always.

The village green where the two-day fair was held was just near our house. On the Sunday before the fair we were up long before it was light to watch the caravans "drawn on", a colourful, magical parade. The vans, all horse-drawn, were painted in exotic colours, with shiny brass buckets and jugs hanging and clanging outside.

Sometimes a giant steam engine would come to the fair. We could hear the chugging and the rattling of the wheels roaring over the flint roads miles away, and a gang of us would rush up to meet it and run behind until it reached the green; like the children of Hamelin we followed the mechanical pied piper.

The coming of a steam engine to the fair meant there would be more than just stalls—perhaps roundabouts, and once a set of chair-a-planes came. We had never seen these flying chairs before and were scared stiff of them; we younger ones couldn't be persuaded to go on them at any cost. When evening came some of the older lads

313

took their girls on this swirling monster and we stood dumbfounded by their flying legs, and were greatly surprised to find that they returned to earth none the worse.

If any of us could cadge or earn a penny it would most likely be spent on a ride on the "Gallopers"—those beautiful, galloping horses with gaping mouths and flaming nostrils. We would mount these gaily painted animals, hanging onto their necks as if they were fiery steeds. They were fixed to the roundabout with brass rods that looked like giant barley sugar sticks. And the organ with its colourful, stiff-jointed figures of men and women who played cymbals, drums and bells, blared lovely loud tunes:

> *I'm one of the nuts from Barcelona,*
> *I clinkety clonk,*
> *I cassidy blonk.*

or

> *I'm for ever blowing bubbles . . .*

—tunes that we hollered and bellowed for months after the fair had gone.

We would stand, mouths watering, watching the gypsy women make the "Claggum"—the name we gave the cream and brown "fair rock" that they sold for 1d a lump. The women would sit crouched round an open fire, their faces grimed with smoke, stirring treacle and brown sugar in a big black saucepan. For ages they seemed to sit there stirring and talking and smoking clay pipes. As soon as the Claggum had reached the right consistency, it was tipped out onto a wooden board.

When it was cool enough to handle the gypsies would spit on their hands and start to "tease" the Claggum, first by flinging it over an old hook that was fixed to the side of the caravan, then pulling it out from the hook—like a huge hank of cream wool it looked— flinging it back over the hook time and time again. Somehow they managed to get a thick brown stripe all through the rock. As soon as the Claggum had been teased to the right length it was slapped back onto the board and cut into lumps.

In the evening the naphtha lights round the stalls hissed and flared, lighting up coconut shies and hoop-la, casting weird shadows over the fairground. A gypsy who always came to the fair was Mrs. Topper, a black-eyed, fierce-looking woman with two wild-looking sons. She made her money by selling water squibs. She would set up a small table and on it put a bucket of water (drawn from our well), and a pile of small shiny tubes, not unlike toothpaste tubes.

She would fill these with water and skilfully twist the open end up tightly with a pair of pliers. These she would sell for a penny. Many a love affair was started at the fair—since this was how the fellows showed their affection, by chasing the girl of their choice and generously squirting her down the neck with one of Mrs. T's squibs.

BONFIRE NIGHT was the next event, not that we had any fireworks, but we did go around the village and peer over the gardens of those who were well-off enough to have a few sparklers.

Before we knew where we were it was time to go carol singing. Our mother wouldn't let us "go plaguin'" people until three or four nights before Christmas—not that there were many places to sing at. It was no good going to ordinary cottagers like ourselves. Real carol singing was confined to "The Big House" and a few large houses where people lived who were much better off than most of us.

One house we loved to sing at was the elderly Miss Holtoms', two spinster ladies whose lives were devoted to the church. Dressed in long full skirts they would swish along the cold stone passages of the house where they lived and invite us to step inside out of the biting wind. Our first carol always, for them, was "While Shepherds 'Washed'" and then, "See Amid the Winter's Snow". The Miss Holtoms' mince pies were the best we ever tasted—all fatty and crumbly. "We will tell the rector how beautifully you sang," they would call as we hurried down the dark drive. But our mouths were too full to answer.

Every year we had a wondrous Christmas party at school. It was given by Major Feilden and his wife. Trestle tables were brought from the parish room and were absolutely groaning with food: thin bread and butter—you could put a slice straight into your mouth it was cut so fine—and lovely square chunks of dough and seedy cake made by Baker Collis.

As well as the lovely feed, we had another treat. In the "big room" was a most wonderful Christmas tree. It touched the ceiling it was so tall, and it dripped with toys: dolls and drums, books and games. It was lit with real candles and dressed with shiny baubles such as we had never seen before. Everyone in the school received a present off the tree.

Then some time in January another special event was held. This was the Parish Tea, which was more a grown-ups' treat and cost a shilling. Men and boys, all scrubbed clean and dressed in their best suits would stand in shy groups at the back of the hall. Women and girls, also in their best, stood about in gossiping groups. First of all there was dancing—this was where we learned the Lancers, the Valeta, the Boston Two-step and the ordinary dances. Then after the "turns" came the tea. We certainly had our shilling's worth on those wonderful nights, which bound us as a village tighter together—making our own fun, sharing and giving.

Sometimes there would be a school concert, too—weeks and weeks of practice were needed to get some of the children to walk on the makeshift stage, but on the final night, when the parish room was again packed to bursting point, we all excelled ourselves.

Once, I remember, Percy Bayliss brought the house down in a nativity play by saying to Mary, "Blessed art thou, for thou art highly flavoured," although he didn't realize what he had said.

In the summer we had another school treat. This one was always held on the rectory lawn—the same trestle tables would be carried from the parish room, the same lovely wafer-thin bread and butter and Baker Collis's cakes. After tea some of the children from the top class would give a display of country dances. I wasn't often chosen to dance because I was big and clumsy and Miss Spencer, our teacher, probably thought I would not be able to produce the white dress and plimsolls that were required for those taking part in the dances.

But one year I assured her that I had a white frock to wear—really, it was the one my sister had worn when she was confirmed. My mother declined to have me confirmed because of my tomboy-ish and unruly behaviour, but I could wear the dress. White lawn it was, with white embroidery, and the edge of the skirt was scalloped, but as it was several sizes too big for me this lovely scalloped piece didn't show because of the huge hem my mother had put on it. Never mind, I was going to be able to do "Rufty Tufty" and "Gathering Peasecods" with the rest.

First we all sat down to eat. Mrs. Edwards came round with a big white enamelled jug full of hot tea. She was just pouring some out for me when Chris Goodwin shoved his great arm across to grab the last bit of cake on the plate, and sent the jug flying out of poor Mrs. Edwards's hand. The tea went all over me and the white lawn frock. When it came to dancing time Miss Spencer eyed the big brown stain on my frock and said, "You can't possibly dance in front of the rector looking like that—Nellie Clark can take your place." How I hated Nellie Clark as she simpered while I sat and sulked.

Never mind, I had my own back later when we ran races, three-legged, sack, and just ordinary fast running. I beat her every time and went proudly home with eightpence winning money—only to get a darned good hiding for spoiling the frock.

Our beloved rector at Ducklington was the Reverend Tristram. He was an ideal village parson and was kindness itself to the villagers. There was a little charity money that he gave out to the poor but our mother often told us that he gave much of his own money away too. "There's some people for ever in and out of that rectory just for what they can get from him. Not good Christian folk neither. Still," she'd go on in her independent voice, "nobody can ever say as I've had a penny charity money. My father used to say to me, 'Ah my girl, an independent woman an' a beggar's purse en't worth a curse;' perhaps it isn't but it's a nice feeling inside."

Most mornings the rector came into the school, sometimes taking us for scripture lessons. He had been educated at Magdalen College, Oxford, and taught us the correct way to pronounce it (Maudlen). It was his idea to have an ancient barn converted into the parish room, and this is still the only meeting place in the village. He started a reading room there too, and got Miss Polly Holtom to run the lending library.

And at his suggestion a girls' club was formed. You had to be between ten and fourteen to be able to join. It was held in the parish room every Thursday when we learned folk dancing and acted little plays and did what we called exercises (P.T.) or just played organized games. I did not join until I was twelve and then was only allowed to because Bern, Bunt and Betty went to choir practice on that night and I could go and come back with them.

APART FROM THESE festivals and teas, nothing spectacular happened in Ducklington. But the place was full of lively characters who brought colour and sometimes excitement into our lives.

There was Edna—poor Edna—subject to fits and "the drink". She was tall and thin and had a pile of black hair above her blotchy purple face. We kids were all scared stiff of her. She would career round the village on her old bicycle, her shiny black straw hat askew, searching for anyone who would get her a bottle of spirits.

The landlords of two pubs had been warned not to serve her but she'd hang about till she found a willing passerby.

The old man who lived next door to us, in the thatched house, was always known as "'e in the corner". Go out on any starlight night and 'e in the corner would be standing by the gate, one eye shut tight and the other pressed to an ancient telescope.

"Venus is clear tonight," he would say if we happened by. "She won't be as near again for a thousand years." We should have listened more intelligently to him.

One night 'e in the corner spied something special through his telescope. Excitedly he shouted, as if he were greeting the heavenly body, "Jupiter, Jupiter!" and a small voice from the darkened roadway replied, "No, it isn't, Mr. Horne, it's me, Claudie, Claudie Collis."

By trade 'e in the corner cut and carved names on tombstones. Lying abed we could hear him chipping away in the outhouse, carving sweet verses to lost villagers.

When 'e in the corner fell ill, our mother used to pop in and do his housework for him or take him some hot pudding or stew. One day, in early summer it was, he said to her, "Missus, stop they dratted birds a-singing, they gets on me nerves, chirp, chirp, chirping away all day long." The thick thatch of his snug cottage was full of sparrows and the garden full of blackbirds and thrushes greedily gorging his fruit. "Poor old fellow," our mother said. "He's complaining about the birds singing—where he's going there'll be no birdsong." The next day 'e in the corner died.

Everybody liked Dick Clarke. Dick would have been called a spastic these days. Poor devil—legs misshapen, bent inwards at the knees, and hands and fingers all knotted up. He shuffled about somehow on two sticks, dragging his feet along the ground. He lived with his brother and sister. The brother was our postman and he also kept a few cows. And each day Dick would prop himself up in the little shed which they used as a dairy and turn the handle of the milk-separating machine; this would take him about a couple of hours to do.

But he was cheerful and chatty, and he would tease us girls about boys. There wasn't much that went on that Dick didn't know about.

Young lads of the village were always on the lookout to make a few coppers, my brothers amongst them. Some of them would make themselves a little wooden truck by using the wheels off an old pram and a box cadged from one of the shops in the town. Then they would go round the village roads picking up horse manure which they would sell for about sixpence for a full truck. Gathering up the horse manure as they did helped our roadman Charlie Hickman, who had a long length of road to keep clean and tidy—nearly seven miles, which included Ducklington.

To me Charlie had always seemed aged, a weather-beaten, gnarled old fellow who rode an old black tricycle. He used to carry his tools tied on the back of his trike and these included a broom, shovel, scythe, sickle, fagging hook and sharpening stone, besides his dinner bag and an old coat. He always wore thick brown cord trousers yorked up below the knee with leather straps and his face was the colour of a bit of old leather.

When we went back to school on some days Charlie would be sitting on the side of the road eating his victuals—usually a great hunk of bread and fat bacon, swilled down with a bottle of cold tea. We used to kick at the neat little piles of dust that he had carefully swept up. "Drat your eyes on you, you little devils. I'll swipe you with me broom handle if I catch you," he'd yell as we ran away.

Besides doing the hard roadwork Charlie kept bees and pigs at home and hand-planted three of his allotments each year with barley, tilling the soil with a breast plough.

Charlie was given notice to quit his job just a month off his eightieth birthday. We had other roadmen, but Ducklington never seemed quite the same without the old man's familiar figure.

A MAN WE WERE SCARED stiff of was called Peter Painter, who lived in the town nearby. He was an expert at biting off puppies' tails. He was never seen without a pail with a lid which was always shut. As kids we thought this was full of bitten-off tails. Mothers would say to disobedient children, at least to the boys, "If you be naughty I'll send for Peter, an' 'e'll do the same fer you as 'e does to they puppy dogs." And for a while the boys would behave and look very solemn at the prospect of their "belongings" being whipped off and carted away in Peter's pail. We found out when we were older that his pail contained pigs' chitterlings, probably given him in lieu of payment for biting off the puppies' tails.

There was never any real tragedy in the village. The worst thing that happened was when foot-and-mouth disease struck Wilsdon's farm. One morning we went to school to find disinfectant pouring over the road. The farm buildings happened to be on both sides of the village street.

The slaughter of the animals came first. All the farmer's men were sent out into Gooseham field where they had to hand-dig a great deep pit. The bottom was lined with cartloads of faggots and paper. Then the bodies of the cattle were thrown in—I can still remember seeing that huge pile—stacks of legs, tails, heads and bodies piled up against the skyline. They set fire to the lot and the awful smell of burning flesh floated over our village for days. After the fire had done its job the workmen poured sacks and sacks of quicklime on the remains, and the hole was covered over with turf. Although there were two other farms very close, the outbreak was confined to Wilsdon's.

At the back of the row of cottages where we lived there were another of three or four. Joe Hill and his wife lived "up the back". They were very old. Joe must have been well over seventy. After Mrs. Hill died he lived on there for a while longer, then he fell ill. Neighbours did what they could but in the end old Joe was taken off to the nearest workhouse.

And one fine morning someone came and put their bits of

furniture out into the yard, and along came a man and sold it. There was a white scrubbed table, and a few kitchen chairs and odds and ends. Most of the items were bought by the nearest neighbours. Our mother paid four shillings for what was probably the most prized possession in the cottage, Joe's wooden armchair.

At some time Mrs. Hill had crocheted a red woolly cover that was fixed over the spars at the back to stop the draught getting on Joe's shoulders. We used "Joe Hill", the name we gave the chair, for years at home. I have it now; the wooden arms are almost white with wear, the crocheted cover has long since worn out and has been replaced by a red cushion, and we still call it "Joe Hill".

In those days the workhouse was the only place for the very old, especially if they were ill and had no relations. By selling their bits of furniture these unfortunate souls could at least have a decent burial—to have to end one's days in the workhouse was dreadful, but to have a pauper's grave was much worse.

What some of the really old folks suffered from was semi-starvation. One dear old lady that our mother used to go to see almost lived on what she called "teakettle broth". This was a piece of dry toast soaked in hot water—no wonder some of them folded up like flowers at eventide and died.

Mollie in her teens

GROWING PAINS

I can remember the excitement, and indeed the sadness, when our sister Betty went off to service—somewhere in Hampshire it was, but it seemed like the other side of the world to us. When girls went to be servants in big houses, their future mistresses would send a list of clothes that the young girls needed. Mothers had to find two of everything, and all had to be marked with the owner's name.

Our mother had such a list and wondered how on earth she was going to get together the necessary items. But the neighbours were wonderful: one made a morning apron, another made two white cambric nightgowns, lace-edged and feather-stitched. And dear, deaf-and-dumb Sally Castle made a morning and an afternoon dress and never charged a penny for the making.

They came to fetch our sister in a car. This was wonderful, because at that time only two or three people in the village had such a luxury. This one was chauffeur-driven, so we knew that the family must have pots of money. But we all cried when she rode away—a forlorn figure she made. This was the first time any member of the family had gone away to work. But one fourteen-year-old out of the house left a bit more room for those that were left.

With her leaving, my elder sister's jobs became mine, and those that I had done became my stepsister's. So now, before I went to school, ashes had to be sifted, and the black grate given a bit of a shine. One of my brother's daily tasks was to get the morning's wood. Every night found him up the hedgerows gleaning dry twigs and little pieces of rotten wood at the base of the hedge. In wintertime he would slip the kindling wood into the fire-oven so it was nice and dry by morning. Then it would light easily and boil a kettle for a cup of tea before he went off to work.

But our mother was rather extravagant with wood and loved to have what she called a "blizzy". Many times Bunt, stumbling from sleep about six o'clock on a winter's morning, came downstairs to find his precious kindling wood had gone. Our mother had burned the lot. "Had one of my blizzies, boy, had to warm myself up a bit before I went to bed," she would say when Bunt chided her. And he would have to go and get some more sticks, probably damp ones. Then he would kneel in front of the grate and blow himself red in the face in an effort to get the wood to catch.

My Saturday job was to scrub the stone-flagged back kitchen, a job I detested. Once, at Christmastime, our stepfather brought home a couple of ducks, and Mother quickly made a bargain with me. "I'll do your scrubbing," she said, "if you'll go and pick the ducks." I was out in that old washhouse for hours and hours; those ducks had half a dozen coats on, I'm sure. The trouble was I did not know that the art of picking ducks is to plunge the thumb and finger right into the thick down as near to the skin as possible. After being out in that freezing washhouse for about three hours, cold and miserable, crying, and covered in feathers, I gave up. The weekly scrubbing of the back kitchen never seemed so bad after that.

Bunt, the more enterprising of my real brothers, used to earn himself a bit extra by catching moles. He would set his traps in Pudney's field, and early every morning he would go out to collect those he had caught. Then he would skin them and carefully tintack the velvet-like skins on a board to dry. When he had got a dozen or more he would take them up to Warburton's in the town, where he would get sixpence each for them.

Both Bern and Bunt helped on a milk round before they went to school. In the very cold weather they wore old socks on their hands in an effort to keep them warm. Handling a steel can on a frosty morning could be murder. They got sixpence each a week for this, a seven-day week at that. But they got a few perks as well: housewives would give them hunks of cake and apples, or perhaps a copper or two at the end of the week.

When Bunt left school he worked for a few months for the milkman, his wages being half a crown a week, but he used to wear out that amount of shoe leather. So, as soon as he could, our stepfather got him a job at the brewery, where he worked until he was called up during the war.

Bern, the eldest, was already holding down quite a good job at one of the big warehouses in the town, where they finished and packed the blankets and dispatched them all over the world. He was lucky to get a job like this because during the 1920s good jobs were few and far between.

Some Sunday mornings after he had started work, Bern would say, "Pop up to Smith's and get a few sweets." Mrs. Smith was a widow who lived in one of the cottages "up the back" and she sold sherbet dabs, cheap toffees and liquorice pipes in her front room. Armed with sixpence we would rush up there with strict instructions on how to spend it. Two penn'orth of toffees at two ounces a penny—hard as a brick but very welcome. Six ha'penny gobstoppers, one each for us younger ones and one each for Bern and Bunt. We loved gobstoppers; they were so big you could hardly move them from one side of your mouth to the other, and as you sucked away at them they kept changing colour—we would fetch them out of our mouths, saying "Mine's pink, now mine's yellow." Then we had to get two penny bars of Cadbury's chocolate for our parents, and a ha'penny bag of popcorn with the last copper. We would hang

round Bern until he had shared the popcorn with us and had doled
out each a toffee. And that was that—everybody had had a treat and
the remaining toffees were his.

OUR MOTHER'S TEMPERAMENT blew hot and cold according to the
weather or the domestic situation. Sunny days found her full of the
joys of spring, light-hearted and loving, taking us for miles, pushing
a pram full of kids on wooding jaunts, blackberrying or mush-
rooming, or just out in God's good air. No doubt there were
occasions when she was very hard up, or maybe just fed up with
everything in general. At times like this you had to watch out—slap,
bang!—you would be smacked for the most trifling thing.

Once I called a boy a "guts", and she rubbed carbolic soap in my
mouth—to wash out the filth, she said—and I sat on the stairs for
ages picking that soap out of my teeth. One thing she could not
abide was any sort of swearing, and although we were surrounded
by people who spoke what she termed "a bit on the rough side", we
were all encouraged to speak properly.

When we became too big for hidings our mother punished us by
sending us up to bed without any tea. In the summer, when all the
other children were out at play, this was a worse punishment than a
good hiding. I don't think any other members of the family were
sent off to bed as often as I was, but then none of them happened to
be as wilful and cheeky.

One of our mother's favourite sayings (and
she had got one for most occasions) was,
"Never let the sun go down on your anger",
and often when I had been sent to bed early
she would bring me up a plate of bread and
dripping just as it was getting dark, and sit
on the bed and talk to me while I ate it.
Then she would give me a goodnight kiss
and ask me to try to be a good girl the next
day. "And don't forget to say your
prayers," she would call as she went back
downstairs, "and ask the dear Lord if He
can make you behave, because I can't."

Every night in wintertime our mother
would fill the oil lamp and trim the wick.
After we had all had a good hot meal and

the crocks were washed up and stacked away, the big table was left clear for us to play for a while before going off to bed.

For hours we girls would make dolls' furniture from conkers—the lovely shiny horse chestnuts made a good base for chairs and tables. Carefully selecting the squat ones we would stick them with pins or spent matches to act as legs, using some as frames for the backs of the chairs and sofas, weaving wool in and out to give a nice upholstered effect. Empty matchboxes were carefully saved and by gluing them together, three high and two across, we made a lovely chest of drawers using pin heads to act as handles to open each box-like drawer.

Other winter evenings were spent doing french knitting. For this you needed an empty cotton reel with four tintacks nailed onto one end. These tintacks acted as needles really, on which were set four stitches. Any odd bits of wool were used. Then, holding the reel in the left hand and a pin in the right, you kept slipping the stitches over the tintacks, gradually pulling the knitting, which was tubular, through the cotton-reel hole. Yards and yards of this we did, sewing it up afterwards to make pretty mats for our mothers to stand pot plants on. Some girls even made fronts of cushion covers with it.

Another indoor game that we played for hours was "I spy with my little eye". Once my brothers and some village lads were playing this game when a fellow called Sid said he spied something beginning with L.L. They tried for ages to guess what began with L.L. and finally all the gang said "Give up." Then Sid announced very proudly "Lectric Light"—it was a battery torch one of the lads had on his bicycle. He was never allowed to forget this and is still referred to as "Old Lectric Light" by fellows who were there.

We often got hold of the wrong end of the stick because we didn't speak or pronounce our words properly. "Our Father Giraffe in heaven," I said for years when repeating the Lord's Prayer, and "God in heaven save my 'soup'" instead of "my 'soul'." And for years I puzzled my brains as to where the Darden hills were. I'd never heard of them except in the song we bellowed:

> *Charlie Chaplin, his shoes are crackin',*
> *And his old baggy trousers, they want mending,*
> *Before descending to the Darden hills.*

But I found out when I got older that the last line should have been—*"Before they send him to the Dardanelles."*

326

WITH BERN AND BUNT at work, Betty away in service and the rest of us at school, life began to be a little easier for our mother, and she gradually refurnished the home by going to house sales, often picking up good bargains. She would career off on her old pushbike and come struggling home hours later with her purchases.

Sometimes she would linger at the sales too long and come puffing down the road about half an hour before our stepfather was due in for tea. With her hat and coat on she would start cooking, with us children rushing about like mad things helping her. "Quick, Mollie—go and find some dry sticks to jostle the fire up, and bring a shovel of little knobs of coal too." Mick would be sent up the garden to pick sprouts, while she herself hurriedly peeled the potatoes, cutting the skins off thick and rough. For a while pandemonium raged.

"Ben," Mother would shout, "pop out to the gate and see if your father's coming," and Ben would come rushing back crying, "He's just up by the milkman's."

"Then you and Denis get off up the road to meet him," she'd yell. "It'll give me an extra five minutes."

Our stepfather would get off his bicycle and sit Ben on the saddle and Denis on the carrier and slowly walk the rest of the way home. When he finally got indoors all was calm. Our mother wearing a clean pinafore would just be in the act of pouring him out a cup of tea. Potatoes and sprouts in separate string nets would be boiling away on the bright fire, and the home-cured bacon was sizzling in a pan on the hob.

She was generous to a fault, often giving away things that we could well do with ourselves. Once she gave a tramp half a bread pudding meant for our stepfather's tea. When he grumbled at her for giving it away she said, "Half of them aren't roaders, just poor devils who can't get work. Surely you don't begrudge them a mouthful of food."

327

Next day one of the neighbours sent us a bucket of chitterlings as a gift.

"There you are!" she cried. "Cast your bread upon the water and it'll come back to you with butter on." And she rolled up her sleeves and set about cleaning the messy innards.

When there were smelly jobs to do, like chitterlings-cleaning or drawing the insides from rabbits and fowls, our mother used to sweeten the air indoors by burning a few sprigs of dried lavender. She would light the stalks and whirl them round and round, filling the room with a sweet summer smell.

As WE GOT OLDER our mother did all she could to encourage us to broaden our outlook, and would cycle miles with us. We explored Roman villas, churches in fields miles from anywhere, holy wells and ancient moats, cruck houses and old preaching crosses.

When we got back from these expeditions she would send us down to the lending library to get books on the things we had seen or on the locality we had visited. She taught us to find pleasure from simple country things—to appreciate sunsets and sunrises and each season in turn. To her, everything had a golden glow: even the common dandelion was a thing of beauty in her eyes.

I never see the sun breaking through the leaves without remembering the simple way she instilled in our minds that beauty was ours for the looking. I have heard her say that, after living in the same cottage for over fifteen years, she could still look out of the window and see something different every morning.

Walking back from Witney, sometimes with the east wind roaring against us, she would quote George Borrow—"There's the wind on the heath, brother". She never minded being out in all weathers; the only thing she objected to was fog—horrible and unhealthy was her opinion of it, and it blocked her vision of the outside world which she loved so much.

Much of her time in later years was spent "catching up" on all the books she had not had time to read when we were small.

She taught us to respect our fellow men, saying, "If you can't say anything good about anybody, don't say anything bad." And as each of us started work she gave us a bit of useful advice: "Keep your job by working hard. Don't try to keep it by telling tales."

One thing she never did was to tell anyone how old she was. And we children never dared ask her. But when friends and relations

brought up the subject she would smilingly answer, "As old as me tongue and a little bit older than me teeth," which was perfectly true anyway. And when she died we found out that she was, in fact, eight years older than any of us had imagined.

Mollie's mother

A TIME TO REMEMBER

By the end of the 1920s a gradual change had come over all our lives. We older ones had begun to spread our wings like a brood of young fledglings, gradually breaking away from the old ways, leaving the elderly to sing at church and camp meetings.

Bern had saved hard and bought himself a fine racing bike. He joined the Oxford Cycling Club and on Sundays he would go along with dozens of other young men, smartly plus-foured, tearing through the countryside, heads down, behinds in the air. A hundred miles or more they would go sometimes! Bunt was courting strong and saving every penny so that he and his Sylvia could marry.

Betty, fed up with service, had come back home to the crowded cottage and had got herself a job at a laundry in the town. She stood ironing all day long with a couple of dozen other girls. The work was hard but quite well paid, and they laughed and sang as they smoothed the creases from the gentry's clothes.

She went dancing on Saturday nights, wearing fancy garters, camisole and French knickers. She curled her already wavy hair with a pair of curling tongs, thrusting them into the fire, then twirling her hair up with the hot irons to make it frizzy. She used lipstick, and strange boys used to wait outside our gate for her, sometimes coming on their pushbikes from other villages to see her. She was beautiful.

When I left school she "spoke for me" at the laundry, asking Mrs. Cameron if she could find me a job. I was put in the sorting-and-packing room. For a while I had to walk backwards and forwards to work until our stepfather picked up a second-hand bicycle cheaply for me. But I was rather a misfit at the laundry: big and clumsy and a bit of a tomboy. Mrs. Cameron used to swear at me and say, "You'll never be the lady your sister is. Why can't you behave nicely like Betty?" But my sister had the advantage over me—that year away in service had taught her a lot, whereas I had come raw, straight from a village school.

I stuck the job as long as I could. Our mother kept saying how lucky I was to be working at such a nice place, but it was no good. One bright Saturday morning the rebel in me surged up. Mrs. Cameron called me "a black-headed bugger" for some trifling thing. I gave her a mouthful of cheek that for once left her speechless and ran out of the laundry—and got another job within the hour.

It was around this time that Alice Spindlow and I used to pretend to go down to church on Sunday nights. Then we would slip back over "The Moors" and up to Witney, to walk up and down the Causeway, or "Bunny Run" as some called it, in an effort to "get off" with boys. One night Alice bought some liquorice allsorts. In them we found a nice round red one and we smeared the red all over our lips, trying to look grown-up. "They 'ad thur mouths made up, they looked as if they'd cut thur throats," one of the villagers told our mother. And that put an end to our walking up the Bunny Run for a while.

The Great Western Railway started to run cheap trips to the seaside. You could go to Brighton or Southsea for about 4s 6d. When we could afford it some of us would go, taking sandwiches enough for the day, for nobody had money to spend on food.

Soon boys began waiting outside the gate for me as well as for Betty; shy lads they were, too—sometimes bringing bunches of flowers with them, carefully tied onto the handlebars of their bicycles—violets and primroses, cowslips and dog roses. Some of the lads wore a great big buttonhole, as big as a saucer, in their lapels, and a nice swank handkerchief in their top pocket.

The lanes and fields that had been our playground for so long now became our courting places. I used to have dreadful crushes on some of these boys—then suddenly it was off with the old and on with the new, until our mother thought that I would never take anyone seriously for any length of time. "You're not bringing any more fellows home," she would say, "making fools of them—you'll go round the orchard and pick up a crab if you're not careful."

In the village, too, things were changing.

Collis's bought a van to deliver their bread in. Benny Clements, the old oil man, no longer came round on Saturdays. Hog  Puddin' Walker and Spetter King passed away too. Now each week on Fridays a pretty ginger-haired girl called, driving a green motor van. She sold all sorts of things to eat, including cold fried fish which our mother used to buy and warm up for our tea.

BETTY FOUND a cheap gramophone in Jacky Brooke's second-hand shop in the town and almost every week she bought a new record— songs by Layton and Johnston, Hutch and Gracie Fields.

The talkies came to The People's Palace in Witney. Waites's ha'penny leg dangle paid their annual visit to the town once again but hardly anyone went—the talkies were much more exciting and we never heard of the Waites travelling theatre again.

Times were changing even faster now. Boys came a-courting us on motorbikes and in cars. We went dancing night after night—Bet and I made most of our own dance dresses, running them up on the old hand sewing machine.

One day our mother went to a jumble sale in the village, bringing back a most lovely dance dress which she had bought for one shilling. Flame georgette it was, with a fringe of real fine ostrich feathers round the bottom. Betty looked like a queen in it. "I shall wear it to the Corn Exchange dance tonight," she said, ripping off the lovely ostrich feather fringe.

"But that makes the dress," Mother protested.

"And how do you think I can explain such luxury to the laundry girls?" Betty cried. "I shall go up to Witney and buy a bit of lamp-shade fringe from Georgie Wickham's and sew it on in place of the feathers and then they'll think I made it myself."

Without knowing one end of a hockey stick from the other, I joined the Witney Ladies' Hockey Club. Mick joined later. We took up tennis and continued to swim in the Windrush from the first of May till the end of September, and all the time thoroughly enjoying ourselves, although we were perpetually hard up.

Bunt and Sylvia got married and Bet and I were bridesmaids for the first and last time in our lives.

IT WAS AROUND THIS time that we moved from "Wayside" to a new bungalow about a mile away from Ducklington. For our mother, especially, the move must have been wonderful after the crowded years at "Wayside". At last we girls had a bedroom of our own, instead of sharing a curtained-off one with our brothers. We had a wardrobe, and a drawer each in a newly acquired chest of drawers. Bern, Ben and Denis shared a second bedroom and our parents the other. We had a front room (for courting), a living room, kitchen and bathroom.

Water was pumped from a spring by a rotary pump and was heated in the copper in the kitchen, and the bathwater had to be carried through into the bathroom, but at least the water ran away on its own into a cesspool in the huge garden. The lavatory, too, was indoors but we still used oil lamps and candles for lighting.

We had a summerhouse and a greenhouse, and kept pigs and chickens and bees.

But I missed the cosiness of the cottage and the nearness of the big family, and I longed to return to the crowded living room at "Wayside" and the cheese box under the bed where I kept my few clothes.

I became restless, walking for miles on my own. I fell out with my boyfriends and began to write poetry and prose. As I walked along the twisty leafy lanes I knew that the magic of my youth was gradually fading away. The funny, familiar things that had happened during those green years were already half-forgotten memories. I was trying desperately to hang on to a world that would never come back again, but it was months before I realized this.

The writing became less now—my sisters teased the life out of me about it, anyhow. But one poem, the only one that finally emerged from that time and yet was not completed until after our mother died, explains the heartbreak of leaving the cottage at Ducklington:

Wild roses of my home,
you climb and circle round my brain,
stirring my aching heart
with your festooned loveliness,
taunting me with your delicate perfume.

Let me return
to those sun-drenched lanes
to press my face
in your bee-kissed blossoms,
brush my cheek
as the gentle breeze
loosens your pale blooms,
spilling your fragrance
over the dew-wet grass,
speckling my path
with confettied profusion,
your thorns
stabbing the memory,
flooding the mind's pool
with nostalgic dreams
of half-forgotten childhood.

Let me return
where the wild rose blooms,
drowning my empty heart
in your summer glory,
cooling my fevered brow
in the lost fields of home.

Mollie Harris

It is now many years since a spirited young girl called Mollie skipped through the lush fields around the Oxfordshire village of Ducklington, or skated on the village pond in winter. Yet Mollie Harris, author and actress, has never lost her affection for that part of the country, and today her home is barely five or six miles from the village she describes so vividly in *A Kind of Magic*. Accompanied these days by Sally, her glossy-coated Golden Cocker spaniel, she spends many hours each week rambling over the fields that lie behind her delightful seventeenth century cottage.

Meeting Mollie Harris, one can't help but be impressed by her energy and enthusiasm. It is not so very surprising, then, to learn that her latest project involves an ambitious 100-mile walk along the Cotswold Way, an ancient drovers' route that runs from Chipping Camden to Bath. With two close friends and Sally, she will be exploring places with such quirky names as Nanny Farmer's Bottom, Nibbley Knoll and Hetty Peggler's Tump. She also plans to visit the Cotswold Olympics, the programme for which includes events that certainly won't be featured at this year's Olympic Games in California—for instance, Shin Kicking and Dwiling, and other equally exotic pursuits. Mollie is hoping to gather enough material from these experiences to write a book on the subject.

Apart from several delightful volumes of childhood memoirs, Mollie Harris has written on all kinds of country topics, including cookery and winemaking. Her latest book, which is to be published soon, has the intriguing title *Cotswold Privies*, and Mollie says she had a lot of fun researching it! She has also written articles for local newspapers on country topics and has for years contributed to radio programmes such as "In the Country" and "The Countryside in the Seasons". One of the highlights of her broadcasting career was her recent guest appearance on Desert Island Discs, which produced an enormous postbag of admiring listeners' letters. But perhaps Mollie Harris is best known for her performance as shopkeeper Martha Woodford in "The Archers".

TIGER, TIGER

A condensation of the book by
PHILIP CAVENEY

Illustrated by Jerry Pinkney
Published by Granada

Harry Sullivan had become a legend among the expatriates in Malaya, both as a respected army officer and as a skilful hunter.

But in retirement the ageing colonial is forced to face disruption of his ordered life. The British influence in Malaya is fading and proud soldiers like Harry "Tiger" Sullivan are being replaced by young men like Bob Beresford, an Australian working on a government repatriation scheme.

As Harry begins to feel Beresford undermining his status—in the community as a whole and also in the emotions of the two people he loves most—a rivalry develops which intensifies with the appearance of a dangerous tiger that is tormenting the local population.

Against the mysterious beauty of dense tropical jungle a spellbinding drama unfolds. *Tiger, Tiger* is a moving tale of honour and courage that will not soon be forgotten.

1

The afternoon sun was still fierce. Haji lay stretched out in the shade of a bamboo thicket, his head resting on his great paws. Aligned with the shadows cast through the bamboo, the jet-black stripes that crisscrossed his tawny body served to render him virtually invisible. He lay stock-still, but he was not comfortable. There was a dull ache of hunger in the pit of his stomach, and his right forepaw throbbed where the quills of a *tok landak* had struck him some weeks ago. He had long since chewed the protruding ends away, but the barbed heads remained buried deep in the flesh of his foot, which had begun to suppurate. The earlier agonizing pain had given way to a nagging ache that was with him day and night.

He was an old tiger, and sixteen years of prowling swamps and jungles should have taught him more caution. But the hunting had been bad for a long time now, and the porcupine's succulent flesh had been tempting. Perhaps Haji was simply not as fast as he had once been, for in attempting to flip the spiny creature over to expose the vulnerable underbelly, something had gone wrong. The *tok landak* had scuttled away to safety, leaving Haji roaring with pain. Since then, the hunting had not got easier.

Haji lifted his head slightly and stared through the screen of bushes. Twenty yards to his right, a group of Upright cubs were playing noisily, kicking a rattan ball to each other. Their strange squeaky shouts echoed on the still air. Haji's yellow eyes took in every movement. He feared the Uprights, but something had called

339

him from the depths of the jungle this day, and he had travelled out into patches of secondary jungle and scrub. Now, here he lay, closer to the Uprights' lair than he had ever been.

The Uprights had always mystified him: these hairless creatures that walked on two legs possessed incredible powers, could march around the jungle, seemingly oblivious to the fact that a bigger and stronger creature was lying mere inches from where their tiny feet trod. On the few occasions when Haji had made his presence known, the Uprights had reacted in extraordinary ways. Some had fled, howling, while others had clambered clumsily onto the branches of trees. On two separate occasions, the Uprights had produced black sticks that roared a moving fire, shattering bushes and earth. At the time of these two incidents it had been Haji who ran away. He knew that the black sticks carried death to those who did not run fast enough.

Haji put out his long rasping tongue and licked absent-mindedly at his paw. The action revived fresh spasms of pain from the wound, and he growled softly. He would have to be very hungry indeed before he tackled another *tok landak*.

An extra loud yell from the cubs focused his attention, and suddenly something crashed into the bushes by his side, almost putting him to flight. But he caught himself as he realized that it was just the rattan ball, which had come to a halt near Haji's paws. He sniffed suspiciously, but it lay quite still and harmless. After a few moments there was a pounding of naked feet on earth, and one of the cubs approached the undergrowth. He began to poke the bushes with a stick, probably wary of snakes. He did not see Haji watching with calm interest. The Upright was small and carried no black stick. He seemed to offer little threat.

The other cubs, tired of the game, were moving on. They beckoned for the lone cub, but he pointed into the bushes and jabbered something in his highpitched voice. Evidently he wanted to retrieve the ball and began to employ the stick more aggressively, muttering softly to himself. He moved a few steps nearer to Haji, stooping down on one knee and pushing the thick leaves aside with his bare arm. He was so close that Haji could smell the aroma of rice and cooked meat on his breath. Now the cub's gaze fell on the shadowy sphere that was his ball. With an exclamation of relief, he moved forward and thrust an arm into the thicket.

Haji gazed at the little brown hand no more than two feet from his own paws. It gripped the ball surely and snatched it out into sunlight. The cub got to his feet as though to walk away, but he hesitated, sniffing the air suspiciously. He gazed intently into the thicket, scratching his head. Then he sank down again onto one knee, reached out to push the screen of bamboo aside. . . .

"Ché!" A voice from somewhere nearby. "Ché!" The cub frowned, half turned, stared at the village of tumbledown dwellings as though reluctant to answer. But then again came the call, more insistent now. With a sigh, he collected his ball and trudged away.

Haji watched the cub walk into the lengthening shadows. Soon the sun would die on the horizon, and the brief twilight would come and go in silence. In the high-stilted houses, lamps would be lit. And for Haji, the long night's hunt would begin.

He got to his feet and, silent as a ghost, he limped away.

HARRY "TIGER" SULLIVAN was occupying his favourite table at the officers' mess, Kuala Hitam barracks. Harry had been using the same table for some eighteen years now, and it was an unspoken custom to leave it free for him. Although he was retired he was still as much a central figure at the mess as he had been when he was a lieutenant-colonel with the resident regiment, the Fourth Gurkha Rifles.

Trimani, the white-coated Malay barman, approached the table with the customary chilled glass of Tiger beer. The glass was wearing a towelling band to make it more agreeable to the touch.

"Thank you, Trimani." Harry put a hand into the pocket of his cotton jacket and pulled out a leather case containing five cigars. He extracted one, cut the end with a silver gadget, and placed the cigar between his lips. Trimani held a match and Harry puffed contentedly, releasing clouds of aromatic smoke.

"The *tuan* has had a good day?" ventured Trimani politely.

"Very good, Trimani, thank you very much." Harry dropped a fifty-cent coin onto the barman's silver tray. With a respectful nod, Trimani retired to his place behind the bar.

Harry sighed. The truth of the matter was, of course, that it had been a very boring day. Most days for him were boring since he had left the forces; more accurately, since he had been obliged to leave the forces. He had always felt bitter about that.

Harry was sixty-seven years old, but few people would have thought it. He was a thin, wiry individual with not a pound of excess fat on his body. Though iron-grey, his hair was thick, and his moustache was immaculately trimmed. He was undoubtedly the most popular officer the regiment had ever possessed, and was still regarded by the men with affection. He had originally served with the Fourth as a junior officer in India and in the Burma campaign, where he had steadily risen through the ranks. He had come across to Malaya in 1962 to help quell the Brunei revolt on the island of Borneo. But a medical examination had discovered a tricky heart problem and he had been promptly—and rather unceremoniously, he thought—dumped. He had been sixty-three years old, and he had reluctantly settled down to a well-pensioned retirement.

And that was where his problems had really begun. A man who had spent his life with energy, authority and decisiveness did not take very kindly to lazing about swimming pools, and there was not a great deal more to do in this lonely outpost. Situated in south Trengganu, on the east coast of the Malay peninsula, the area was little more than the barracks and several isolated villages, called *kampongs*, dotted at intervals of a mile or so along the main coast road to the state capital. All around lay thick and virtually inaccessible jungle. The barracks, established in the campaign against the Communist terrorists, was now maintained by a skeleton crew: worse still, the Gurkha regiments were soon to be whittled down to a mere ten thousand men. For the rest of them, the prospect was a meagre pension and a one-way ticket back to their homes in India, where they were expected to pick up where they had left off in 1940. The decision meant poverty and heartbreak for the majority of them, but, as always, the Gurkhas had accepted their fate with quiet humility. Now it was simply a question of waiting. Harry shared their feeling of regret, but was unable to change anything.

Harry raised the beer and drank a silent toast to an old adversary, the head of which glowered down at him from above the doorway of the mess. The taxidermist had done a good job, except that the tiger's expression of rage was totally contrived. He had died with a look of complete peace on his face, and in dying he had gazed up at Harry with a decidedly questioning expression.

Why? he had seemed to be imploring.

Because you're a cattle killer, Harry had answered in his mind, knowing in his soul that this was not really the truth. After some deliberation he had had to admit that the months of tracking and sitting up at night over the stinking carcasses of slain cows and goats had really been done for the sport of it. Cattle killing was merely the excuse. The look in that dying tiger's eyes had shaken Harry badly, and he had never gone hunting again. That had been back in 1958. He had impulsively bequeathed the trophy to his regiment, having no desire to mount it in his own home. He had realized too late that the beast would always be there in the mess, staring down at him in silent accusation. Thus a little ceremony was born, a toast from one tiger to another. After all, it was the death of this cat and many others like him that had earned Harry his nickname. And what more fitting than to drink to the creature in Tiger beer, that infamous beverage that was both the delight and the ruin of the armed forces in Malaya?

The beer was a delicious shock to Harry's dehydrated insides. He set the glass down carefully and tilted back his head, allowing the electric fan above him to direct a cooling breeze onto his face and neck. He closed his eyes and gave a sigh of contentment.

"Hey, now, Trim, pour me a big one! I've got a mouth like a badger's behind! Oh no you don't, lads, this round is mine. . . ."

Harry opened his eyes again, the peace shattered by an unfamiliar Australian voice that had all the delicacy of a drum kit falling down a flight of stairs. A group of young officers had just trooped into the mess, headed by a tall, athletic fellow with close-cropped fair hair. Evidently a civilian, judging by his sloppy T-shirt and blue jeans. It was to this man that the brash voice belonged.

"All right, Jim, what're you having? What? I should bloody well say so. Aw, have what you like! Make that a double, Trim, and make sure it *is* a bloody double, too! Have one yerself while you're about it."

Harry frowned. There was not a man in the world who could call him a racist. After all, he had worked side by side with the Gurkhas for half his life, and he thought them some of the most agreeable people he had ever encountered. Likewise, he loved and respected the Malays, Indians and Chinese who inhabited the peninsula. But try as he might, he could not bring himself to like Australians. He imagined that somewhere there must exist an antipodean male who was not loud, boorish and obsessed with dirty stories. Unfortunately he had yet to meet that man.

"Here, this one'll kill ya! There's this bloke, see, goes to the doctor 'cause his sheila's goin' berserk with 'im, reckons he don't love her any more. Anyway, the doctor tells 'im to . . ." The rest of the story was obliterated by a burst of raucous laughter from the young officers.

Harry was quietly outraged. In his day, the mess had been a place where gentlemen congregated. There had always been room for a certain amount of high spirits, but the telling of off-colour jokes in a loud voice seemed to illustrate how drastically standards had dropped. Most upsetting to Harry were the young officers, openly encouraging this oaf to do his worst. Well, somebody had to draw the line. Harry drained his glass, banged it down on the table with just enough force to turn a few heads at the bar. Then he stood up, nodded curtly to Trimani, and strolled out of the room. Trimani smiled apologetically as Harry passed by him. He, at least, understood.

Outside, the night was humid and cacophonous with the chirping of myriad insects. Large fat moths flapped vainly around the lantern that overhung the entrance to the mess. The grizzled old man who had appointed himself Harry's customary driver for this journey eased his creaking trishaw, a kind of bicycle-driven taxi, round to the base of the white stone steps. In the glow of his oil lamp, beneath the wide brim of his coolie hat, he grinned gummily.

"Good evening, tuan. You leave early, yes?"

"Yes, we leave now." Harry smiled warmly at the old Chinese driver. "Tonight not good for me. Too noisy."

The old man waited patiently while Harry climbed onto the seat, then gratefully accepted the cigar that Harry passed to him. He leaned forward as Harry's lighter flared. He inhaled with slow satisfaction, and grinned again.

"Good," he murmured. "Good cigar. I thank the tuan." He engaged his sandalled feet on the pedals, and the trishaw accelerated away from the mess, crunching on the gravel drive and turning out onto the deserted road. The wheels made a dry whirring sound as they sped past the black silhouettes of secondary jungle that flanked their path. Riding in this way, smoking with his old travelling companion, Harry felt a peculiar peace settle around him.

IN THE DARKNESS Haji was patrolling the western end of his home range. It was necessary to keep on the move, because potential prey soon became alerted to his presence and promptly moved on.

344

It took Haji ten to twelve days to complete a trip round his territory, a rough triangle of fifteen square miles. Right now he was prowling the jungle beside the coast road; troops of monkeys often chose to congregate there, carelessly thinking themselves safe so near to the wandering-grounds of the Uprights. But tonight, somehow, they had got wind of Haji's notion and stayed safely in the top limbs of the *meranti* trees.

Haji was used to such hard times. The rest of the jungle creatures conspired against him. Monkeys gibbered his presence from the tall trees, and the birds quickly took up the cry. The sambar deer uttered their "pooking" sound to alert their brothers whenever their sharp noses picked up the merest trace of that distinctive, musky, tiger smell. Hampered by his wound and his advancing years, Haji was doing well to bring down one kill in about thirty stalks, and in between he could expect long bouts of frantic hunger. When he did succeed in killing something, a sambar, a wild pig, sometimes even a fat wild calf, he would gorge himself, consuming maybe eighty pounds of meat in one sitting. It had been three days since his last kill, an unsubstantial mouse deer, and hunger kept him moving.

He paused for a moment to listen. Far to his right, deep in jungle sanctuary, a barking deer sounded an alarm. Haji growled softly and was about to move on when an unfamiliar sound came to his sensitive ears. He froze in his tracks, snapped his gaze to the roadside at his left. The sound was a rapid whirring noise, much too loud to be produced by the wings of any insect. Haji slunk beneath the cover of some large ferns as a light came soaring out of the darkness.

A vehicle on which two Uprights were riding sped into view. Haji could see them quite clearly in the glow of the light that swung from side to side in front of their heads. He could see the wrinkled sternness of their faces as they gazed unswervingly at the road ahead of them. How foolish to travel in such a manner, always looking forwards when danger might lie in the shadows at either side, or was it simply that the Uprights were so powerful that they did not fear the beasts of the jungle? They did not *look* very powerful.

The Uprights left a fragrant smell behind, a burning-leaf smell that lingered on the warm air. Haji sniffed, watched as the Uprights sped away, the constant whirring noise fading gradually into the distance. Then his thoughts returned to the barking deer he had heard before the interruption. He emerged from the bushes and moved deeper into the jungle, his head down, his mind on the long hunt ahead of him.

THE TRISHAW DRIVER came to a halt outside Harry's bungalow, part of a small estate a mile south of the nearest village, Kampong Panjang, which they had passed on the two-mile journey from the mess. Harry alighted and pressed a dollar into the driver's arthritic hand. The fare was always the same, whatever the distance, and the old man would have been insulted if Harry had tried to give him more. "Safe journey back," Harry told him.

"Of course, tuan!" He grinned, and pedalled gamely away to his own home. Few trishaw owners ventured out at night, preferring to leave the taxiing to car drivers, but this engaging fellow had somehow discovered Harry's regular mess nights and would not have dreamed of missing a single one. Neither, for that matter, would Harry have dreamed of using another driver.

You get to a certain age, thought Harry, and your life becomes a ritual. Has to. The only way you can make sense of it.

He unfastened the metal gate and strolled into the large, neatly ordered garden. The path was wide enough to take a car, but he had never learned to drive. In his years in the army there had always been somebody to ferry him about, and that was the way he preferred to keep things. He strolled up the path, past banana and papaya trees, whistling tunelessly to himself. The bungalow was like many others built for British tenants: long, low, white-painted, with a green slate roof and an adjoining veranda. It was compact, practical, and possessed no style whatsoever.

No sooner had Harry inserted his key in the front door and stepped into the house than Pawn, his aged *amah*, came bustling up to greet him. There was a toothy smile of welcome on the servant's wizened little face, and she held a straw broom with which she had been sweeping. Pawn never stopped work while she was in the house. She lived at Kampong Panjang and usually went home to her family at five o'clock. But on the nights that Harry went to the mess, she insisted on staying in to ensure that the tuan was properly looked after when he came in. Harry would quite happily have looked after himself, but once Pawn had fixed on an idea, it was impossible to shake her.

"Tuan have good time soldiers' mess?" she inquired, and without waiting for a reply, she hurried off to the kitchen to prepare cocoa and biscuits.

He shook his head ruefully, wondering just how it was that he had managed to get himself saddled with creaky old Pawn. Most of his acquaintances had pretty young Chinese amahs, but Pawn had been a legacy of sorts. She'd worked for the previous occupant of the house, and the day Harry had moved in she'd just arrived on his doorstep. Mind you, she was an excellent worker, worth every cent of the one hundred and twenty dollars a month she received, a decent wage by Malay standards. She was far too proud to accept anything more, but she was not averse to accepting Harry's little gifts from time to time, particularly if they were intended for her grandson, Ché. The boy was a bright, articulate twelve-year-old who sometimes accompanied his grandmother to the house and had become a great friend of the tuan's. In fact, Harry doted on Ché, reserving for him the kind of affection he would have given to his own son, if he had ever sired one.

A photograph of his late wife, Meg, stood on a small table. Harry walked over to it, as he often did, picked it up, and stared thoughtfully at the face he had loved for so many years. She had died quite suddenly in 1950 from a cerebral haemorrhage. They had always wanted children, and ironically, the evening before Meg had died, the two of them had discussed the possibility of adopting a Malay child. They had both been strongly in favour of the idea. Later that night, Meg had woken complaining of a terrible headache. She got up to fetch some aspirin, but halfway to the bathroom door she had spun round to look at Harry, her face suddenly drained of colour, and she had spoken his name once, softly. In that instant he had somehow known that it was all over for her. She had crumpled lifelessly to the floor before Harry could reach her. His grief and torment had been indescribable. But now, with the advantage of hindsight, he knew that when his time came, this is how he would want it to be. Quick, clean, a minimum of fuss and pain. In Harry's opinion, all a man had was his dignity. Lose that and you had lost the reason for living.

Pawn came bustling in with a silver tray bearing the mug of cocoa and two digestive biscuits that constituted Harry's usual bedtime snack. He sat down in his armchair and glanced through the day's news in the *New Straits Times*. There was little that took

347

his interest. Harry sipped his cocoa and watched a couple of chit-chats on the ceiling above his head. The smaller of the lizards, presumably the male, was chasing his mate around the room. Harry soon tired of them, and retired to his bedroom. He changed into silk pyjamas, climbed into bed and let the mosquito net down around him. He thought for a few moments of the boorish Australian he had seen in the mess earlier. He felt that this man represented the new order here on the archipelago, and vaguely threatened by his presence.

He smiled wryly. "I'm an endangered species," he murmured, and reaching out he switched off the bedside light.

Haji woke from a fitful doze. The flame of dawn was still an unfulfilled promise on the far horizon, and the damp, shivering land awaited the first rays of warmth. Haji stretched and yawned, throwing out a long, rumbling growl. Wasting little time, he struck out along a well-worn cattle track into deep jungle, his eyes and ears alert. They were his greatest aids, and the day they began to fail him would be the day that Haji would admit defeat. But now there was a terrible hunger knotting his belly, and while his legs still possessed the strength to carry him he would hunt to stay alive.

The jungle was beginning to come awake. There was a distant whooping of gibbons in the forest canopy. Black-and-yellow hornbills fluttered among the foliage, and there were the familiar weeping tones of the bird that the Malays had named *burung anak mati*, bird whose child has died. None of this distracted Haji from his quest. Presently his ears were rewarded by a rustling in the undergrowth some eighty yards ahead. He stopped and listened intently. He could hear quite clearly the crunching of a deer's wide jaws on a bunch of leaves. Haji flattened himself against the ground and moved to his right, keeping himself downwind of his intended prey. Slowly, slowly, setting down each foot in a carefully considered spot, knowing that one telltale rustle would be enough to frighten the creature away, he began to shorten the distance between himself and the deer. After twenty minutes he had worked himself close enough to see it: a sambar. He could glimpse the rust-red hide, dappled by the rising sun. The sambar lifted his head between mouthfuls, staring skittishly this way and that, and Haji remained still. Each time the deer returned to its meal, Haji inched forward. In this way another half hour passed. Haji was within twenty yards of the sambar; but here there was a clearing through which he could not pass undetected. His only hope was to rush upon the beast like an arrow from a bow and trust that panic would confuse his prey long enough for him to leap upon it. He flexed his muscles, craned forward, ready; and in that instant, a deer upwind caught the smell of tiger and gave a loud cry of warning.

The sambar wheeled about, and with a bellow of rage Haji broke from cover, propelling his four-hundred-pound body along with tremendous bursts of power. For an instant the sambar seemed frozen with fear, but abruptly the instinct for survival reasserted itself and the deer bolted across the clearing with Haji mere inches from its flying heels. The sambar lengthened its stride, sailed effortlessly across a fallen tree stump and was off, gathering speed. Haji knew he was beaten. He dropped down onto the grass, panting, while he watched the sambar recede into the distance.

Haji fashioned his frustration into a great blasting roar that shook the ground on which he lay. A troop of pigtailed monkeys, safe in the top of a nearby *kapok* tree, began to chatter and shriek abuse at him. Haji, blind to everything but his own anger, flung himself at the tree in a frenzy, his great claws scattering bits of bark in every direction. The monkeys quietened for a moment, but then, seeing they were still safe, began their impudent mockery again, while Haji raged vainly far below them.

At last he drew back from the tree, growling bitterly beneath his breath. The deer's panic would have alerted every creature for miles in the direction it had taken. Haji gave one last roar, and struck out along a path to his left, which led to secondary jungle and eventually to Kampong Panjang.

The monkeys watched him stalk away.

HARRY STROLLED in through the open glass doors of the Kuala Hitam Sports Club and nodded to the pretty Chinese receptionist, who rewarded him with a radiant smile. He passed through another doorway and turned right, towards the long, open-air bar that overlooked three well-maintained tennis courts. Harry had come for his regular game with Captain Dennis Tremayne, a longstanding friend who was still serving with the Fourth and who, at the age of forty-four, was considerably younger than Harry. Harry cut a more imposing figure in tennis shorts than Dennis, who was already a little on the stout side.

Harry spotted Dennis sitting at a table and made his way over.

"Hello, old chap!" Dennis grinned. "It seems we're a bit early for our game. Let me get you a drink."

"Fresh orange juice, please." Harry settled into a chair as his companion signalled to the barman.

Dennis turned his attention back to the game in progress. "All action out there today," he observed. "Hope they don't expect that sort of routine from us." He had a plump, ruddy face that always wore a happy expression. His cornflower-blue eyes were today hidden behind mirrored sunglasses. "Is it just me or does it get hotter here all the time?" He motioned to the sweater Harry wore. "Beats me how you can wear that thing."

"Well, don't forget, Dennis, I've been living in this climate for most of my adult life. India, Burma, Malaya have one thing in common—they're all hot. Couldn't stand it any other way now."

"You, er . . . wouldn't fancy going back to Blighty ever?"

"England? I should say not! I'd freeze to death." Harry narrowed his eyes suspiciously. "Why did you ask? C'mon, Dennis, spill the beans, you never could hide anything from me."

Dennis chuckled, raised his hands in capitulation. "All right, all right!" He leaned forward, lowered his voice slightly. "It's just that word came through today about more cuts in the forces and—"

"*More* cuts!" Harry shook his head. "Surely they've cut the Gurkhas down as much as they can."

Dennis nodded sympathetically. "Well, you know I couldn't agree with you more. But the top brass have got it into their heads that Kuala Hitam is unnecessary. It's got to go, old son. Complete demobilization. Heard it just this morning."

"What? You mean everything?"

"Lock, stock and barrel. What troops we leave in Malaya will be based in Singapore. As for this lot—" He made a sawing motion across his throat with his index finger. "Which is why I asked if you ever thought of going home."

Harry stared at the table top. "Dennis, this *is* my home. What would there be for me over there? My relatives are all dead."

"You've a nephew, haven't you?"

"Oh yes, and very pleased he'd be to have an old devil like me descending on his household from the far-off tropics. No, Dennis, here I stay, until the Lord in all His infinite wisdom sees fit to reorganize my accommodation. What will you be doing?"

"Oh, I'll be going back. Expecting confirmation any day now. Suffolk, I hope, where my roots are. The fact is, I'm quite looking forward to it. I keep imagining snow at Christmas, that sort of thing. And Kate's thrilled to bits. There's lots she misses: good shops, fashions, family. She's all but got the bags packed."

Harry nodded. "And what of your pretty young daughter?"

"I think Melissa is pleased too. Things are a bit quiet around these parts for her liking."

The barman arrived with tall glasses filled with orange juice and crushed ice. He set them down on the table and left.

"I'll miss you," observed Harry. "I'll miss you all."

"Yes, well, look here, old chap, if you ever want to come on a visit, we'll always have a place for you. I hope you realize that."

Harry sipped at his drink thoughtfully. It was so cold that his breath turned to vapour as his mouth touched the rim of the glass. He stared impatiently at the action on the tennis court. "Are they never going to finish?" he muttered. "In the old days, these games always finished on . . ." His voice trailed off as he recognized one of the players, the loudmouthed Australian from the night before. "I say, Dennis, who *is* that fellow on the court?"

Dennis peered in the direction that Harry was indicating. "Oh, you mean Bob Beresford. He's a civvy. He's working at Kuala Hitam on the Gurkha repatriation scheme, though, so he's been given the run of the place."

"Indeed. He was in the mess last night. Just what is he supposed to be teaching the Gurkhas? How to tell dirty stories?"

"Farming techniques, I believe. Irrigation, animal husbandry. How to make the most out of limited resources, basically. He's certainly well liked by the men." Dennis smiled warily. "I get the impression he hasn't made an instant hit with you, though."

Harry grimaced and shrugged. "Well, you know how I feel about the Aussies, Dennis. And that one—well, he shows a lack of respect, that's all."

Dennis chuckled. "It just comes down to what you're used to, really. Beresford isn't so bad, and you've got something in common with him."

Harry looked suspicious. "And what might that be?"

"He fancies himself as a bit of a crack shot. Done some hunting in his time, he tells me."

Harry shook his head. "I haven't hunted for years, as well you know. If this Beresford chap still does, it just confirms that he's got some growing up to—ah, they've finally called it a day!"

Beresford and his opponent were leaving the court. The Australian was pumping his opponent's hand in an exaggerated display of good sportsmanship. "Great game, Ron! Let me buy you a drink."

Dennis and Harry collected their gear and walked out towards the court. Beresford eyed the two of them. As Harry walked past, he distinctly heard the Australian say, "Strewth, look at those two old blokes goin' out for a bash!" Beresford's companion smothered a laugh, but Harry pretended he had heard nothing. He wasn't going to let some jumped-up sheep farmer from the outback make any impression on him.

Dennis had heard nothing of the brief exchange. "Let's have a quick warm-up," he suggested. He trotted to the far end of the court, and Harry served a lazy ball over to him. They played for some time in silence. They rarely bothered to score the games; it was playing that they relished, not winning. The white surface reflected the fierce sun up at them, and it was like playing tennis on a vast electric hotplate. After a few moments their clothes were sticking to them.

Harry played mechanically, his thoughts not really on the game. His mind had slipped back to a memory of Britain before the last war. It had been a fine summer, and there was a tennis court not far from his family home in Sussex. He had been in his twenties then, with no thought of enlisting in the army, no thought of doing anything in particular. His family was rich, and life seemed to be an endless succession of parties. Marriage had been the last thing on his mind, at least until that particular day when they had all gone to play tennis and Harry had spotted an exquisite young female on the court, a frail little thing dressed in white, who played tennis like nobody's business. Harry had fallen in love with her then and there, and when his mother had wandered over to him to inquire what he was looking at, he had smiled and replied, "My future wife, I think."

How distant it all seemed now. England. And Meg. Sometimes in the night he lay in the darkness, trying to conjure up a vision of her face. He could not do it. Her features were blurred by time. He would have to switch on the light and fetch her photograph, just to reassure himself that she *had* existed. It frightened him, this loss of definition. The past was just a series of hazy ghosts.

"Come on, Harry, wake up! You missed that by a mile."

"Hmm?" The present came abruptly back into focus. Dennis was peering at him over the net.

"Do you want to rest for a moment?"

"Certainly not!" Harry retrieved the ball and stepped up to the serving line. He flung the ball skyward, whipped back his arm to serve. A pain lanced through his chest, making his breath escape in an exclamation of surprise. The ball dropped untouched beside him, and he stood swaying slightly. He could not seem to get his breath, and his heart was thudding like a great hammer.

"Harry? Are you all right? You've gone as white as a sheet."

"Yes, yes! I'm fine." Harry stooped for the ball, but as he stood up the court seesawed crazily. His racket clattered to the ground, and suddenly Dennis was at his side, supporting his arm.

"Here, here, you've been in the sun too long, I think."

"Ridiculous," protested Harry feebly. "Let's play on."

"I don't think we better had." Dennis was easing him towards the exit. "Come and sit down for a while."

"This is really quite silly. . . ." Harry was aware of anxious faces peering at him from the tables. He tried to detach his arm from Dennis's grasp so that he might walk under his own steam, but the dizziness seemed to get worse, filling his head with a powerful red hum. He felt vaguely nauseated.

"Here, old chap, this way. Our table's just a few more feet."

Out of the corner of his eye Harry could see Beresford and his companion watching the scene with amusement. The Australian muttered something, and the two of them collapsed into fits of laughter. Harry wanted to die of shame. He was lowered into a seat, and a cold drink was thrust into his hand.

"How do you feel?" Dennis's voice seemed terribly distant.

Harry forced a smile. "I'll survive," he muttered. "Just a dizzy spell, that's all."

"All right." Dennis sounded far from reassured. "I'll go and fetch your stuff."

He walked away, leaving Harry to brave the stares of two hundred sympathetic eyes. Harry could imagine the crowd thinking, "Poor old man. Must be his dodgy old ticker." And he knew that after this dizzy spell, he would never have the courage to come to this place again.

BOB BERESFORD threw his kit bag into the back of his beaten-up old Land-Rover, kicking the engine into life, and drove away from the sports club, chuckling to himself. Honestly, these old men who thought they were still fighting a war! Malaya seemed to be full of them. Bob still wasn't quite sure what to think about Malaya. He missed the social life he had back in Oz, but it was plain that he'd landed himself a cushy number here with the repatriation scheme. The Gurkhas were a likable bunch of blokes, who followed their courses with quiet dedication. The pay was excellent, considering that he only worked three mornings a week.

As he drove, his eyes kept scanning the secondary jungle on either side for signs of life. It was his old man's influence that had turned Bob into a keen amateur hunter: Roy Beresford hunted animals obsessively, forever undertaking extensive trips in New Zealand, after deer and boar mostly. Bob's earliest memories were of Roy's trophy room, standing beneath the gigantic spread of antlers belonging to a fine stag. Roy had told him the story of that particular hunt a hundred times. Bob's greatest regret was that his father had died of cancer long before he was big enough to accompany him on an expedition. Since then, Bob had been doing his utmost to wear his father's boots, and the need to do so had become a singular obsession.

As yet, Bob had not organized himself into hunting in Malaya. For one thing, the territory was completely new to him, and he would need a good guide. But the locals he had talked to had displayed an astonishing ignorance of their native wildlife. Oh indeed, there were tigers and deer and wild pigs and even the occasional elephant out there somewhere, but why any man should be interested in going after the creatures was quite beyond them. It was the Malays' simple policy to get on with their lives and leave the beasts of the jungle to do likewise. Bob lived in hope of finding a Malay with a more adventurous attitude.

He turned left off the coast road and entered the group of houses where the army had allotted him a bungalow. He lurched the Land-Rover into the drive, clambered out, grabbed his kit, and entered the house. Lim hurried into the room at the sound of his arrival.

Lim. Now there was one benefit of living in Malaya. Lim was his amah, slim, pretty, eighteen years old, and Chinese. In the few weeks that Bob had been at Kuala Hitam, his relationship with Lim had developed beyond that of servant and master. She lived in full time, and when the nights were long and lonely—which they invariably were—it was not *her* tiny room to which she retired, but the tuan's. Bob was careful to keep the situation under control, showing little emotion for her. He was well aware that a large percentage of Chinese girls here aspired to marriage to a white man, followed by a one-way trip out of the country of their birth. Lim knew that once his work was finished, the tuan would be heading home to Australia, and she never lost an opportunity to tell him how much she would love to see the Sydney Harbour Bridge or a kangaroo or an aborigine. Unfortunately for her, Bob was planning to remain a bachelor for many years to come.

She stood now, smiling welcome. "Bob want drink?"

"No, thanks." He stripped off his tennis gear without further ado and strode to his room. "I'm going to have a shower."

"There is letter for you in bedroom," Lim called after him.

It was lying on the bedside table, airmail from Australia. He recognized his mother's handwriting. He picked it up, looked at it blankly for a moment, and then turned to gaze thoughtfully out through the slatted window. He could see next door's amah, pinning ranks of billowing washing on the line. Bob looked back at the envelope and frowned. He pulled open the drawer of the table, slipped the letter inside with four others, none of which had been read.

HARRY PREPARED himself for bed. He felt fine now, as good as ever. He regretted all the fuss at the tennis court earlier that day. The trouble was that the grapevine was so efficient here. Word would soon get around that old Tiger Sullivan had had a bit of a turn. Well, let them talk! Why should it bother him?

He undressed slowly, hanging his clothes neatly over the back of a chair. Then, turning to look for his pyjamas, he caught sight of his reflection in the wardrobe mirror. He froze, momentarily horrified by this vision of stark, skinny manhood. Lord, the ravages that time made!

Harry's gaze moved sideways to the dressing table, where a photograph of himself stood. Taken shortly after his arrival in

Burma, it showed a tall, suntanned individual in khaki battle dress, his muscular arms crossed over his chest, a mischievous grin on his handsome face. His thick black curls had yet to be taken in hand by the regimental barber, and he had not yet grown a moustache. As he moved over to the photograph and examined it more closely, a dark rage flared up in his heart. Why, he was unrecognizable! He snatched the picture up, with the intention of flinging it across the room. But in that instant his rage died, and he felt vaguely ridiculous.

"Old fool," he murmured softly. He laid the picture face down on the polished wood. If he did not see it again, it could not antagonize him.

He moved back to his bed and found the pyjamas he had been looking for. He did not look in the mirror again that night.

THE HUNGER THAT HAJI felt in his belly was now a wide, gaping scream. Yet, as he crept through the darkness, he kept control, every sense alert. His pupils had dilated to their fullest, enabling him to see quite clearly. He was patrolling the road just below Kampong Panjang, his usual fear of the Uprights dissipated some-what by his current predicament. He worked his way along a monsoon ditch at the base of a short decline that led down from the road. The night was clear and silent save for the steady back-ground of insect noise. Haji paused for a moment to listen, his head tilted to one side. Now he could faintly discern another sound—distant, mournful, it rose and fell in a cadence. Haji dropped low on his belly and crept silently up the slope to peer over the rise.

The sound was the singing of an Upright cub strolling along the road. More interestingly, the boy was leading a skinny white cow on a piece of rope. All this Haji saw in an instant, and then he dropped down to glide along the ditch so as to come up again behind the cow. The nearness of the Upright made him nervous, but the prospect of the cow's flesh was too tempting. He waited, his ears alert to the sound of bare feet and hard hooves on the dry dirt surface of the road. At last he moved swiftly up the bank until he was crouched on the edge, some ten yards behind the Upright and his cow. The beast's flanks waddled in invitation. Haji began to inch forward.

The cow, abruptly nervous, snorted and pulled back on the rope.

The cub stopped singing, and turning, yelled something at the frightened creature. He tugged at the rope, but the cow began to low in a deep, distressed tone. Haji, afraid the sounds would attract more Uprights, began his attack at a steady run. Glancing up, the cub saw Haji and stood transfixed, still clutching the rope.

Haji launched himself onto the cow's back, his claws extended to grip the animal's shoulders. At the same time he bit down into the nape of the skinny neck with all his force. The weight and impetus of his leap bore the cow to her knees, bawling. Haji swung sideways, twisting his prey round, while his jaws took a firmer hold on the creature's throat.

At last the cub had the presence of mind to relinquish his grip on the rope. He stumbled backwards, away from the nightmare that had suddenly engulfed his most precious possession. The cow was kicking feebly as the tiger's great yellowed teeth slowly throttled the life from her. The cub tripped, sprawled on the road. Screaming with terror, he staggered up and began to run towards the kampong.

Haji gave a couple of powerful wrenches from side to side to hasten the cow's end. At last she gave a final convulsive shudder and was still. Anxious not to waste time, Haji swung the creature round and began to drag it towards the bank in a series of violent jerks. It would have taken six strong Uprights to move the cow, but within moments Haji had the white carcass across the road and over the steep bank. He leaped down beside it and began to jerk it along, deeper into the jungle. The long horns were jamming in roots and behind tree trunks, and Haji had to keep backtracking in order to release them. Displaying the characteristic guilt that tigers feel when they kill a domestic animal, he dragged the cow much further than he would have had it been his natural prey—a wild pig or a sambar. Despite his hunger, he did not halt until he was a mile and a half from the scene of the kill. Then he dropped the cow in a sheltered hollow where there was a flowing stream in which he could slake his thirst.

He began tearing ravenously at the flesh, in huge mouthfuls that he virtually swallowed whole, such was his haste. By the time his appetite was satisfied, he had eaten almost half of the carcass. He crept to the stream and drank deeply, lapping up the water until his stomach was bloated. With a deep rumble of fulfilment, he strolled back to the carcass, walked proudly round it a few times, then backed up to it and with his slender rear legs began to kick dry grass over the remains. He did this for several minutes, but the white hide was still visible.

He went over to a thick clump of ferns, tore them from the ground with his mouth, and turning back, deposited the whole clump on top of the cow. He paraded round the slain beast again, and paused a couple of times to kick more grass over it. At last he moved away from the kill and sat licking his paws. For the first time in days he felt contented, and he shaped the feeling of wellbeing into a blasting roar of triumph, which echoed in the night and sent flocks of slumbering birds flapping from the treetops in alarm. The sound of his own voice pleased him, and he sent out another roar, and another, great sonorous exultations that could be heard for miles, in every direction.

Then, well pleased with his night's hunting, he sauntered away to find a secure place to sleep.

A DISTANT SOUND woke Bob Beresford. He lay staring up at the darkened ceiling, listening intently. After a couple of minutes he could discern the sound again, a long, mournful wail, distorted by distance. A locomotive horn, perhaps, from the iron mine over at Padang Pulst.

Lim stirred in her sleep beside him. "Bob not sleep?" she murmured, her voice a dreamy slur. "You want me fetch drink?" But then she was gone again, submerged in the pool of slumber from which she had briefly surfaced. Bob smiled. He closed his own eyes, tried to settle down, but then the noise came again, long, constant, not a mechanical sound at all. It went on for some time, repeated at intervals, and then it stopped abruptly as though the animal responsible had drifted away in search of sleep.

Wish *I* could find some, thought Bob; but he knew that once disturbed in this way, he would lie awake till dawn, thinking of his father who lay in the cold earth and of his mother, whom he had abandoned because she had remarried. Bob had worshipped his father. He could never understand how she could have forgotten him so readily; worse still, how she could have chosen a no-account bank clerk to marry. Well, Bob had fixed her wagon, right enough. It didn't matter how many letters she wrote to him, he was just going to let her stew, along with the little twerp she called her husband.

358

3

Haji woke with new spirit. His hunger was satisfied, his pride restored. He stretched luxuriously for a few minutes. Then he moved off, stopping from time to time to spray the trees and bushes with the aid of a scent gland beneath his tail. This was simply a way of marking out his territory. The secretion possessed a powerful odour that could linger for weeks, provided it did not rain.

The track Haji was on led down a slope to a sluggish yellow river between sandbanks and boulders. Without hesitation, he plunged into the water and submerged his body, leaving just his head above the surface. The water was wonderfully cooling, especially to the wound on his leg; but then his keen eyes caught a telltale swirl in the water that spoke of a large crocodile. Haji had no real enemies in nature, unless one counted the Uprights; but he knew that the only other beast likely to attack him would be a crocodile, and in their natural element, water, those were unbeatable. Haji decided to move on. But he waded out with dignity, refusing to hurry. When he finally reached dry land, he half turned and directed a threatening roar at the pair of beady eyes surveying him from the surface of the water. The crocodile dropped from sight. Haji growled and shook himself to remove the water from his fur. Then he went on his way.

As he moved along another track into deeper jungle he was astonished to find the powerful scent of a male tiger sprayed on the bushes and trees. Haji came to a halt, sniffing. It was rare for one male tiger to invade another's territory. Young tigers who did not possess their own home ranges sometimes crossed through an established run, but such creatures were merely transients, en route to another place. They didn't mark out territory in such a brazen way. Haji was very angry that his authority should be challenged in this manner. He paced up and down, growling to himself. Then he lifted his tail and blanketed the area with his own scent, so that if the intruder should return, he would be left in no doubt about Haji's outrage. This accomplished, Haji moved to the centre of the track and made two distinct scrape marks in the dirt with his hind feet, a further indication that the territory was his.

He moved on again, stopping to spray at regular intervals. The scent of the other cat kept recurring for some distance, until Haji reached a place where the intruder had veered towards the river. Haji growled, sniffed at the ground, and gave one last obliterating spray. Then he moved along, trotting briskly. His aim was to make a wide, rambling circle within his territory and arrive back for a second feed on his kill around dusk. His intentions became more positive when, a mile or two along the track, he came across yet another scent. This one did not antagonize him, for it belonged to Timah, one of the two tigresses that shared Haji's range.

As is the accustomed way with tigers, Haji lived a solitary existence, as did his two mates. They would only meet up to copulate, or sometimes to share a kill, and the latter was Haji's intention now. Timah's scent was still fresh, and he was able to locate her by a series of calls that she promptly answered. A short while later he found her waiting on the track ahead. They made the familiar coughing greeting to each other that tigers invariably use, and rubbed against each other, flank to flank, purring contentedly like overgrown domestic tabbies.

Haji had not yet mated with Timah, for she was only just coming to maturity. She was a particularly handsome creature, some three years old, considerably smaller than Haji and shorter in length by over a foot. Her fine dark coat was smooth and glossy, and her green eyes glittered with quick intelligence. In old age, Haji's coat had grown tattered and pale, and there were many grey hairs about his face and throat. But for all that, Timah was his mate.

In many ways he preferred Timah to the older tigress, Seti, who had borne him four litters over the years. Raising cubs was an arduous business for any tigress, for she was obliged to keep them with her for two years until they were adept at looking after themselves. Then they either left of their own accord or were physically driven away so that they might search for territories of their own. Often there would not be one available, and they would have to be transients for a year or so until a resident cat died or moved away, leaving a range free. It was rare to have to wait long, but there were instances of a maturing cat fighting an old male for possession of his territory, and it was such a circumstance that Haji feared might be the outcome of the intruder's scent-spraying.

But all that was quickly put out of his mind by the playful, mischievous Timah. In some ways still a cub at heart, she obviously wanted to romp, and she began to leap around Haji, pawing at him in a display of mock fighting and then, when he reciprocated, gambolling off into the bushes for a game of hide-and-seek. Dour old Haji felt all this beneath his dignity, and after going along with it for a short while, he gripped Timah firmly by the nape of the neck and bit her just a little harder than qualified as play. She quietened down considerably after that and contented herself with trotting obediently along behind him, especially when he intimated that a meal was waiting at the end of the journey.

They set off, with keen appetites and high expectations, into the dappled green depths of the jungle.

THE TIGER'S HEAD above the doorway seemed to have acquired a grin. Harry settled into his familiar seat with a decided feeling of wellbeing. Trimani must have caught on to the tuan's feeling of contentment, for he brought the glass of beer with a dazzling smile across his face. He lit Harry's cigar and received a Havana for himself, along with the usual fifty-cent tip.

After a while Dennis came in with his daughter, Melissa, in tow. She hurried over to Harry's table while her father sorted out some business at the bar.

"Hello, Uncle Harry!" She kissed him energetically on the cheek. She had always called him uncle, though they were not related.

He beamed at her. "How are you?" he inquired. "Found anything to occupy yourself yet?"

"I'm afraid not. Everything's so quiet around here!" Melissa had recently finished school in Singapore and was anxious now to do a little living. Harry sympathized with her; the most energetic preoccupation here being the acquisition of a suntan.

"I expect you're itching to get back to England, aren't you?"

"I should say so! But Uncle Harry, I wish you were coming with us. Writing letters just won't be the same somehow."

Dennis arrived carrying drinks, one of which he passed to Melissa.

"Good heavens, what is she drinking now?" cried Harry in mock horror.

"Gin fizz," announced Melissa. "And don't forget, it's legal—I was eighteen last week, in case you've forgotten." She winked slyly. "Age of consent."

Harry laughed. He was extremely fond of Melissa and would accept things from her that he would not have tolerated in others. She was a lean, very attractive girl, with thick dark hair and enchanting hazel eyes. Harry's affection for her was paternal, in many

361

ways similar to the relationship he had with Pawn's grandson, Ché.

"You're a lucky fellow," he told Dennis. "Lovely wife, lovely daughter. Where is Kate, by the way?"

"Oh, you know her. More content to sit at home with a good book. Can't say I blame her. There's not much here if you don't enjoy a drink. Say, old chap, I've got to pop over to my office for a moment. Would you mind keeping this young lady out of mischief?"

"Delighted."

Dennis went out of the room and Harry motioned to Trimani, who came hurrying over from the bar.

"One Tiger beer. One . . . gin fizz, please."

"Right away, tuan!" And he was gone.

Melissa shook her head. "Look at the way they run around for you, Uncle Harry. If anybody else tried to get that kind of service, they'd just be ignored. Why is that?"

"Because I'm a relic, I suppose." He shrugged. "In my day, that's how it was always done. Trimani has served in this mess a long time. I expect he remembers the old ways too, but lately he's been told by a lot of people that he doesn't have to bow and scrape to the white sahibs any more. Still, he chooses to keep one memory of the old days alive, and that memory is me. Nobody else here goes back as far as me and Trimani. We're the only dinosaurs left in this particular patch of swamp."

"You're not a dinosaur," cried Melissa emphatically. "And neither is Trimani."

"Pardon, missy?" inquired the barman, who had just arrived with the drinks.

She stared at him, flustered. "Ah, I was just saying, Trimani, you're not a . . . dinosaur."

"No, missy, that is right. I am a Buddhist." He set down the drinks, smiled proudly, and walked away. Melissa managed to hold back her laughter until he was out of earshot.

She found herself musing that she was rarely happier than when she was in Uncle Harry's company. She had meant what she said about missing him. Harry Sullivan had always represented a reassuring steadfastness that she had come to rely on. When she was a little girl, she had relished the visits to his house. She would sit on his lap, inhaling the familiar cigar-smoke smell of him and listening, enthralled, to his wonderful stories of adventure in faraway places.

Even then he'd been alone, of course. The Tremaynes had not come to Malaya until 1956, when Melissa was eight. Harry had already been a widower for six years. He always spoke of his late wife with a reverence that Melissa found touching, and she quickly learned that underneath his blustery, austere exterior lay a heart of pure gold.

"Do you remember much of England?" he asked her now.

"Little things." She smiled. "I remember building a snowman one Christmas and I remember a field, I think, outside our back garden." She shook her head. "Everyone keeps telling me how cold it is over there and . . ."

Her voice trailed away as her attention was distracted by the entrance of a stranger, a tall, blond-haired man wearing jeans and a white T-shirt. He was walking slowly, his hands in his pockets, with a rather glum expression on his handsome face. He moved to the bar and began chatting with Trimani.

"Is something wrong?" inquired Harry, who had not noticed the focus of her attention.

"I was just wondering who the dish was."

He stared at her. "Dish?" he echoed. "I'm sorry, I don't . . ."

She smiled apologetically. "It's just an expression I picked up from a magazine. It means dishy fellow—good-looking." She leaned closer to whisper. "I'm talking about the chap by the bar there, wearing blue jeans."

Harry looked in the direction she was indicating. "Him?" he cried. "That's Beresford!"

"Shush! Yes, him. He's very handsome."

"But he's Australian!"

Melissa giggled. "Well, all right then, he's a handsome Australian. I say, why is Trimani pointing at us like that?"

Harry looked up. Sure enough, Beresford was chatting with Trimani, and Trimani *did* seem to be pointing at the table where Harry and Melissa were sitting. Then the Australian was sailing towards them with a disarming grin on his face. A few steps brought him to the side of the table.

"Hello there. I'm Bob Beresford. You must be Harry Sullivan." He thrust out a hand, but Harry just sat there staring at him; so he swivelled to the left and offered the hand to Melissa, who shook it readily. "I'm afraid I don't know your name, miss."

"Melissa Tremayne. Pleased to meet you, Mr. Beresford."

"Well now!" There was a brief, rather uncomfortable silence as Bob turned back to Harry. "I hope you don't mind me coming forward like this, but I had to buy you a drink the moment I learned it was you what bagged the big stripey over there."

"Bagged the . . ?" Harry was beginning to suspect that the rest of the local population had decided to switch to a new language overnight. He glanced at Melissa for some support.

"I think he means the tiger," she said cautiously. "Won't you sit down, Mr. Beresford?"

"Ah, thanks very much, Miss Tremayne."

"Melissa."

"Right. Melissa." Bob pulled up a chair and sat at the table. "And you must both call me Bob. Now, I took the liberty of asking Trim to bring over another round. You see, Mr. Sullivan, we're birds of a feather. I do a bit of hunting meself, and . . ."

Harry took a deep breath. "Mr. Beresford—"

"Bob. My friends call me Bob."

"Mr. Beresford. I can assure you that—"

" 'Course, I've never gone after tigers before. That's where you come in. See, I've heard that a big tiger killed a cow last night, on the coast road just outside of Kampong Panjang. I was thinking that you and me, the two of us together, could team up and . . ."

"*Mister* Beresford!" Harry's voice was as harsh as a whipcrack. "Let me assure you that I have not gone hunting tiger, nor anything else, for something like eight years. I am sixty-seven years old, and frankly I do not feel in the least bit interested in renewing the hobby. I hope I have made myself clear."

It became very quiet again. Trimani arrived with the drinks, sensed the uncomfortable atmosphere, and departed as rapidly as possible. Bob took a packet of cigarettes from his back pocket, offered one to Melissa, who shook her head dumbly. He lit his own and then tried another angle.

"Of course, Mr. Sullivan, you wouldn't actually have to join in the hunt. See, what I'm really lookin' for is a good guide, a tracker, someone who knows the ropes. I'd be willin' to pay." He saw from the outrage on Harry's face that he had put his foot in it again, and he glanced wildly at Melissa, hoping she might bail him out.

"You know," exclaimed Melissa with exaggerated jollity, "I was saying to Daddy only the other day, I wouldn't mind learning to shoot."

"Oh, well, Miss Tremayne—Melissa—I'd be only too glad to give you some lessons."

"If Miss Tremayne wants shooting lessons, I think she knows only too well that *I* can provide them," said Harry tonelessly.

"You *can* still shoot then?" murmured Bob.

"I beg your pardon?"

"I thought perhaps the reason you didn't hunt any more was because your eyes had gone, something like that."

"My eyesight is perfect, thank you."

"Well, if you feel up to it, me and some of the junior officers have organized a little target shooting for Saturday. We've got permission to use the rifle range at the barracks. Officially the prize is a crate of beer. But just to make it more fun everybody puts in fifty dollars, and the winner takes the lot."

"Gambling." Harry said the word in an icy tone.

"Yeah. Well, you've got to do something to pass the hours."

"Why don't you go? I could come and cheer you on."

"Maybe Mr. Sullivan really *doesn't* feel up to it." Bob glanced slyly at Harry. "Could be he doesn't want to risk his fifty dollars."

"What time is this competition?" snapped Harry.

"We're starting off at ten in the morning."

"I'll be there," announced Harry calmly.

"Fantastic!" Melissa clapped her hands in anticipation. "I've always wanted to see you in action, Uncle Harry!" She lifted her gin fizz. "Here's to Saturday," she said.

"Cheers." Bob raised his beer and drank. Then the two of them glanced at Harry, but he remained impassive. The awkward silence returned.

"About this tiger, Mr. Sullivan," ventured Bob warily, "couldn't you give me some advice, at least? I've been asking around the kampongs for guides, but nobody seems to have much idea. I suppose the obvious thing to do is to find the carcass of the cow he killed and then try tracking him into the jungle from there."

Harry let out an exclamation of contempt. "Mr. Beresford, that is the last thing you do! I only once resorted to trailing a tiger through its home ground, and I was lucky to escape with my life. The tiger was wounded. The only possible reason for following a cat into the jungle is to put it out of its misery after your first shot has failed to finish it off."

"Fair enough. But how do you get that first shot in?"

365

"You build a *machan*, Mr. Beresford."

"A what?"

"A tree platform. You place it in a tree overlooking the half-eaten kill. A tiger will return every night to feed. You fix a flashlight to the barrel of your gun, and when you hear the cat eating, you aim, switch on the light, and shoot." He spread his hands. "One dead tiger," he said calmly. "Or one wounded tiger, which is when you come down from the tree and trail him."

"Ah. That part sounds a bit more sporting! So, er, how do I go about making this . . . *machan*?"

"There will be someone in the kampongs who remembers. Ask the older men to help you. It's a long time since I heard of a tiger venturing out of the jungle. It may just kill this once and go back; in which case there's no reason to shoot it."

"Reason?" Bob chuckled. " 'Course there's a reason!" He jerked a thumb over his shoulder at the tiger's head on the wall. "I want to put a trophy on *my* wall." He leaned forward as though confiding a secret. "From what I've heard, this new tiger is a lot bigger than the one you've got there."

"Oh, I don't doubt it! One of the villagers told you about it?"

"Well, yes—"

"The Malays have a marvellous capacity for exaggeration." Harry pointed to the trophy. "That fellow there, on several occasions, was described to me as being over twelve feet long. A beast as big as a horse, with jaws like a crocodile. When I'd finished him off, he went eight feet, six inches, between pegs. Not small by Malay standards, but not exactly a monster."

Bob looked puzzled. "Between pegs?"

"There are two ways of measuring tigers, Mr. Beresford. The honest way is to drive a wooden peg into the ground by the tip of his nose and another at the tip of his tail, then measure a straight line between. *Some* hunters prefer to lay the tape along the contours of the body. That can add another four or five inches. Very good for the ego. Of course, the rajahs in India had the most ingenious method. They had special tape measures constructed that had a couple of inches taken out of every foot. Hence all those records of eleven- and twelve-foot cats. . . ." He went silent for a few moments, his eyes narrowing as though squinting into some misty world that his companions could not see. Then he said, "I really wish you would leave that tiger alone, Mr. Beresford."

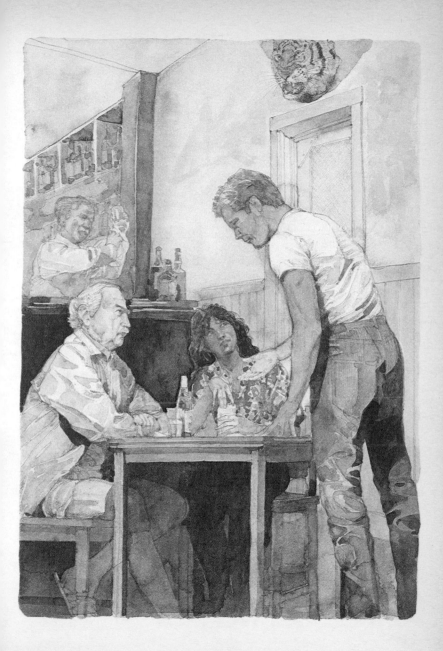

"Why?" The other man stared at him defiantly. "He *is* a cattle killer."

Harry smiled sardonically. "Ah yes. Of course he is. I'd forgotten."

Melissa had been listening quietly to the conversation, but now she saw the need to move in and referee again. The atmosphere of antagonism was extraordinary, though it did seem to stem more from Harry than from the young Australian.

"I understand you're working on repatriating the Gurkhas, Bob," she ventured, and managed to steer him successfully onto a new topic of conversation. Harry simply sat regarding the two of them. For Melissa's part, she was quite happy to chat with Bob Beresford, who was not only strikingly handsome but cheerful and easy to talk to. Still, Harry's presence made the whole thing rather uncomfortable, and Melissa was relieved when she saw her father returning with a bundle of papers under his arm. Harry immediately excused himself, mumbling something about work he had to do.

HAJI WAS JUST ABOUT at his wits' end with Timah. His repeated cuffings and bites served to discipline her for only a short time. Then her spirits would rise again and she would resume her antics, hiding among the bushes, pouncing out at him unexpectedly, pursuing him like some overgrown cub. It was more than his dignity could bear, and in the end he indicated to her by growls that if she did not curb her frivolity, he would not take her to the kill. This did the trick, for she was every bit as hungry as he was, and now she trotted obediently along in his wake.

After some time they neared the place where Haji had hidden the kill. They could smell the meat that had lain in the hot sun all day. This was tantalizing and Timah would have gone straight to the feast, but Haji growled a warning and she flopped down in the grass to wait. He took a long, slow stroll around the area, until he was sure that everything was as he had left it. Then, circling back to Timah, he indicated that all was well.

Haji flopped down, waiting while Timah ate her fill. This she did eagerly, throwing herself upon the carcass in a frenzy. She consumed over half the meat that was left and at last, satisfied, she moved off to the river to quench her thirst. Haji's appetite was less keen, but even so, he had little trouble in stripping the cow down to bare bones. Then he too moved to the river to drink. They stretched out beside the kill, but Haji was always restless in the vicinity of an eating place, and after a short while he got up and led the way along a familiar cattle trail.

Timah followed him for several miles, but then they came to a place where the trail forked. Haji started to the right. After he had gone a little way he sensed that Timah was no longer following him. He turned to gaze back. She was looking at him, and everything about her stance and expression told him that she wished to take the left-hand path. He growled once, a half-hearted command for her to follow; she would not heed him. He continued on his way, and when he glanced back a second time the trail behind him was empty. He was not surprised to see this. The solitary life was the way of the tiger.

4

Harry stepped out of the taxicab onto the crowded pavement of the main street of Kuala Trengganu, the state capital. The taxi took off into a melee of cars and bicycles, and Harry glanced about. Kuala Trengganu, like most sizable Malay towns, was a riot of sounds, smells and visual peculiarities. Harry didn't make the trip often, but the only real shops were here and he had something special in mind.

Harry moved past a market stall where the revolting smell of *durians*, a popular local fruit, assailed his nostrils. As he walked, he was quite aware of the ridiculous spectacle he presented to the Malays, this wiry old Englishman in khaki shirt, shorts and leather sandals. For all that, he walked proudly, his back straight and his chest forward, for his military background had woven itself into the very fibres of his being.

He noticed a couple of bedraggled beggars coming towards him, and he increased his pace to avoid them, advancing deeper into chaos: street stalls topped by brightly coloured canvas parasols; masses of tiny Chinese women in patterned trousers and tunics, each more brilliant than the one before; Tamil traders in turbans and white shirts and baggy trousers, proffering rattan bowls of spices and sweetmeats; hundreds of ramshackle cabins made of plywood and corrugated iron, offering a bewildering array of clothes, toys, incense, soap, razor blades, candy, battery-operated fans.

Harry climbed up the steps alongside a monsoon drain and onto a raised pavement. This was the area he was heading for. After a few moments he came to the particular shop he wanted. It was packed tight with electrical goods, and ranks of glittering watches were displayed beneath glass counters.

In an instant the Chinese proprietor, a tubby, bespectacled little man called Hong, bustled over. "Hello, sir! You look for something special?" He indicated the watches. "Good watches, best in Trengganu. Best in Malaya!"

Harry smiled. "I am looking for a watch. A gift for a very good friend."

"Ah! You want special watch! I show!" Hong indicated some beautiful Japanese chronometers. "Fine made, got two-year guarantee." He was already removing them from the glass case, but Harry shook his head.

"Those are very good watches. But not what I'm looking for." Harry rubbed his chin, scanned the ranks of merchandise. "I want something easy to understand. It's for a young boy, you see."

"Ah! I got good watch for young boy. This one! Shockproof, dustproof, waterproof, antimagnetic, one-year guarantee."

"No. It's not quite . . . *that's* the sort of thing!" He pointed to a simple silver pocket watch on a leather fob. "Let me see that one."

"This watch, sir?" Hong could scarcely believe his eyes. "But this one not show date! Not dustproof, not waterproof!"

"Yes, well, I'd like to see it anyway."

"OK, sir." Hong bobbed down behind the counter, extracted the watch and, as Harry had expected, emerged with a whole new point of view. "This very fine watch, Swiss mechanism. Twenty-one jewel, shockproof, waterproof."

Harry suppressed a smile. "I thought you said it didn't have those things."

The Chinese spread his hands and smiled sheepishly. "But, sir, that was when I didn't want you to buy this watch."

In spite of himself, Harry had to laugh. It was an outlandish explanation, but it could have been uttered appropriately by any of the merchants in this town. He picked up the watch and examined it critically. It showed the time clearly and looked as if it could take some rough handling. "All right," he said. "How much?"

"You good man. I good man. I make you special price. Twenty dollars."

"Twenty? That's robbery. I'll give you six dollars for it."

Hong was outraged. "Six? If I sell for that, I go out of business. You give me fifteen dollar. I cannot go less."

"Well . . . all right, ten dollars, my last offer."

"Ten dollars! Madness!" Hong shook his head adamantly. "Twelve my lowest price!"

"Then I don't want the watch." Harry made as if to walk away.

"All right, all right!" Hong tore at his hair. "I give you for ten."

"Eight?" ventured Harry with a grin, but Hong's look of horror told him that this was clearly not playing the game. "Only joking." He counted out the notes and put the watch in his pocket.

With a brief wave Harry set out again into the crowds. He went next to a small barber's shop where he had a haircut and a beautifully close shave that was administered with a horrifying cut-throat razor. As he sat back in his chair, he brought out the silver watch and examined it again.

"Nice watch," observed the barber. "How much you pay?"

"Ten dollars."

"I can get watch like that for six dollar."

Harry nodded. "This shave is costing me one dollar," he said. "If I were a Malay, I could get it for twenty-five cents."

And the barber threw back his head and laughed merrily, his dark eyes twinkling. Harry laughed along with him. No further explanation was necessary.

BOB BERESFORD brought the Land-Rover to an abrupt, squealing halt on the stretch of road alongside Kampong Panjang. He clambered out, took his rifle from the back seat, and slinging the weapon carelessly over his shoulder, he headed into the village.

The kampong was a jumble of rattan and corrugated-iron dwellings, all supported three or four feet above the ground on stout posts, a practical necessity in a land that swarmed with venomous snakes, scorpions and centipedes. The village seemed to have been constructed with no sense of order, one building close upon the next, with a well-trampled muddy walkway in between. As Bob approached, groups of children flocked around him excitedly, pointing to his gun and jabbering in Malay. He could barely speak their language. Over and over he inquired, "*Penghulu?*" Somebody had told him that this was the Malay word for the village headman. It took some time to make his wishes known, but at last the laughing

371

children drew him deeper into the village. They deposited him outside a dwelling that looked no grander than the others; the children began to shout and yell until a little, wizened monkey of a man, dressed in a red sarong, emerged from the house and climbed down the stairs. He smiled at Bob and bowed his head.

"Good day, tuan. Can I be a help?" His English was very good. The children began to giggle. The *penghulu* gave a shout and stepped menacingly towards them, at which point they scattered in every direction. The *penghulu* turned back and inquired politely, "Will the tuan take some tea?"

"Ah, no, thanks very much. I came about the tiger."

The *penghulu* looked puzzled. Evidently he had not come across this word before.

"*Harimau*," prompted Bob, who had taken the trouble to find out the Malay word for tiger from one of his pupils.

"Ah!" The *penghulu* nodded gravely. He eyed Bob's rifle. "You want shoot him?"

"If I can. Can you show me the place where he took the cow?"

The *penghulu* smiled, showing large, discoloured teeth liberally dotted with bright gold fillings. "Come," he said, and he led Bob away from the house.

Bob took out a packet of English cigarettes, offered one to the old man, then put one between his own lips. He lit both with his silver lighter. The *penghulu* gazed at the lighter admiringly and then strolled happily beside the Australian, puffing ostentatiously on his cigarette, aware that people in the surrounding houses were observing him.

"Is it far away?" inquired Bob.

"Not far, tuan. *Si-pudong*, old hairy-face, kill cow on road, out by kampong. Then he carry away. Herdboy very frightened, but *si-pudong* not touch him. He read words on boy here." The *penghulu* tapped his own forehead and smiled. "So, *si-pudong* 'fraid to eat boy. Take cow 'stead."

Bob did not understand this at all and resolved to ask somebody to explain it to him in the near future. The two of them moved out of the village, walking in silence, glancing occasionally into the jungle that flanked the road. The afternoon sun was fierce, and Bob felt the tickle of sweat as it ran down his back beneath his khaki shirt. After a surprisingly short distance the *penghulu* announced, "Cow killed here!"

He pointed to some marks in the hard dirt surface, and peering closer, Bob could see patches of dried blood. Now the *penghulu* pointed to the right, where the ground declined sharply into a monsoon ditch. *"Si-pudong,* he come up out of ditch, attack from behind," he explained. Bob slid down into the ditch, closely followed by the *penghulu*. The ground was comparatively moist here, and they found a series of pugmarks.

"Ai!" exclaimed the *penghulu*. "There were two of them! See, tuan." He indicated a pair of large, squarish paw prints. "Man cat go up bank to kill." He pointed out smaller tracks a little distance back. "His woman wait here, while he do all work." He thought for a moment, then added, "Just like my wife."

Bob smiled, scratched his head. He certainly hadn't expected two tigers. He moved along the ditch until he reached the place where the cow had been dropped down the bank. The grass was crushed and there was a long, deep furrow, presumably where one of the creature's horns had gouged into the soil. A distinct trail led off through the undergrowth. Bob indicated to the *penghulu* that he intended to follow it. The old man looked far from eager, so Bob took out his cigarettes and lighter, handed them over, and suggested that he wait up on the road. With a grateful nod, the *penghulu* scrambled up the bank, and Bob set off into the jungle.

It was as though somebody had switched off the sun.

The instant he passed into the shadow of the trees, he was immersed in a chilly world of green-dappled mystery. As he moved onwards, the foliage high above formed a thick, dark canopy through which rays of light could only occasionally stab. The drag-marks he found led through lush ferns and tangled vines, around the gnarled roots of *balau* trees, through the heart of seemingly impenetrable bamboo thickets. Bob followed silently, glancing nervously this way and that. It was his first experience of real jungle, and the dank humidity made him feel very claustrophobic. But he kept doggedly onward. From time to time he came across chafed roots of trees and bushes where the horns of the cow had evidently lodged. The torn bark suggested that the cat had exercised prodigious power in pulling the carcass free.

The trail led on through green shadow, and Bob's nerves began to get the better of him. On two occasions, he had the impression that something was gliding intently along behind him. Each time, he snapped fearfully round, his rifle ready to fire, only to find nothing but empty jungle mocking him. He was on the verge of giving up when unexpectedly the trail culminated at the edge of a sluggish-looking stream. It was a disappointing end to his search, for there was nothing here but a sorry-looking pile of bones and offal. No tiger would bother to return to this meal.

The return journey seemed to take twice the time. Bob saw not a living thing on the way save for a brilliantly coloured tree snake hanging from an overhead branch. It had a glossy black body marked with green and red spots, and he gave the creature a wide berth, not being sure whether it was poisonous. After an uneventful eternity of trekking, he emerged into sunlight again.

The *penghulu* was sitting beside the road, smoking and humming happily to himself. As the Australian's head appeared above the bank, the old man smiled, his gold teeth throwing out a dazzling welcome. "Ah, tuan! You find *si-pudong*, yes?"

"No." Bob stepped onto the road and flopped down to rest. "The cow was all eaten up," he announced. "If I'm going to shoot that tiger, I need to be on to the kill much quicker next time." He thought for a moment, then reached into his pocket and pulled out a notebook and pencil. "I tell you what. I'm going to write the address of my house down here. And I'm going to give you twenty dollars. . . ."

The *penghulu*'s eyes lit up.

"Now, the next time you hear of a tiger killing a cow anywhere around here, you come and let me know, understand?" He drew out his wallet and handed a twenty-dollar bill to the *penghulu*, who accepted it eagerly. "Another thing. You got any friends who can work with wood? Savvy? A carpenter, you know?" He mimed the action of sawing and hammering, and the *penghulu* nodded.

"My cousin," he said with conviction.

"All right. Let's go and see your cousin. I want him to make me a special seat that I can rope up into the trees, a seat I can shoot from. And look, I'm going to need men to help me later on, and they'll all get paid too. You'll be able to buy a lot of cigarettes before we're through. What do you say, are you going to help me out?"

The *penghulu* crumpled the twenty-dollar bill in his hand. "You not worry, tuan, I keep ears open, all over! I hear something, I send word, never fear!" And he grinned. "Now, you come talk my cousin. He make you good shooting seat, you will see."

IT WAS A LITTLE after eight o'clock, and Harry had already been up for three hours. He sat in his favourite rattan chair on the veranda, remembering how when he was younger he had possessed the ability to sleep like a proverbial log. Now, the advent of the night was no longer a pleasure but an irksome task to be endured in endless tossing and turning. More often than not he would rise with the dawn and pace about, searching for little jobs to occupy him while the hours crept past.

It was with a feeling of elation that he heard the garden gate clang open. Pawn had arrived to make breakfast and, more important, today was the day she always brought Ché with her. They advanced up the drive, an incongruous couple, she small and creaking, he a spindly hyperactive twelve-year-old. He bounded onto the porch, his dark eyes flashing in merry greeting. "Good morning, tuan!"

"Good morning, Ché, Pawn." The old woman bowed very slightly and moved on into the house.

Ché pulled over the spare seat and sat down, lifting his bare legs so that he could rest his chin on his knees. He regarded Harry with a good-natured grin. "The tuan is well today?" he inquired.

"Oh, well enough, Ché, well enough. Now, what's been happening over in Kampong Panjang?"

Ché's face became very animated. "Well, tuan, such excitement two nights ago! A great *tok belang* killed a cow just beyond the kampong. The cow belonged to my best friend, Majid, and he stood as close to the beast as I am to you!"

Harry smiled. He noted that, like many Malays, Ché had a terrible reluctance to say the word tiger. The boy had called it *tok belang*, the striped prince. Other locals named it *si-pudong*, old hairy-face. This stemmed from the superstition that the very mention of the word *harimau* was enough to bring the creature's wrath down on one's head. In most areas of Malaya the superstition had faded except among the very old, but here in Trengganu it persisted among many inhabitants.

"A big tiger, you say? How big?"

"Majid said he was fifteen feet long and stood as high as a fully grown deer. His eyes blazed like hot coals, and his teeth were like great white daggers, this long!" Ché held the palms of his hands six inches apart. "Poor Majid was fixed to the spot, but of course the beast did not attack him, for he was facing it."

Harry knew all about the fervent Malay belief that every good man had a verse from the Koran written on his forehead, proclaiming mankind's superiority over the beasts of the jungle. This is why, of course, nine times out of ten, a tiger will attack a man from behind. Harry could easily explain that Majid had probably been in no danger because a tiger only attacks humans if it is very old or badly wounded, unable to catch its usual prey. Moreover, tigers naturally attack from the rear to maintain an element of surprise. But no amount of reasoning would shake Ché's belief. So Harry simply asked, "Where do you think this tiger came from?"

The question was more complicated than it might seem to Western ears. To a Malay's way of thinking, no tiger could just *be* there wandering out of its jungle home. Ché thought for a moment before replying. "Some people say that it might be a weretiger. There is an old *bomoh*, a witch doctor, who lives alone near Kampong Machis, and he claims to have the power of turning into a *hari—tok belang*. But more likely it is the other way round. A beast from Kandong Balok has been living among us and now is seeking his old ways."

Harry knew better than to laugh and cause offence. He knew about Kandong Balok, the mythical kingdom of tigers that lay far beneath the earth. There ruled Dato Uban, king of all tigers, in a home made of human bones and thatched with human hair. From time to time one of Dato's subjects would yearn to live as a human, and this tiger would leave Kandong Balok by a secret tunnel. En route, a mysterious transformation would occur. The tiger would take human form and would go to live in some kampong. Sometimes the changeling would hunger for raw flesh and would revert to its other form and kill cattle or even human beings.

The kampongs were rife with stories about weretigers, usually told to a huddled family late at night in the glow of a solitary oil lamp. Details varied, but the basis was always more or less the same. A woman would be happily married to a good provider, a gentle husband. A tiger would start to prey on luckless villagers at night, and the poor woman would never suspect a thing until she awoke one morning to see her husband coming up the short ladder into the house, his head supported by the crouching body of a tiger! This was her husband, caught in mid-transformation. What happened to the marriage at this point was generally left to conjecture. Of the countless similar stories, Harry had his favourite, and he now asked Ché to recount it for him, for he loved the boy's excitement whenever he told such a tale.

"Well, tuan, in the days before the *tok belang* looked as he does now, he was nothing more than a wild little boy, wandering in the jungle. One day he was befriended by a strange old man who lived in a hut alone. The old man was kind to the boy and taught him how to eat properly, how to speak and wear clothes, for the boy had been quite naked. Well, the people in the nearest kampong came to hear about this and sent a man to insist that the wild boy must go to school. The old man was sad to lose his friend, but at last he agreed. Now, the schoolteacher was very stern, and he quickly lost patience with the wild boy, for he was always fighting with others, biting and scratching most cruelly. The teacher warned the wild one that he must be quiet or he would suffer. But the boy began to fight again and the teacher snatched up a strong cane, shouting, 'Now I shall beat you, for you are truly nothing but a wild animal!' And he hit the boy with the cane. At this instant the boy dropped onto his hands and knees. The teacher hit him again and the boy growled. He hit him a third time and whiskers grew from his cheeks. A fourth time and a tail grew. The teacher kept striking the boy so hard that the cane scarred his body with black stripes, and suddenly the creature leaped to the door and ran away to the jungle. And to this day he carries the stripes on his back to remind him of that terrible beating."

Ché sat back with a smile of satisfaction, for he felt that he had told the story well. Harry applauded him gently. Then he announced slyly, "I went into Kuala Trengganu yesterday."

"Oh?" Ché tried to sound casual, but he knew that the tuan was leading up to something.

Harry took a small leather box out of his pocket. Ché's eyes lit up. "What have you there, tuan?" he inquired.

"Oh, just something I bought. For a friend of mine. I wonder if he'll like it." He opened the box, removed the watch, and let it dangle on its leather fob before Ché's eyes.

"Oh, tuan! It shines like the sun! I think your friend will like it very much." He gazed at Harry suspiciously for a moment. "Who is this friend you speak of?"

"A very special friend of mine. He tells me marvellous stories."

"Me? It is for me, tuan? Oh, thank you!"

Ché stretched out his hand, but a sudden rush of perversity took

377

Harry and he moved the watch away a little. "But I cannot give it to my friend yet," he continued. "First, he would have to say something else for me."

Ché laughed merrily. "What must I say, tuan? Another story?"

Harry shook his head. "Just one word. Just to prove to me that he has his wits about him. I want him to say 'tiger'."

Ché's face fell. "Tuan, I cannot! It is unlucky!"

"Oh, well." Harry feigned disappointment. "If you can't say that one word . . ."

"But, tuan." Ché glanced at his feet. "You don't understand. Of course, I don't really believe the old stories, but—"

"You mean this marvellous watch must go back to the shop?"

"No, I, uh . . ." Ché fixed his gaze stubbornly on the floor, then glanced up at the glittering silver watch in Harry's grasp. "Tiger," he mumbled. "There, tuan, I've said it."

"So you have," admitted Harry. And he gave the watch to the boy. Ché's misgivings were swept aside by his rush of delight as he held the watch to his ear.

"Oh, it is beautiful, the most wonderful watch ever! I can hear it ticking so loudly! Thank you, tuan, thank you!" He rushed to hug Harry, tears of gratitude in his eyes. "May I take it to show my grandmother?"

"Of course!" Harry was as delighted as the boy was. Ché rushed into the house, yelling for Pawn. But once he was gone, Harry felt vaguely annoyed with himself. Why had he taxed the poor little devil so cruelly? Surely in all the years he'd lived here, he'd learned that the one thing you shouldn't fool around with was the beliefs that people held dear, no matter how ridiculous they seemed. Still, he told himself, there was no harm done. He settled back in his chair and closed his eyes.

MELISSA GAZED CRITICALLY at her reflection in the hand mirror as she methodically ran a brush through her long dark hair. She had been sunbathing on the lawn with her mother for most of the morning and had become bored to distraction.

She put down the hand mirror, got up, and strolled to the slatted bedroom window. She could see her mother stretched out on a sunbed, apparently asleep. Beyond the large, empty garden lay the silent, sunbaked street, and not a soul moved along it in the heat of the afternoon.

Melissa felt a great wave of dissatisfaction welling up inside her, but she willed herself to control it. There was at least one area of hope on the horizon: the shooting contest in two days' time. Of course she had not the remotest interest in shooting, but Bob Beresford would be there, and that particular young man was beginning to receive more and more of her attention. She found herself thinking about him constantly, and her thoughts frequently turned into the most torrid fantasies. Her conception of men was still surprisingly childish, nurtured by the overprotective life-style of the girls' boarding school. She simply had not been given the opportunity of being with boys. Now that she had "done her time", that was one matter she intended to put right at the earliest opportunity.

Melissa felt suddenly ashamed of her thoughts and she blushed, glancing round nervously as though afraid that somebody might be observing her. She moved back to her desk and picked up the mirror. She was pretty, there was no doubt of that. But Bob did not seem to be making a move. It might be up to her.

"Melissa? Aren't you coming out again?" Her mother's voice from the garden.

"Coming," she replied wearily. She put the mirror down, but it was dangerously close to the edge of the desk, and it fell with a crash onto the tiled floor. With an exclamation of anger, Melissa stooped and retrieved it. There was a wide diagonal crack across its surface. "Just what I needed," she muttered darkly. "Seven years' bad luck."

ON WEDNESDAYS it was Harry's custom to meet Dennis at the officers' mess for a lunchtime drink. The ever-faithful Chinese trishaw driver would turn up at Harry's doorstep around twelve o'clock and whisk him over to the barracks. This morning, however, the trishaw was uncharacteristically late. It was twelve thirty, and Harry was just about to go in search of a cab, when he saw the old man pedalling up to the garden gate.

Harry hurried out of the house and was concerned to see that the driver looked far from healthy. His thin face was more haggard than ever, his eyes were red, and there was an overall weariness about him. "Sorry for lateness, tuan," he croaked.

"Sorry nothing! You look terrible. Are you ill?"

The old man shrugged. "It is nothing, tuan, Come, climb in."

Harry shook his head. "Don't be ridiculous! You can't drive me anywhere in that condition. You should be in bed."

"Tuan, I must work. Please, we go now, yes?"

Harry frowned. Then a solution occurred to him. "Here, come along, off the bike." He grasped the driver by the elbow and helped him down. "Now, you climb in," he insisted.

"But, tuan, surely, you cannot . . ." Harry pushed him firmly but gently into the passenger seat and then climbed astride the bicycle. "Tuan, you cannot do this! It is not proper," protested the driver, but Harry waved him to silence.

"Nonsense. You go pedalling this thing and you're liable to collapse. Now then . . ." He began to pedal the trishaw slowly along the road. "There, nothing to it. We'll soon have you home. Your kampong is near the mess, isn't it? I can walk from there."

The old man was clearly not happy, but it was plain that protesting would do no good. He slumped back in his seat, trying to keep as much out of sight as possible. Meanwhile, Harry was rather enjoying the experience. It was harder going than he would have imagined, but there was a certain exhilaration involved, and he soon had the vehicle speeding along the coast road. He overtook a couple of villagers strolling along the verge, who became quite excited when they saw what was going on. They shouted loudly and gesticulated, and Harry gave them a dignified wave as he sped by.

He handed the old man a couple of cigars and his lighter. "Thank you, tuan." He took them, lit both and handed one back. "You are a very good man. Very kind."

Harry shrugged. "I don't know about that, but I'm beginning to think I'd make a pretty good trishaw driver."

When they reached the old man's village, Harry pressed a twenty-dollar bill into the driver's hand, and insisted that he go straight to bed. "If you call for me in such a state again," he warned, "I shall be very angry." And ignoring the barrage of profuse thanks, he set off at a brisk pace to walk the remaining half mile to the mess. He arrived a little after one o'clock and found Dennis at the bar.

"Hello, old chap. Thought you'd deserted me!"

"Had a bit of trouble on the way in." Harry recounted what had happened, much to Dennis's delight.

"I'd have given anything to see that!" Dennis laughed. They ordered drinks, and the Tiger beer was very refreshing to Harry's somewhat parched throat.

381

"What's new at the barracks?" he asked.

"I've had my marching orders. Go in three months' time. Little camp in Suffolk, actually the place I requested. The girls are over the moon."

Harry sipped thoughtfully at his beer. "That's it, then. I kept hoping for a change of plan." It was said with such heartfelt sadness that Dennis felt momentarily at a loss how to reply. There was a brief silence before he came back with the usual reassurances.

"Well, look here, old man, we'll write to each other. And if you should ever fancy a holiday over there, I don't have to tell you again, I'm sure. . . ."

Dennis made an attempt to swing the conversation round to something else. "I hear there was another cow killed last night, over in Kampong Wau this time. Apparently the cattle were penned up in the middle of the village, and the tiger came in and took a calf. I, uh, also hear that your friend Bob Beresford has been riding around in his Land-Rover all day, mobilizing the villagers. He's intending to finish off the tiger's career very shortly."

Harry grunted. "When does he find the time to fulfil his duties?" he said sarcastically.

Dennis shrugged. "Mr. Beresford finds himself with a lot of free time on his hands. At least he's putting it to some use."

"Use? Shooting some poor beast who's so desperate for food he has to pilfer from kampongs? Listen, Beresford told me exactly why he wanted that tiger. For a trophy to display."

"You know, Harry, nobody around here knows more about hunting tigers than you. Couldn't you give him a little help?"

"For heaven's sake! I refuse to get drawn into this business. The death of a couple of skinny cows doesn't constitute a crisis."

"But once a cat starts killing . . ."

"Not necessarily, Dennis. Perhaps if he's old or injured, he might begin to make a regular nuisance of himself. But let's face it, there are plenty of cussed old devils around here who haven't changed their habits in years." He concluded this sentence with a sly wink, leaving Dennis in no doubt as to which particular tiger Harry was referring to.

IN THE LATE AFTERNOON Haji returned to the place where he had left the carcass of the calf. But as he neared the area, his keen ears picked up the sound of Uprights' voices and he went into cover, creeping slowly through the undergrowth until he could observe what was going on. A short distance from the kill, a couple of dusky Uprights were at the base of a tall *kapok* tree, hauling a curious wooden thing up into its branches. A third Upright, paler than his companions, strutted about barking authoritatively. Everything about their actions suggested that they were in a hurry, and Haji settled down to wait.

After a little while the pale Upright climbed awkwardly up the tree, and a black stick was handed to him. He seated himself on the wooden contraption that had been hoisted skyward, and remained there, his long, thin legs dangling some eight feet from the ground. The two other Uprights shouted their farewells and hurried away.

Haji could smell the appetizing aroma of decaying meat wafting across the clearing, but he certainly wasn't foolish enough to go and eat while an Upright kept watch, especially one armed with a black stick. He had seen the terrible power such sticks could unleash. Still, it was early. Perhaps if he waited long enough, the Upright would abandon his curious game. So Haji stretched out in the soft grass and had a catnap, waking every so often to see if the Upright was still in position.

Twilight came and went with a hypnotic chirping of insects. Then the night sky deepened and filled with stars, but the Upright did not budge, although he had begun to fidget in his seat. Haji stretched lazily and took a long stroll around the area. At one point he came very close to the kill. The smell was overpoweringly delicious, and for a moment he was tempted to sneak out to it; but the memory of the black stick returned, and he backed away into cover.

Now he circled back behind the tree in which the Upright sat and, flattening himself against the ground, he cautiously crept nearer until he was directly under it. Gazing up, he could see the Upright's strange leathery feet dangling enticingly. What a simple matter it would have been to snatch him off his perch! But Haji's fear of the Uprights persisted and he lay where he was, listening intently. From time to time there would be a slapping noise and muttering, which suggested that this Upright was having problems with mosquitoes. His presence must have been known to every inhabitant of the jungle.

Haji was puzzled by the Upright's presence here, in a place where that species rarely visited. Why had he forsaken the safety of his home? The black stick was a clue, of course. The black sticks, with their moving fire, roared death at other creatures. Perhaps it was the Upright's intention to fling death at something he thought might stray here; Haji lay beneath the tree watching to see if any such action might occur. But the hours passed relentlessly and nothing happened. Tiring of the whole affair, Haji was about to go elsewhere in search of prey, when he became aware of soft rhythmic sounds coming from the tree seat. It did seem that the Upright had gone to sleep. Just to be sure Haji waited for several more minutes before moving in a wide circle that brought him slowly, cautiously, up to the kill.

He lifted the half-consumed carcass in his great jaws in order to drag it away; then abruptly he came to a halt. The carcass would not move! Setting it down, Haji examined a thick rope fastened around the calf's middle. The other end was attached to a stout stake that had been hammered deep into the ground. Haji sniffed at the attachment suspiciously. Then, glancing back nervously at the tree, he took the carcass up again and began to pull. At first his efforts seemed fruitless, but then the stake slowly began to come free of the earth. Haji spread his forepaws wide and gave one enormous heave that wrenched the wood completely out of the ground. With the rope and stake trailing behind him, he carried the food triumphantly away into the jungle. Behind him, slumped on the *machan*, a lone Upright slept, dreaming of success.

5

The constant hunt for food was disrupted by the long, wailing cries of a tigress whose time for mating was at hand. Haji recognized the voice of Timah, and all thought of food was momentarily forgotten. The sound echoed eerily through the jungle clearings, a loud, prolonged caterwauling, impossible to ignore. Haji began to answer with calls of his own, and moving quickly along cattle trails, he soon reached an area where she had recently passed, the ferns and bushes reeking with the musky scent that she had copiously sprayed. Her cries were nearer now, but Haji was alarmed to hear a third voice, calling from another direction. This voice too was answering Timah, and it was unmistakably male. Haji thought of the unfamiliar sprayings he had recently found, and he bristled with anger. He threw back his head and roared shatteringly, warning the stranger to keep his distance. The third voice kept up its arrogant barrage, and the three cats began to converge.

At last Haji emerged into a small clearing, to find·Timah awaiting him. She moved towards him flirtatiously, prowling with a slow sensuous grace that she had newly discovered. When she reached him, she moved her soft flank invitingly against his and curled the end of her tail over to trail along the length of Haji's spine. But the stranger's voice was still calling, very close now. Timah halted her caresses and started off, puzzled, in the direction of the call. After a few moments she returned to her shameless advances.

Suddenly, the newcomer burst into the clearing, a handsome young male, just reaching maturity. He could not have been much over four summers old, and while he looked Haji's dimensions, he was clearly at the peak of his strength. He stood with his legs braced, snarling defiance. Haji responded with a roar that would have scared most competitors away, but the newcomer stood his ground, his ears raised to show the white spots on the back of them, a sign of aggression. Haji paced silently towards the youngster until they stood about ten feet apart. Timah plumped herself down in the grass to await the outcome of the contest.

Now began a long show of power, as the two males paced restlessly up and down, bellowing and raging, bristling the white ruffs round their necks and making short ritual dashes at each other. The display went on for some time before the young male made the first real attack. He took a sudden lunging run at Haji, his great clawed feet slashing at the older cat's eyes; but Haji twisted aside, turned in against his adversary's flank, and sank his claws and teeth into the thick neck. The youngster roared in pain and whirled about, striking back with a series of blows that thrust Haji away from him. He followed straight after, lunging full length, his jaws seeking the older cat's throat. But Haji's legs raked savagely against his opponent's chest, driving him off with another cry of pain.

The two drew back and prowled cautiously around each other, both of them seeking an opening. The younger cat now became aware of Haji's injured leg and instinctively directed his next attack to that area. He leaped in to sink his teeth into the swollen flesh, but he received such a devastating flurry of blows about the head that he turned away again. Then Haji's claws sank into his flank and the two of them locked together. Their struggles took them over the edge of a steep slope, a tumble of kicking legs and foaming jaws. At the base of the hill they struck a tree trunk and sprawled heavily apart. The youngster was up first. He struck head-on, three hundred and fifty pounds of ferocious power pushing the older cat backwards with a series of relentless blows. Haji felt one of his ears rip into bloody tatters. He was weakening rapidly. A decisive attack now could turn the tables. . . .

The youngster retreated abruptly onto more open ground, and Haji followed closely, realizing only too well that his adversary was rallying for an all-out assault. In this next confrontation the outcome of the fight would be resolved. There was silence while two pairs of yellow eyes flashed hatred. Then the two great cats ran at each other and collided in a fury of claw and fang. Haji struck badly, twisting his injured foot inwards against the other cat's chest. He howled in pain, and sensing an advantage, the youngster struck home, pounding and tearing with incredible force. Haji could do nothing but retreat. In that instant he knew he had lost the fight. The triumphant roar of the youngster mocked him as he turned and ran away into the jungle, for to stay longer was to die, and Haji had always been a survivor.

But his shame weighed terribly on him as he plunged into the undergrowth with his tormentor hard on his heels. He raced into a bamboo thicket and buried himself deep in the cool, leafy sanctuary. The younger cat gave up the chase now, contenting himself with parading up and down outside the thicket, roaring triumphantly and telling the jungle at large about his victory.

Haji slumped down and began to lick at his wounds in humiliation. He was an exile now. Not only would the victor take his mate, he would lay claim to his territory and would waste no time in chasing Haji off it. The old cat would be a transient, allowed to linger no more than a day or so in any one place. In such a situation he could not hope to live very much longer.

He lapped weakly at his injured leg. The fight had unsettled the porcupine quills in their fleshy beds, and new pain coursed spasmodically through him. His head, neck and flanks were scarred deeply, and blood dripped from the wounds. Peering back, he saw the youngster strutting in the direction of Timah. He let his head drop onto his forepaws and gave a long low moan, deep in his throat. And he lay slumped and unmoving all through the rest of the day and far into the night.

HARRY EMERGED from a taxicab outside Kuala Hitam barracks. He reached in for the rifle in its leather carrying case and slung it over his shoulder, paid the driver, and then strolled towards the gates. The young Gurkha sentry recognized him and began instinctively to salute; then he hesitated, smiling foolishly.

"Force of habit," he explained. "I never know what to do."

"Try saying 'Hello, Harry,' " suggested Harry with a grin. "How are you, Hernam?"

"I am most well, sir. It is good to see you again."

"Heard anything yet? About your transfer, I mean."

Hernam shook his head. He had the typical delicate features of a Gurkha, handsome dusky skin and large brown eyes. "Nothing for sure yet. But the first wave leaves in two weeks' time." He shrugged helplessly, then forced a smile. "You are here for the shooting, yes? You are expected."

"Good. Well, goodbye, Hernam."

Harry strolled on, and out to the shooting range. A large crowd had assembled by the firing line, and it was obvious that everybody who had a dollar to spare was going to have a bet. A couple of young Gurkha officers were taking odds, and a lot of money was changing hands.

Harry moved into the crowd and instantly people started recognizing him. He had long since earned the dubious status of a local celebrity, and at gatherings he tended to find himself being greeted by people whom he scarcely knew. He moved towards the shooting line, nodding and keeping his best professional smile glued to his face; but the smile faded as he noticed Melissa talking earnestly to Bob Beresford. She glanced up as he approached.

"Uncle Harry! We were beginning to think you'd changed your mind!" Harry winced at the word *we*, as if she and Beresford had already formed some kind of partnership. Well, it was probably just a matter of time, he realized that now. He tried not to feel resentment towards the Australian, but felt it rising again the moment he heard the man's droning accent.

"Great to see you, Harry! I hope you don't mind me callin' you that." Bob paused for a reply, didn't get one, and hurried on. "Now, first off, you give your fifty dollars to Harun over there." He indicated one of the young officers. "There's eight of us altogether, so we pair off, see, we have a sort of elimination series. Whoever wins out of the first pair goes on to meet the winner of the next pair and so on. The eventual winner takes the pot."

Harry nodded. "What are the targets?"

"Standard bull's-eyes. You get six shots each, and the highest number of inner rings gets it. They aren't too big. Think you'll be able to see them OK?"

"I'll manage," snapped Harry.

"Yeah, well, we've drawn lots for partners already. You're paired against me, as it happens."

"You'd better be good," announced Melissa brightly. "I've put down five dollars on you, Uncle Harry."

Bob spread his hands in a gesture of benevolence. "I told Melissa she should put her money on me. I'm going to win this."

Harry glared at him. "Are you always so sure of yourself, Mr. Beresford?" he asked.

"Only where shootin's concerned. I never miss."

"Well, Uncle Harry's no slouch either," Melissa chuckled. "I tell you what! This will be a good way to settle that little dispute the other night, about my shooting lessons! Whoever wins out of the pair of you is hired. How about that?"

The two men gazed at each other in silence. Melissa instantly wished she hadn't said it. "No, look, that's a silly idea," she began, but Bob waved her to silence.

"Sounds fine to me! What do you say, Mr. Sullivan?"

Harry shrugged. "Just as you wish," he muttered. He turned abruptly away and went to find a seat where he could await his turn. When the young officer approached him, he dutifully handed over his fifty dollars.

"What has the silly old geezer got against me?" murmured Bob irritably.

"He's not a silly old geezer," retorted Melissa, and was vaguely surprised by her defensiveness. "But it's true, you do rub him up the wrong way. I hate to think of the two of you as enemies. Why don't you let him win?"

"What? I couldn't do that!"

"Why not?"

He stared at her. "Well, because . . . it wouldn't be the truth. Anyway, I always shoot to win."

Melissa sighed. "I had a feeling you'd say something like that."

The contest got under way, and soon it was the turn of Harry and Bob.

388

Harry took his rifle from its case and approached the shooting line. Bob let out a low whistle of admiration when he saw the weapon. "Here, that's a beaut. An old Martini-Henry, isn't it?"

"That's right. A 450/400."

"Well, it's a nice gun, but not the sort I'd choose. Bit old-fashioned if you ask me." Bob hefted his own rifle. "Now, you take my gun here. Had it custom-made in Oz. It's got a—"

"Mr. Beresford, this is the only rifle that I possess, and furthermore the only weapon that I'd ever feel truly happy with. Now, after you."

"Suit yourself." Bob took his position on the line in the designated kneeling position and sighted on the target thirty feet away. He began to fire rapidly, methodically, loading a cartridge into the chamber after each shot. After the sixth shot he stood up confidently as the shouter raced over to check the score. The man waved his arms excitedly.

"Six bulls!" he cried. The crowd broke into applause. Bob leaned towards Harry with a triumphant smile on his face.

Harry approached the firing line, knowing that the very best he could hope for was a draw. He called to the shouter, "Announce them one at a time! I don't want to waste any bullets!" This brought laughter from the crowd, who were rooting for him.

"Go on, Tiger!" yelled a couple of voices. He knelt and slid the wooden stock of the rifle against his right shoulder. It was a long time since he had felt it there, and it was oddly reassuring. He took long, careful aim. He had to stare very hard at the small white target before it came into focus. He steadied himself, squeezed the trigger, felt the jolting kick of the old rifle. The crowd held its breath as the shouter hurried to the target.

"One bull!" he yelled, and scuttled back to safety.

Harry took his time with the reloading, knowing that hurrying made a man clumsy. Again he took a long aim, wanting to be absolutely sure. He squeezed the trigger.

"Two bulls!" A murmur of anticipation ran through the crowd. Maybe the first shot had been a fluke, but two in a row wasn't bad at all. Over in the crowd, Melissa glanced at Bob. "You could have missed one shot," she whispered.

"I told you," he hissed. "I never miss."

Harry squared up for his third shot and got another bull. Likewise with his fourth. The crowd was growing tense with excitement.

389

Taking aim for his fifth shot, Harry paused to mop his brow. He took a deep breath, squeezed the trigger.

"Five bulls!" The crowd broke into applause, then corrected itself, remembering that there was one more shot to go.

Harry took a cartridge from his belt, fumbled it, picked it up. His eyes were watering from the effort of peering with such concentration. One more shot and he was home. Then, of course, there would be another shoot-off, because a draw was no use to anybody. He wilted at the thought. He wasn't sure if his eyes, or his nerves, could take another round of this kind of punishment. He shook his head, wiped the sweat from his forehead, and lifted the rifle. The target seemed to fade to a white fuzzy blob, then redefine itself, dissolve, sharpen, dissolve . . .

The gun recoiled, the shot felt good, but Harry had doubts about it. He waited in silence while the shouter raced eagerly to the target. The man came to a halt, gazing at the rings as though they foretold his own destiny. Then his shoulders sagged.

"One outer," he said flatly.

A great collective groan spilled from the crowd. They had so much wanted the old man to win. He took his loss with all the good grace he could muster, turning away with a shrug and a smile, and they loved him for it. He strolled back to much applause and a consoling hug from Melissa. Ironically, for the moment at least, he was the winner.

"Oh, Uncle Harry, that was *so* close."

"Yeah, great shootin', Mr. Sullivan. You're a tough man to beat." Bob cranked Harry's hand enthusiastically, but his eyes suggested that he resented losing the adoration of the crowd. "But look here, now that you've proved what a good shot you are, surely you'll help me tackle this tiger?"

Harry raised his eyebrows ever so slightly. "You mean to say you haven't bagged him yet?"

Bob was quite unaware of the sarcasm in Harry's voice. "Sat up all last night over his kill. When I fell asleep he managed to make off with the carcass without waking me. I mean, the calf was roped to the ground! What I know about tracking, you could print on the back of a matchbox. Mr. Sullivan, if you'd only come out to the place I was last night, give me a bit of advice. What do you say?"

Harry glanced not at Bob but at Melissa. She was gazing at him hopefully, the same expression she used to use when she was

390

younger and the pair of them were walking past the ice-cream parlour in Kuala Trengganu. He had never been able to resist the look then, and time had in no way hardened him.

"Well," he answered, "I appear to be fifty dollars down today. And as a professional tracker, I suppose I should ask a fee. So if you're prepared to pay me fifty dollars, I suppose it's all right."

"Done! We could drive out there tomorrow afternoon, after my lessons. I'll pick you up around three o'clock."

At this moment Bob was called for the next round of the shoot-off, so Harry and Melissa settled down to watch.

There was something awesome about the Australian's ability on the firing range. Round after round he came up with a perfect score. But, thought Harry, there was a disagreeable arrogance in the way he swaggered out to take his turn, and a marked insincerity whenever he shook the hand of a man he had just bettered. Melissa, however, seemed blind to these traits, and as each round went by she would applaud Bob wildly.

The final round came. Matched against one of the Gurkha officers, Bob cracked away quickly, almost carelessly, yet his aim never faltered. The day that young man misses an important shot, thought Harry to himself, there will be hell to pay. Somebody that sure of himself could never live with failure.

The Gurkha's luck failed when a shot went wide, and Bob Beresford was the winner. He strode back, basking in the applause, to receive his crate of beer and the prize money.

"Well," observed Harry drily to Melissa. "It looks as if you should have put your five dollars on our friend there. . . . Hello, what's going on now?" Bob was at the centre of a large crowd of people, mostly officers, and more money was changing hands. A Malay youth had suddenly appeared, and people were talking excitedly to him. He was grim-faced, but after a while he nodded. There was some laughter, and several notes were passed to the boy. He turned and began to walk towards the targets, carrying a beer bottle in his hand.

"This must be the trick shooting," announced Melissa gleefully. "Bob said something about it before."

The boy came to a halt by the targets. The crowd backed away, and Bob went down on one knee. The boy reached up and put the bottle on his own head, then waited, a look of dread on his face.

"Good Lord," whispered Harry, "he's going to . . ." He stood

391

up, horrified, and began to walk towards the firing line. But he had taken only two steps when he heard the report of the rifle and saw the bottle shatter above the boy's head. The crowd applauded enthusiastically; the boy ran forward, much relieved. But Harry felt a surge of anger erupt within him. He strode forward and reached Bob just as the Australian was getting to his feet.

"You idiot!" exploded Harry. "What the hell do you think you're playing at?"

Bob was astonished. "What's the matter, Mr. Sullivan?"

"What's the matter? Of all the irresponsible, dangerous tricks I've ever seen . . . Supposing you'd missed? Supposing the cartridge had misfired? That boy could have been killed, and you stand there asking me what's wrong!"

Bob realized just how public this little scene was.

"Look," he said quietly. "You're making too much of this. I've done that stunt a thousand times. It's perfectly safe. Here!" Melissa had hurried over to referee the bout, and now Bob grabbed hold of her arm. "Just to show you how simple it is, I'll shoot a bottle off Melissa's head too!"

"You will not!" exclaimed Harry.

"Oh, why not?" retorted Melissa brightly. "It sounds like fun!"

"Fun?" roared Harry. "For heaven's sake, girl, you're as mad as he is." He took hold of her other arm. "Come along now, it's time you went home."

"Uncle Harry! Let go!" For a moment Melissa was the object of a furious tug-of-war between the two men. It was Bob who relinquished his hold first, embarrassed by the looks of delight on the faces of the onlookers.

Harry began to drag Melissa away through the crowd. "Let go of me! How *dare* you!" Her face was crimson. "Uncle Harry, I don't want to go yet! For heaven's sake, I'm eighteen years old!"

"Not old enough to have learned any sense though," growled Harry. "Melissa, I refuse to leave you with that—that maniac. I'm merely doing what your father would do if he were here."

"Don't be ridiculous." They were away from the crowd now, and Melissa's voice rose. "The plain fact is that you're *jealous!*"

He rounded on her in amazement. "I'm not jealous, Melissa. I'm concerned for your welfare, that's all. That oaf, Beresford . . ."

"Oh, he's an oaf, is he?" Melissa had tears in her eyes now. She

392

wanted to hurt him for humiliating her. "An oaf who's young and handsome, who can shoot better than you!"

She regretted her words the instant they had left her lips. Harry stood still for a moment, his head slightly bowed. He looked suddenly weary. Abruptly he turned to walk in the direction of the gates. She followed, a few faltering steps. "Oh, Uncle Harry, I didn't mean that."

He stopped, not looking back at her. "Of course you did, my dear. And you're quite right. You go back to the others now. As you said, you're eighteen years old." And he walked on again.

Melissa stood where she was for a moment. She glanced through a blur of tears at the crowd she had just left. They were applauding some new stunt, and she could see Bob on the firing line, the object of their attention. Ahead of her a lonely figure trudged slowly away. She hesitated only a moment longer.

"Uncle Harry, wait for me!" She ran after him until she was walking alongside. "You were right, it *was* a dangerous thing to do. I wasn't thinking, that's all." She bit her lip. "We could share a taxi home if you like. Uncle Harry? I'm so sorry. You aren't angry with me, are you?"

He said nothing, but his lean, gnarled hand reached out and took hers. Harry was silent, he seemed to have retreated into a world of his own. He kept hold of Melissa's hand, but he did not speak once all through the taxi journey home.

6

Melissa's hair was dry already. Ten minutes earlier she had been splashing aimlessly in the cool water of the local swimming pool; now she was walking home. The two girls with her were school-mates, rather on the empty-headed side, she thought. For this reason she rarely bothered to seek them out, but they had called at her house that morning to ask if she would like to go swimming. The girls' names were Victoria Plumly and Alison Weathers. Victoria was rather plump, with medium-length curly red hair and attractive green eyes. Though she possessed an innocent air, she was a holy terror where boys were concerned, and some of the stories she came out with at school were quite lurid. Alison, on the other hand, was a tall, thin, plain girl whose most striking feature was a set of buck-teeth. Her one saving grace was her long blonde hair that fell in silken tresses. She was one of those unfortunate creatures who is prone to fits of giggling whenever the subject of boys is brought up. As this was the chief interest of both Victoria and Melissa, she had been giggling all afternoon and was now looking rather worn-out. Still, for the moment, the subject had switched to another topic: going home to England.

"Actually," Alison observed, "I'm going to miss Malaya."

"What?" The other two stared at her.

"Well, we won't have servants and things. And England is supposed to be very cold in the winter."

"Nonsense!" cried Victoria. She was able to say this with some authority. Her parents had been posted to Malaya for only two and a half years, whereas the other girls couldn't remember what the old country was like. "You'll soon get used to it. Besides, there's so much to do there. Pubs, discos, pop concerts. Fish-and-chip shops." She raised her eyebrows. "Boys . . ."

Alison began to giggle. The other two girls gazed at her wearily. They walked on for some distance in silence, letting the mirth subside. "Anyway," said Melissa after some thought, "I can't wait to kiss this place goodbye. Nothing ever happens here."

"*Some* of us are all right," said Victoria meaningfully. "*Some* of us get invited to shooting contests!"

Melissa smiled. "How did you know I was there?"

"Oh, a little bird, dear. I also understand," Victoria continued, "that you were in the company of Mr. Bob Beresford."

Alison began to giggle uncontrollably.

"Yes, well, I was talking to him quite a bit," admitted Melissa. "What's wrong with that?"

"Nothing! He's *gorgeous*. What a shame he's tied up though." She glanced sneakily at Melissa to gauge her reaction.

"What do you mean?" asked Melissa. "Oh, for heaven's sake, Alison, stop giggling!"

Victoria sauntered along for a moment, relishing her own power.

"I thought everybody knew," she said. "By all accounts, he's very fond of his little Chinese amah. I mean, very fond. I've seen her, she is an extraordinarily pretty girl."

"I don't believe it!" snapped Melissa.

"Oh, it's true enough." Victoria was adamant. "They're quite open about it apparently. It's a wonder you hadn't heard."

"Bob and I are very good friends," persisted Melissa. "He's promised to give me shooting lessons."

The two girls gazed at her with new respect. "Lucky you," murmured Victoria.

"In fact, that's not all I'm planning to do with him!" Having got their attention, Melissa was determined to press her advantage. "He's been very . . . attentive."

"Do you fancy him?" inquired Alison breathlessly.

"Of course she fancies him, you gonk! Who wouldn't? Did you see him at the tennis club last week? Talk about poetry in motion."

"And he does look quite clean," reasoned Alison. The others looked at her in quiet desperation.

"I wouldn't care if Bob Beresford had just crawled through a cesspit," Victoria said. "A *real* man like that. How old is he, Melissa?"

"Twenty-four."

"Mmm. Do you think you've got a chance of making home base with him?"

"Sure! Just a question of time, really."

"I bet you won't."

"I bet I will!" Melissa retorted.

"How much? Twenty dollars?"

"All right then."

"That's silly!" said Alison. "For one thing, how will we know?"

"True," agreed Victoria. "The buck-toothed one has a point. You could simply tell me that you'd been with him and I wouldn't know any better. We'll have to think about this carefully."

The three of them walked for some distance while Victoria thought out the possibilities.

"One way," she mused at last, "would be to bring something of his back to show us . . . a sort of a trophy." She snapped her fingers. "I've got it! Bob wears a special necklace. At the swimming pool a couple of weeks ago he was wearing this thing round his neck, a silver charm like a bullet or something. He told Angela Cartwright it had belonged to his father and that he never took it off, because it means a lot to him. Now, if you brought *that* back to show us, I think that would be proof enough."

"But supposing he won't give it to me," said Melissa.

"My dear girl." Victoria smiled mysteriously. "I'm told that when a man wants a woman enough, he'll give her anything she asks for.

There's no need to set a time limit either. You'll be heading back to England in three months. If you haven't caught him by then, you never will. So—if you haven't presented the locket to me no later than three days before you leave, then you pay me twenty dollars. And if you do show the locket, I'll pay you."

"All right," agreed Melissa. "I'll try."

HARRY WAS SNATCHED from a shallow snooze by the sound of a car roaring up to his garden gate. He sat up, blinking, unsure for the moment of where he was. He found himself in his favourite rattan chair on the veranda. He muttered something beneath his breath and then turned at the sound of the gate. Bob Beresford came strolling up the driveway.

"Hello there!" He waved a greeting. Harry sat staring in silent disbelief. "Er, am I a little early?"

"Early for what?"

"Well, we made an arrangement yesterday. Here." He reached into his back pocket and extracted fifty dollars, which he set down on the table. "There y'go. Cash in advance."

"Yes, but that was before you pulled that awful silly shooting stunt! I didn't expect you to show up after . . ."

Bob spread his arms in a gesture of goodwill. "Forgive and forget, Mr. Sullivan, that's my motto. I'm prepared to forget it!"

"You're prepared . . !" In spite of himself, Harry had to smile. The Australian's sheer gall was unbelievable. "Well, Beresford, for your cheek, I will go along. That is, if you promise not to try shooting bottles off the heads of any tigers we meet."

"You've got yourself a deal there!"

"Very well. You'll have to hang on for a moment while I change." Harry disappeared into the house, and it was twenty minutes before he emerged again. He was now wearing canvas jungle boots that laced up almost to the knee. Into these were tucked a pair of khaki trousers, and he wore a matching shirt and a bush hat. His rifle was slung over his shoulder, and a thick ammunition belt around his middle was heavy with cartridges; also hanging from this was a water flask and a formidable-looking *parang*, a long-bladed knife in a leather sheath.

At least he's not wearing jodhpurs and a pith helmet, thought Bob. But he said, "You look ready for a nine-day march!"

"It's always been a rule of mine," declared Harry firmly. "Never go into the jungle, even for a few hours, unless you're prepared for every eventuality." He shouted goodbye to Pawn, then followed Bob to the Land-Rover. Soon they were racing along jungle roads, en route to the scene of Bob's unsuccessful hunt.

Bob tried to make conversation, asking questions about Harry's experiences as a hunter and an officer with the Gurkhas, but the old man's answers were curt. He had agreed to help the Australian out, but he had in no way consented to be his friend.

As they neared Kampong Wau, Bob brought the Land-Rover to a halt on the side of the road. "This is where we go in," he announced. Bob led the way, and as they walked, Harry found his gaze sweeping instinctively left and right, looking for signs. He spotted some wild-pig tracks, but they looked weeks old. Harry knew that a good way of telling if a tiger was in the neighbourhood was to see how many pigs were encountered on the trail. If they were abundant, it meant the cat had moved on to a new part of its range; when there were none, it indicated that he was around somewhere, looking for food. But in such instances one usually found evidence of his recent presence—pugmarks, droppings—and Harry was puzzled to find none.

He asked the Australian if he had encountered any wild pigs on his marches through the jungle.

"No, not one. Why?"

Harry shrugged. "Pigs are the tiger's main source of food. A shortage of them could explain these cattle killings."

"Hmm. Well, I'll keep my eyes open for them in future. Ah . . . now this is where we join the drag, I think."

Sure enough, a trail of crushed vegetation and broken grass moved directly across their path, and they could see where the calf's hooves had ploughed furrows in the damp earth. Bob let Harry take the lead, interested to see what the old man could do. Harry moved along, stopping occasionally to examine half-formed pugmarks. At last he found some clear imprints and he knelt down to study them.

"Well, it's a male," he announced. "And old. I'd say very old."

"How do you know that?"

"The forepaws of a male are larger and squarer than the average female; also, the feet splay out as he gets older. See the large gaps between his toes? The pads seem very scarred too. That long diagonal scar on his left forepaw will be easy to spot again."

"What about these smaller tracks?" asked Bob. "The *penghulu* at Kampong Panjang reckons there's two tigers, male and female."

Harry chuckled. "Standard mistake," he replied. "A tiger's back feet are smaller than his front ones, that's all. No, there's only one cat here and a big devil too, judging by his pugs." He stood up and followed the prints across the soft ground. "Hmm, that caps it," he murmured. "He's wounded in the right foreleg. He's dragging the foot to the side at each step, see there? That must be quite a pronounced limp."

Bob scratched his head. "Strewth, you do know a thing or two. With this kind of information we'll soon have him bagged."

"Well, yes, perhaps it's not such a bad thing after all. He's wounded. Be best to put him out of his pain."

Harry continued along the trail for nearly a mile, watching for more signs. At last they reached Bob's *machan*, still hung in the branches of the *kapok* tree. Bob was about to point it out, but Harry had already spotted it.

"No wonder the tiger didn't get taken in!" he exclaimed. "You can see that contraption a mile away." He turned back to Bob. "You mustn't assume that because he's an animal he's stupid, you know! A tiger's eyesight is much more developed than yours or mine. If he sees the slightest thing out of the ordinary, he'll be alerted that something's wrong. Next time, disguise the *machan* with a covering of foliage. But make sure you cut the branches from some distant place. A tiger would notice cut-down shrubbery in the area of a kill and be warned off. When that happens he normally leaves the kill and never goes back."

"Well, this fellow last night didn't react like that. As I told you, he came and stole the pegged meat when I was asleep."

"Yes . . . curious that. I imagine he could hear you snoring or something. Oh, that's the other rule about sitting up on a *machan*. Keep the noise down. Don't fidget. Anyway, let's have a look."

Harry strolled around in a wide circle, until he came across some pugmarks emerging from the jungle to the left of the *machan*. They followed the tracks to the place where Haji had moved to within a few yards of the carcass. Harry saw that the tiger had doubled back, and he retraced his own steps until he came up behind the *kapok* tree.

"I'll be damned." He indicated a longish depression in the soft ground. "He must have been lying here for some time."

398

"Here?" Bob looked horrified. He glanced up at the *machan*.

"Exactly, Mr. Beresford. If he'd taken it into his head to reach up and grab hold of one of your legs, you wouldn't be talking to me now. In future, you should build your *machans* a little higher. Also, curb your need for cigarettes if you can." He indicated a couple of cigarette stubs at the base of the tree.

Bob frowned. "Did I do anything right?" he mumbled sourly.

"Just one thing. You consulted me. Well, when he gets hungry enough, he'll kill again. Then you'll have another chance."

"All right, thanks, Mr. Sullivan. Now, I've just got to get the *machan* unroped so I can put it back in the Land-Rover." He glanced at Harry hopefully, but the old man sat down on a tree stump and brought out a packet of cigars.

"You carry on," Harry suggested. "I'm in no great hurry."

IN THE EARLY HOURS before dawn, a thick, low-lying mist wreathed the surface of the road to the north of Kampong Panjang. Only a brief swirl marked Haji's passing as he moved down into a monsoon ditch, then along it for some distance. There was considerable urgency about his movements. He had summoned his last reserves of strength for a quest that had taken him out of familiar jungle haunts, into places where he might find the slower game he had been seeking. This was his only chance of survival.

He slunk into a straggle of secondary jungle and emerged into an area that was unfamiliar to him. This was a large rubber plantation, and the countless evenly spaced trees rearing up out of the mist looked somehow threatening. Haji paused nervously on the edge of the land. Then his attention was caught by a moving, bobbing light out in the midst of the trees, and he began to creep cautiously forward, hugging what cover was available, though it was unnecessary in such a mist.

The light was a helmet with a lantern fixed onto it, worn by a solitary Upright. He had come early to the plantation to collect the little cups of rubber that had been left out overnight. He had a large container slung over one shoulder, and he was moving slowly along a line of trees, removing the cups, tipping their contents into the larger vessel and replacing each in a new position on the trunk. He spent several minutes at each tree, his back turned as he fiddled over his task. Haji moved forward until he was hidden behind the line of trees parallel to the ones at which the Upright busied

399

himself, and trailed him from trunk to trunk. He would wait until the Upright reached the very last tree, near the edge of the field. From there it would be fairly simple to drag the kill into the jungle.

The Upright was three trees away from the end of the line, humming to himself as Haji watched. Suddenly, the Upright seemed to become nervous. He stopped humming and stared this way and that into the mist; but he did not see Haji, crouched fifteen feet away from him. He smiled at his own foolishness and moved to the next tree.

Haji watched for a moment, then slunk forward, placing his wounded leg with great care. The humming sounds were serving to unnerve him.

A shout rang out among the trees! A second yellow light was bobbing amid the forest of trunks. The Upright stood up, called something to his approaching friend, then broke off as a brief snarl at his rear alerted him. He saw a long, striped phantom emerging from a sea of mist, and he opened his mouth to scream.

Haji struck with terrible force, flinging the Upright back against the base of the tree by which he had been standing. The container of rubber clattered to the ground. The breath was driven out of the man's body in an instant and his arms dropped marionette-like to his sides. Then Haji's great jaws clamped around his throat. Haji was momentarily surprised by the ease with which he had taken his prey. He began to pull the carcass away from the scene, aware that the second Upright was now dangerously close.

A few moments later the second man reached the tree and realized that his friend was no longer there. He saw the overturned container, its precious contents spilled on the ground. Moving closer, he noticed a splash of crimson on the smooth bark of the tree. A feeling of dread overtook him. He ran to the edge of the secondary jungle. There he found his friend's bloody sarong snagged on a root, and two narrow lines in the dust where the dead man's heels had dragged as his killer bore him away.

The man let out a scream of terror and fled back towards the buildings at the far end of the plantation, the light of his lantern bobbing and leaping weirdly through the mist.

BOB WAS DREAMING, but someone was shaking him roughly.

"Bob! Wake up! Somebody comes to see you!"

He blinked up at Lim's excited face. Then he shifted his attention

400

to the bedside clock. It was past ten o'clock; he had slept late. "What's the matter?" he demanded.

"The *penghulu* of Kampong Panjang asks to speak with you."

Bob pulled on his dressing gown and strode out onto the porch, where he found the *penghulu* standing with a man he did not recognize.

"Good morning, tuan." The *penghulu* indicated his companion. "This is my brother from Kampong Machis. *Si-pudong* strike near there, early this morning. Brother take you to place, rubber plantation just outside kampong."

Bob scratched his head, thinking that he had misheard the man. "Since when do they keep cows on a rubber plantation?"

The *penghulu* shook his head emphatically. "No, tuan. This time he kill a man. A rubber tapper. Creep up behind him."

Bob's face drained abruptly of colour. Only three nights before, that same tiger had lain under a tree gazing up at him, waiting for him to sleep. Supposing it had taken the notion to turn man-eater then? He shuddered. "Wait here while I get dressed," he said.

Ten minutes later Bob, the *penghulu*, and his brother were bouncing along the road in the Land-Rover, and the *penghulu* was richer by twenty dollars. Bob drove even more recklessly than usual, anxious to get to the scene of the kill. He was quite relieved when they passed Kampong Machis and came to a halt by the entrance to the rubber plantation. They alighted, and Bob was quickly directed to the foreman, a grim-faced Chinese in a white short-sleeved shirt. He was standing on the edge of the crowd, his hands on his plump hips, and he looked very unhappy.

"You speak English?" asked Bob.

"Sure, boss! You come shoot tiger?" It was refreshing to find somebody who didn't mind using the word.

"If I can." He asked the foreman to take him to the scene of the kill, and the two of them strode away.

There was little indication of a struggle where the killing had occurred, just a couple of items of bloodstained clothing.

"I'll need a few men to help me," announced Bob. "There's a shooting seat in my Land-Rover. Once we find the body, I'll rig that up over it."

But the foreman stared at him. "The body already found," he replied, and then grimaced. "Very horrible. The workers bring it back to family in kampong. They arrange for burial."

402

Bob cursed beneath his breath. Of course, he should have expected this. A human corpse was not the carcass of a cow.

"Well, I'll still need a couple of men to come and help me prepare," he told the foreman. "I've got a plan for tonight, savvy? Now, come on, we've a lot to do." He snatched up the articles of clothing belonging to the victim. The foreman glanced at him in surprise.

"What you want those for, boss?" he inquired. An expression of revulsion came into his face as he saw the torn white shirt.

"In the absence of a corpse," explained Bob calmly, "we'll have to make one of our own."

HARRY WAS ENGROSSED in the morning's edition of the *New Straits Times* when the peace of midafternoon was rudely shattered by Ché, pounding down the driveway, his flip-flops slapping loudly.

"Tuan, tuan! The great *tok belang* that killed Majid's cow has turned man-killer!"

Harry glanced up sternly from his reading as Ché thundered onto the veranda.

"Has he now?" he replied icily. "And is that any reason to make so much noise when I'm trying to rest?" Harry felt decidedly crotchety today. The weather wasn't helping much. The atmosphere had grown muggy and oppressive, and the air smelled strongly of sulphur. A storm was due.

"Are you not going to do anything, tuan?" Ché moved closer now, staring at the old man inquiringly. "You are the greatest hunter for miles around. It is only right that you should be the one to put an end to this devil."

"Ché, I haven't killed a tiger in years!" A note of exasperation crept into Harry's voice. "When are people going to realize that? I'm not interested, it's as simple as that." He frowned. "Besides, Tuan Beresford will be after the old devil's hide soon enough."

"But," Ché persisted doggedly, "it is not right that the glory should go to him."

"Glory?" cried Harry, losing his temper. "You think there's any glory in seeing off a poor beast who's too old and lame to live as nature intended him to? Well, do you?" He stopped speaking as a sharp pain coursed across his chest. He massaged it with the palm of his hand and took a deep breath. "There, you see, now you've given me heartburn," he complained.

Ché was still intent on his one theme. "Tuan, the people would wish you to shoot the *tok*—"

"You don't give up easily, do you?" cried Harry. "Go away. Your chatter's beginning to tire me."

Crestfallen, the boy backed away a little, an expression of pain on his face, as though he had been physically struck. Then he turned and strode grim-faced into the house in search of his grandmother.

Harry felt like a villain but was too annoyed to call after the boy. He got up from his chair, thrust his hands into his pockets, and walked out into the garden. The late-afternoon sun was being choked as the sky took on a flat, bruise-black tone, and all bird-song had ceased as the creatures anticipated the storm.

Harry moved past ranks of carefully tended orchids, hardly aware of them. His mind was dark with resentment. Why was everybody so keen to associate that tiger with him? If Beresford was so anxious to assume the mantle of Great White Hunter, let him, with pleasure!

A large olive-green lizard skittered along the base of the garden wall, searching for a nook to shield him from the coming rain. Harry sighed, then turned back to the house. As he went in he could hear Ché jabbering to his grandmother. Harry closed his bedroom door quietly. Then thunder split the sky in two.

7

Bob Beresford was getting soaked to the skin. He had been in position on the *machan* for three hours, but the last thirty minutes or so had been a nightmare. The canopy of foliage above him offered no respite from the downpour, and he was cold and miserable; yet he would not give up his position while there was even the faintest chance of the tiger coming back to feed. From time to time a flash of searingly bright lightning illuminated the crudely made manikin that he had substituted for the corpse. Consisting of the victim's clothing stuffed with straw, it certainly looked convincing from a distance. But whether it would fool the tiger was another matter.

The rain gushed down Bob's collar. Even his sturdy boots were waterlogged, and the sensation of being wet through made sitting on hard wooden planks still more disagreeable. I must be crazy to do this, he thought glumly.

He reached into the pocket of his shirt and pulled out his packet of cigarettes, now a sodden lump of cardboard and tobacco. He flung it away with a curse as a flash of lightning lit up the sky, closely followed by an awesome clap of thunder. Bob stiffened in surprise. For an instant the eerie light had picked out everything in incredible detail: the tangled undergrowth below, the blood-spattered shirt and sarong on the straw dummy, the raindrops momentarily frozen in midair . . . and something else, slinking from a patch of long grass off to the left. Bob had glimpsed it only briefly, but there was no mistaking the long, lithe shape of a tiger. His heart leaped into his mouth, and he literally had to stifle a cry of excitement. He brought his rifle up and waited, hardly daring to draw breath.

Again lightning flashed, and his senses thrilled as he saw, quite clearly, a large tiger prowling nervously from the undergrowth, in the direction of the bait. There was not a moment to be lost. The tiger would soon realize that a switch had been made. Bob would have to be ready to fire at the next flash of lightning, flicking on his flashlight at the same instant in order to prolong the light. He steeled himself, tried to settle into a comfortable shooting position. He sighted along the rifle, keeping it trained on the faint whiteness of the shirt and sarong.

Abruptly the lightning flared again. Bob hit the flashlight button and there was the cat, standing over the manikin, sniffing it suspiciously. He looked enormous, how could anybody miss? Bob sighted high behind the creature's shoulder, and then events seemed to slip into a hazy slow motion. The cat sensed that something was wrong. As thunder roared from the sky, he turned his head to gaze up into the trees, and the orbs of his eyes glowed red in the beam of light. Bob squeezed the trigger, the gun bucked against his shoulder. The tiger began to wheel away in alarm, but a concussion shook his whole body, a patch of hair flew up from his shoulder. He reeled sideways, seemed to recover, and began to race towards the jungle to his left. But his front legs failed him, and he flipped upwards in the rain, turned a slow, agonizing somersault, his open mouth roaring pain and surprise. He crashed to the ground, rolled over, and lay clawing the air with a single front paw. He attempted to get up just once, then slid back again, his tongue lolling.

Bob gazed down at the dead beast, his heart beating wildly. For the moment he could hardly believe that he had achieved what he had set out to do. Then he gave vent to a cry of pure exultation and he fired three shots into the sky, the signal for the villagers that the man-eater was dead. He hoped that they would hear the shots in the midst of the storm. He half climbed, half fell down to the ground and sloshed through the undergrowth to claim his prize. The tiger lay quite close to the bait, looking strangely ethereal under a haze of deflected rain, his great yellow eyes already clouding over in death. Bob felt a ridiculous sense of elation, and he began to dance childishly around his victim, laughing out loud.

AFTER THE COMMOTION of the previous night, the morning seemed a gentle absolution. Harry rose a little after dawn, made some tea and took it out to the veranda. He felt rather grieved at the way he had treated Ché the evening before, and since this was the boy's usual day for visiting, he was determined to make it up to him in some way. But he was disappointed and a little shocked when at eight o'clock Pawn arrived for work without her grandson. She came slowly up the path, smiling sheepishly, for she was well aware of the old man's affection for Ché.

"Good morning, tuan. Ché not here yet. He go to Kampong Machis to see dead man-eater, but he come later."

"Dead?" Harry had not expected Beresford to be successful so soon. The hunting down of a cat usually required considerable persistence.

"Yes, tuan!" Pawn grinned. "Tuan Beresford shoot him. When Ché and his friends hear of it, they must go to see!" She shrugged expressively. "Boys . . . what can one do?"

"Yes, well, never mind," snapped Harry. He did not want his concern to show. "I expect he will come along soon."

Pawn bowed slightly and went on into the house. Harry remained where he was, a faint scowl on his face. It's only natural, he thought; any boy would rather go to see a dead tiger than pass the time of day with an old man. Still, he felt rather put out, and though he sat gazing at the garden gate for the next few hours, Ché did not come.

Harry fell into a shallow doze that was interrupted by the creak of the gate. He opened his eyes, expecting Ché, but it was Melissa. She waved cheerfully as she approached. Beyond the gate he could see her father's car, with Dennis at the wheel.

"Hello, what brings you here?" asked Harry with a smile.

"We're going over to Kampong Machis to look at Bob's tiger. We wondered if you'd like to come along."

Harry was somewhat taken aback. "They'll be organizing coach parties next," he observed drily.

Melissa laughed. "What do you say?"

Harry was as curious as the next man to see what the man-eater looked like; also, he might have the opportunity to apologize to Ché—if he was still there. "I'll get my jacket," he announced simply, and went into the house.

When he came back out, Melissa and he strolled arm in arm to the car. Dennis looked pleased, if a little surprised, that Harry had consented to the trip.

"Hello there, old chap!" He swung open the door on the passenger side and Harry climbed in. Melissa clambered into the back beside her mother. Harry glanced at Kate Tremayne in astonishment. It took a great deal to tempt her away from home.

"My goodness, it must be an event," he said. "Hello, Kate. I wouldn't have thought this was your sort of thing."

"It isn't!" Kate assured him. "Going along to gawp at a poor dead animal is certainly not my idea of fun. But I'm interested in getting a look at this man that Melissa's taken such a fancy to."

She winked slyly at Harry, and Melissa blushed bright red. "Mummy!" she protested.

The car sped along the coast road until they reached a bumpy dirt track leading up to Kampong Machis. They parked on the outskirts of the village and continued on foot from there. A large crowd of people were gathered in the centre of the kampong, and in the midst of them Harry could see Bob Beresford looking rather tired, but proud.

The atmosphere was like that of a public holiday. Large numbers of children were racing about, and among one group Harry spotted Ché. He was carrying a crudely made wooden rifle with which he was energetically shooting his comrades. Harry detached himself from Dennis's party and went over to the boy.

"Hey there!"

Ché stopped, gave Harry a guilty glance. "Good day, tuan," he muttered. "I was going to come later."

"Oh, that's all right! What have you got here?" Harry took the rifle from the boy's hand and examined it critically.

"It is only a toy, tuan. Have you seen the tiger yet?"

407

Harry raised his eyebrows at Ché's use of the word tiger, an unexpected show of recklessness.

The boy laughed. "I have no need to fear it now," he explained. "Tuan Beresford has killed him, so he can hunt me no more." And he glanced in Bob's direction with an expression on his face that could only be described as hero worship. "When I grow up, tuan, I too will be a great hunter. I will go into the jungle and kill all the tigers that hide there."

Harry stared down at the boy in dismay, wondering what in the world had got into him.

Meanwhile, Harry's companions had managed to push through the crowd to get a look at the slain beast. Melissa knelt beside the tiger, ran her hand along the striped fur. "He's fantastic!" she exclaimed. "So huge!" A cough from Kate prompted her to make a hasty introduction. "Oh, Bob, this is my mother."

"Pleased to meet you, Mrs. Tremayne." The two of them shook hands across the dead tiger. "Well, what do you think of him?"

"I'd rather see him alive," replied Kate thoughtfully. "But as Dennis keeps reminding me, he *was* a man-eater."

"He's a magnificent specimen," observed Dennis. "No doubt you'll be having him skinned, Mr. Beresford?"

"Just as soon as I can find somebody who knows how to do it! I expect we'll get it done tonight, when everybody's had a good look at him." Bob indicated the crush all around him. "I wasn't expecting so much interest."

"Of course everybody's interested!" exclaimed Melissa. "You're a hero, Bob!" And impulsively she leaned forward and kissed him on the cheek. "A kiss for the victor!" she announced dramatically. Bob stared at her for a moment, then grinned.

Dennis gave an embarrassed cough. "Ahem! Perhaps Harry Sullivan might know some skinners. Now where did he go to?"

He swivelled round, shielding his eyes with the palm of his hand, while he scanned the crowd. He spotted Harry talking earnestly to Ché, but the boy hardly seemed to be listening. Suddenly a group of children raced past and Ché took off after them, leaving Harry in mid-sentence. The old man gazed after him.

"Harry! Come over here. You haven't seen the tiger yet!" Dennis beckoned energetically, and Harry glanced up in surprise, as if he had forgotten all about their reason for coming. He forced a smile, and trudged slowly over.

408

"Hello, Mr. Sullivan. Take a look at this beauty!" Bob watched as Harry stooped to examine the kill. The old man crouched in silence, gazing fixedly at the long, striped carcass. The rest of the crowd, it seemed, was waiting for his blessing. After a little while the tension became unbearable, and Dennis prompted him.

"Well, what do you think, Harry?"

"Beautiful," murmured Harry, his voice barely more than a whisper. "Beautiful." Abruptly he snapped his head up and glared at Bob. "You fool," he said coldly.

Bob's jaw dropped open. "Mr. Sullivan, I'm getting a bit tired of this! Why, only the other day you told me this cat ought to be shot, to put it out of its misery. And that was before it turned man-eater."

"You're quite correct, Mr. Beresford, I did say that. And you may also recall that I checked out some pugmarks for you and gave you a fairly precise description of the man-eater."

"Well, yeah, I remember."

"Would you like to explain to me, then, how it is that you've managed to go out and shoot the wrong tiger?"

"The what?"

"The wrong tiger, Mr. Beresford. The cat that we tracked was fifteen to twenty years old and had a wound in its right forepaw. This cat is barely in its prime, four years old at most. I don't see any evidence of a wound in the leg, do you?"

Bob stood staring down at the tiger. "But . . ." he managed to blurt out, "I . . ."

Harry held up one of the creature's front paws for inspection. "You may also remember that the cat's pugs showed that his front feet were splayed out and badly scarred. Does that look as if it might be capable of making such tracks? Well, does it?"

Bob gestured helplessly. "It must be the man-eater! I mean, it came down to take the bait. It has to be. Otherwise—"

"Otherwise you've shot a beautiful rare animal that has caused no harm to anybody. Well, Mr. Beresford, I hope you feel very proud of your efforts."

"Uncle Harry, leave him alone!" Everybody turned at this unexpected outburst from Melissa. "You're just fed up because Bob's managed to do something you're no longer capable of!"

"Melissa," warned Kate, "I don't think that's entirely fair."

"Fair! Everybody's afraid of hurting Uncle Harry's feelings, but it doesn't work the other way round, does it? He's been picking on Bob ever since he found out what a good hunter he is."

Harry gazed at her for several moments. "Don't you understand?" he said calmly. "He shot the wrong animal. This is just some poor brute that happened to wander in the wrong direction."

Bob Beresford took a step forward. "Now just a minute. For all we know the tracks found under my *machan* may have belonged to another tiger that was just . . . passing by. What makes you so sure you know better than anybody else, Mr. Sullivan?"

Harry's body suddenly went rigid, his face drained of colour. When he spoke again, his voice shuddered with emotion.

"Mr. Beresford. I have had considerable experience of so-called man-eating tigers. I have shot them on six different occasions, and in each case the cat was either very old or wounded. You can believe me or not, as you wish, but I tell you that you have made a mistake. You have a moral obligation to so inform the villagers, otherwise they'll go back to strolling about on the jungle roads at night. And the next death will be on your conscience. One more thing. You like to think of yourself as a sportsman, but it's quite obvious that you don't know the meaning of the word."

"Now look here, you silly old—"

Bob broke off as Harry stepped forward and brought his hand across the Australian's face in an unexpectedly powerful slap. Bob reeled back with an oath, and Harry turned smartly on his heel and strode away through a shocked and silent crowd.

"Well, of all the . . ." Bob massaged his stinging cheek. "I ought to knock his head in. I would if he wasn't old enough to be my father!"

"Are you all right?" cried Melissa anxiously.

"I'm sure Mr. Beresford is still in one piece, dear," Kate said.

Dennis scratched his head. "Well, I suppose we'd better go."

"Oh, I'll stay on," Melissa said. "If Bob can give me a lift home later on?"

"Uh, yeah, sure, if you like."

Kate gazed at her daughter. Her eyes said, We'll talk about this later, my girl! but her mouth said, "Goodbye, dear. We'd better get after Uncle Harry. Come along, Dennis." The two of them edged through the crowd.

Harry was standing beside Dennis's car, leaning on the roof as if to support himself. His head was bowed and his shoulders seemed to be heaving. Fearing that the old man was suffering another attack, Dennis ran forward and grabbed him by the arm. Harry glanced up, and Dennis could see two trails of moisture running down his cheeks.

"Here, here now." Dennis was flustered. He had never seen his friend so openly displaying emotion.

"I'm all right, really." Harry straightened up, dashed at his eyes with his sleeve as Kate approached. He cleared his throat awkwardly. "Silly of me. Shouldn't have lost my temper like that. Damned idiot Beresford. He'll discover soon enough, when that tiger gets hungry again. . . ."

He quietened as Kate took his hand and squeezed it gently. "I feel I should apologize about Melissa," she told him.

Harry forced a smile. "Children are different these days," he said. "So strong-willed. I'm sure when she's had a chance to think about it, she'll see that I was right."

"She's not a child any more, Harry. She may act like one, but she's not."

He sighed. "Well, I could use a drink!" He was trying to sound hearty, but it was unconvincing. "What say we head back to my house for a cold beer?"

"Yes, why not?" replied Dennis. The three of them got into the car and lapsed into a sombre silence. It was a long and uncomfortable drive to their destination.

THE SMALL CAVE was cool and comforting, a welcome relief from the heat of the day. Haji had come here with the intention of having a nap, but the incidents of the previous night still troubled him, as a succession of vague images. He had lain in the bushes while the storm exploded, hungry but as yet too nervous to go out and reclaim his kill. Then, from the bushes on the other side of the clearing his arch-enemy had emerged, moving towards the dead Upright with the bold, aggressive stride of the victor. The youngster had seen Haji lying in the grass, and he was going to brazenly snatch the old tiger's food from under his nose. But then there had been the roar of the black stick, and the young tiger had whirled up beneath the rain to die in the long grass. Terrified, Haji had slunk into the deepest cover of the bushes, and he had watched an Upright descend from the tree and perform some kind of gleeful dance around his victim. Later more Uprights had arrived, and,

411

cutting down some stout logs, they had bound the dead tiger between them and carried the body into the village.

Haji had stayed put for another hour before cautiously emerging and making his way over to his kill. And strangest mystery of all, the kill was no longer the kill, just a tasteless piece of Upright's clothing filled with dead jungle. The long wait had all been for nothing. Slinking dejectedly away, Haji had come face to face with a young tapir who had got separated from his parents in the confusion of the storm. The calf had provided enough meat for a sumptuous repast, after which Haji sought out one of his favourite resting places. The Upright had unwittingly been of great help to him: with the youngster eliminated, the range was returned to its original owner. And the usurper's brief rule had taught Haji how easy it was to turn his attention to the new game that would feed him through his declining years. Though in many ways he still feared the Uprights, he had tasted of them now, and would not hesitate to take another.

In the coolness of the cave, Haji stretched out and let his head rest on his paws, while out in the jungle the afternoon sun burned down with relentless ferocity.

8

It was late afternoon and the shadows were lengthening rapidly as Bob Beresford's Land-Rover sped along the coast road. Sitting in the passenger seat, her long hair streaming back in the wind, Melissa clung grimly to the dashboard and tried to think of something interesting to say. She glanced across at Bob, who was hunched over the wheel, and wondered if he always drove like a maniac or if he was trying to impress her. She glimpsed a glitter of metal beneath the open collar of his khaki shirt, and for an instant she could see the bullet-shaped locket that Victoria Plumly had mentioned. This provided a chance to strike up a conversation.

"What an interesting necklace!" She leaned forward to look.

"Yeah. My old man wore it when he was out huntin'. Sort of a good-luck charm."

He swerved round a tight bend and noticed the alarm on Melissa's face. He dropped to a more reasonable speed. "Sorry. I'm just a bit anxious to get back to the tiger. That feller I left to guard it, I don't really know him. I guess I won't relax until the brute's skinned and hung on my wall."

"You've done very well," she reassured him. "I'm just sorry about that fuss with Uncle Harry." She sighed. "The sad thing is, he's old now and can't do the things he used to. It's not really surprising that he's so crotchety."

Bob nodded. "It's sad, but there's nothing you can do. Mind you, I keep wondering about what he said. Supposing the man-eater isn't dead? Maybe I ought to spread the word for everyone to take care, just in case."

"The whole thing was done to discredit you," retorted Melissa firmly, "that's all."

He gazed at her for a moment. "You really think so?"

She smiled, nodded. "I'm sure of it."

Bob reached out a hand impulsively to stroke her arm. She was startled but made no attempt to pull away from his hand. She felt excited and oddly flattered by the gesture.

"How old are you, Melissa?" he asked unexpectedly.

"Eighteen."

He smiled wickedly. "You're quite legal then," he observed. She felt her face colour dramatically. "It's the best age," continued Bob. "So, er, this is where you live," he muttered. He glanced mechanically about as though inspecting the place. "This is your place on the left here, isn't it?"

"What? Oh, yes." She had momentarily forgotten where she was. "My house is over there." But he was already easing the Land-Rover to a halt on the outskirts of the estate. The light was fading rapidly, and there was nobody about. Bob glanced at her meaning-fully, then switched the ignition off. The two of them sat for a few moments, abruptly awkward in the silence, and Melissa felt a mingling of anticipation and fear flooding through her. All the confident scenes of her fantasies evaporated like steam, and she was left tongue-tied. Finally she glanced at her watch. "Well I . . . I suppose I ought to be . . ."

She broke off in surprise as he edged suddenly and decisively against her. His arms came round her in a powerful embrace, and his mouth was against hers. She resisted for only an instant, a token display of indignation; then she relaxed and returned his kisses. The experience was new to her and oddly exciting. But somehow the cramped Land-Rover was not as she had imagined the scene.

His kisses became more hungry, but she was nervous at being so near the estate, and she pushed him away, glancing quickly around.

"What's the matter?" he asked.

"Another time," she whispered breathlessly. "I'll meet you somewhere else. Somewhere where we can be alone. . . ." She stroked his face reassuringly. "Somebody might see us here."

He frowned, nodded. "When then?" There was a trace of irritation in his voice, and she feared that she might have offended him.

"Tomorrow. I'll go to the Chinese Swimming Club with some friends. Can you meet me there?"

"I work in the morning, but I could get there by two o'clock."

"That would be fine. You could offer me a lift home and we'll go off by ourselves. . . ." She hesitated, embarrassed by her own boldness. "That is, if you want to."

"Of course I do!" His eyes promised excitement, but there was a familiarity in them that worried her. "We'll have a great time."

She smiled. "Tomorrow," she assured him, and she got out of the Land-Rover. "You . . . will be there, won't you?"

"Try and stop me!" He roared the engine and accelerated away without glancing back.

Melissa gave a slow smile of satisfaction. Well, that hadn't been so difficult! She turned and strolled in the direction of her parents' house, humming serenely to herself.

As soon as Bob arrived back at Kampong Machis, he knew that something was wrong. In the glare of the headlights, he could see that the open area in the centre of the kampong was now deserted. The oil lamps that had been left beside the tiger were not in use, and there was no sign of the man that Bob had paid to guard his property. He brought the Land-Rover to an abrupt halt and hurried out, suspecting for a moment that the tiger had been stolen. But he breathed a sigh of relief when he perceived the dim shape of its carcass stretched out on the grass. Cursing the uselessness of a guard who had wandered off, he took a box of matches from his shirt pocket, and squatting down he lit one of the lanterns. He still had to find somebody to do the skinning, and decide whether he wanted a head trophy, a rug, or a fully stuffed and mounted animal.

He moved to the carcass and held the lantern above it. The smile of triumph on his face turned to horrified amazement. He stood for several long moments, looking angrily at the tiger.

414

The carcass had been nearly destroyed. Bob had not realized the attraction that tiger charms and talismans held for the villagers. During his absence, no doubt with the cooperation of the guard, there had been a massive free-for-all of souvenir taking. They had wrenched out the teeth, had pulled out the creature's claws. Either of these items, worn as an amulet, would protect a superstitious villager whenever he ventured into the jungle. The whiskers had been snipped off, and these would find their way into the potions and balms of herbalists. Even the ground-up bones of its skeleton were sought after for their supposed healing qualities: a wine made from the substance could cure rheumatic ailments. And because the ashes of burnt tiger hair were also a highly prized ingredient in magic charms, large patches of the tiger's hide had been hacked away. The tiger would be of no use whatsoever to a taxidermist.

Bob gave a low moan and sank to his knees. A deep, cold rage settled in his heart. He turned and stared up at the dwellings around him, where he could perceive faces peering fearfully from the windows. Emotion welled up in his chest, and he threw back his head and screamed.

"Thieves!" He felt cheated, betrayed. The cat was his. Now the villagers had robbed him of his triumph. He strode towards the nearest building. "Come out of there," he shrieked. "Come out and see what you've done! The tiger was *mine!*" He aimed a kick at one of the thick supporting poles on which the building stood, and the rickety construction shuddered. Shouts of alarm sounded from within. Raging, Bob moved to the next building and directed a few well-chosen curses in that direction, but the natives chose to stay inside their homes.

"Gutless cowards!" screamed Bob. "I should have let the tiger go on killing you all!" A wild impulse took him, and he ran to the Land-Rover, snatched out his rifle. Ramming a cartridge into the chamber, he sighted up on the first object that caught his attention, a goatskin gourd full of water that was hanging from the side of a house. He squeezed the trigger and the gourd convulsed, its contents streaming through the rent in its side.

Suddenly, the windows were crammed with staring faces. Bob laughed almost hysterically, pumped the rifle bolt, and took aim at a clay chimneypot on the roof nearest to him. It shattered and came down in a shower of broken bits. Lights were going on all through the village, and shouting people were running out of doorways.

"Stop this!" The command came from behind him with unexpected force. Bob whipped round. It was the *penghulu* from Kampong Panjang. The little man stood with his arms spread and his eyes fixed unwaveringly on the rifle pointing at his chest.

"The tuan is angry?" he asked.

Bob slowly lowered the rifle. "Yes, I'm angry," he snarled. "What are you doing here?"

"I come today to see dead *si-pudong*. I stay with my cousin." The *penghulu* gestured vaguely at the buildings behind him. "But tuan, why do you do this wickedness?"

Bob grasped the *penghulu* roughly by his skinny elbow and marched him over to the mutilated carcass. "Look at that! You see what they've done to my tiger?"

"*Yours*, tuan? Forgive me, but surely this was a creature of the jungle. Who can say that it belonged to anyone?"

"Don't give me that! A tiger belongs to the bloke who went out and got him. I risked my neck for the village, and this is how they repay me. I mean, where's the fairness in that?"

The *penghulu* shook his head. "The tuan must remember," he said, "to these people, *si-pudong* is a great and magical beast. To own a part of him is everyone's wish."

"Well then, why don't they go and shoot one themselves?"

The *penghulu* gave a little laugh. "To say such a thing, you do not know Malays well," he observed. "A Malay has a special outlook on life, tuan. Things are done only when they must be. A man's roof leaks, water falls on him. Then, he fixes roof, not before. You understand?"

"Yeah, it means he's bone idle!"

The *penghulu* shook his head. "You say this because you think like a white man, and the white man must be always doing something. For a Malay to hunt *si-pudong*, he needs a strong reason. Like revenge—tiger eat his wife or children—or he has to have money." The *penghulu* spread his arms in inquiry. "What would you have done with the beast, tuan? Stuffed him and stood him in your fine house? Made a rug of him? You have no beliefs about him, for you are not of his land. You do not share the same trials as he, you do not drink of the same water. Surely, if *si-pudong* belongs to anyone, he belongs to us."

The *penghulu*'s words shamed Bob, but he did not want to admit it. "It's easy for you to talk," he blustered. "You didn't sit up that

416

tree in the rainstorm! Anyway, I'm not going to leave the rest of the carcass here."

He strode to the Land-Rover, threw his rifle in the back, and returned to the tiger. Going down on one knee, he attempted to drag the beast along, but he could not even budge it. "Give me a hand," he grunted to the *penghulu*. "At least I should get a few quid for it in Kuala Trengganu. They say the bones bring a good price." The two men heaved at the tiger for a few minutes, but it had taken four strong men to carry it out of the jungle and it was apparent that they would never lift it.

"Call some of your pals out of their houses," gasped Bob.

The *penghulu* shook his head. "Alas, tuan, I fear they will be too frightened by your shooting! They will not come."

Bob's face reddened with anger. He took a long look around him at the grim faces watching from the doorways, and then he gave a shout of exasperation. He went back to the Land-Rover, got into the seat. The *penghulu* ran after him.

"The tuan is leaving?" he inquired politely.

"Too right I am! You can keep the blasted tiger and good riddance to it! I'm going home to get some sleep." A glint of moonlight caught something lying on the passenger seat. Bob picked it up and examined it carefully. It was a silver lipstick case. In his rage, Bob found a target on which to focus. If it hadn't been for driving her home, he would never have left the tiger.

Cursing, he flung the lipstick away and accelerated out of the kampong, leaving the *penghulu* staring after him. The little man reached thoughtfully beneath his white shirt, where the tiger's claw hung in a tiny leather pouch. He had felt quite confident about coming down to confront the white man, and sure enough, the power in the claw had saved him from being shot. He glanced at the carcass and grinned. On impulse, he walked over to the tiger and placed one foot on it, mimicking the traditional pose of the victorious white hunter. He received a burst of applause from the watching villagers, who appreciated that he'd scored a sizable victory over the aggressive Australian.

HAJI AWOKE to a familiar sound: the distant mournful cry of Timah, who was still seeking a mate. Her roars suggested that the young male, for all his strength, had been unable to mate with her because of his lack of experience. Haji felt much stronger now, and he did not hesitate to leave the cool sanctuary of the cave and go in search of Timah, responding to her call with his own, deeper roar.

He found her pacing restlessly up and down beside a wide jungle stream. She displayed no surprise when Haji emerged from the undergrowth, but moved forward to greet him, rubbing her flank against his and pausing to give a slow, sensuous stretch. He nuzzled at her neck with his mouth and she flopped down in the grass for a moment, purring luxuriously as he lapped at her ear. She rose to her feet, prowled a short distance, then went down again. Haji followed silently.

The union was brief, twenty seconds at most, with Timah emitting a series of low guttural cries as Haji gripped the fold of skin around her neck tightly in his jaws. The first consummation completed, Timah felt abruptly insecure, and she whipped around and launched a boisterous attack on Haji, boxing at his head with her heavy forepaws. He fell back, blocking the most severe of her swings but not attempting to counter the attack. After a few moments Timah seemed to lose strength and she flopped down, rolling onto her back. Haji sat quietly a few feet away, watching her intently. The only movement was the occasional twitch of her tail. Five minutes passed, and it was deadly silent in the jungle. Now Timah's head lifted a little, and Haji crept forward to nuzzle at her face again. Growling softly, she got to her feet and walked a short distance, and the entire process was repeated, right down to the brief quarrel afterwards. Indeed, it was repeated all through the day and the following night. During this time Haji and Timah had no thought of food, and only during the late hours, after they had mated some forty or fifty times, did they allow themselves a brief nap. While Timah's oestrus lasted, the pair would stay constantly together, and when it was at an end they would separate and return to their usual patterns. If the union was successful, Timah would have the task of raising the resulting litter for up to two years. In that time, save for chance encounters, she would not expect to have Haji's companionship again. Such was the simple and solitary life that nature had evolved for the tiger.

MELISSA WAS FUMING. She stalked along the coast road, her hands in the pockets of her shorts, painfully aware that she had made a complete fool of herself. Bob Beresford had not turned up at the swimming pool that afternoon. That much would have been bad

418

enough, but she had invited Victoria Plumly and Alison Weathers along to witness her triumph. At first she had been quietly confident, but as the afternoon wore slowly on and there was no sign of Bob, she had begun to feel quite wretched. Of course, Victoria had lost no opportunity to feign wide-eyed innocence as she said, "Perhaps his jeep broke down," or, "Are you sure it was today?" At last Melissa could stand it no more and left.

Now, walking home, she began to examine the possibilities. Had she come on too strong with him? She'd always been led to believe that men liked girls who showed a little initiative. Or perhaps he really had got into an unavoidable situation at work. Maybe he would get in touch with her soon. . . .

The sound of a car engine interrupted her thoughts and she turned, half expecting to see a battered Land-Rover pursuing her. But it was her father's car, returning from the barracks. He was smiling and opening the passenger door for her. She walked to the car and clambered in, slamming the door.

"What have you been up to today?" inquired Dennis.

"Swimming pool."

He raised his eyebrows. "Did you forget your towel then?"

"I didn't go there to *swim*."

"Ah. That would explain it." He started up the car again. "Go by yourself?" he asked.

"With Victoria and Alison."

"I thought you didn't like them."

"I don't. They're disgusting."

"Ah. Yes . . ." Dennis noted that his daughter was in a singularly strange mood, but he had learned from experience that it was pointless to pursue any of her more puzzling remarks.

"Did you see Bob Beresford at all today?" asked Melissa.

"No. But I did hear something interesting about him."

Melissa sat up and took notice. "Oh? What was that?"

"Well, it seems he had a bit of a nasty trick played on him. He left somebody to guard the tiger while he went away for a bit, and the villagers chopped the tiger up. Apparently it was good for nothing by the time Beresford got back to it. A shame, really."

Melissa turned to gaze blankly at the straight strip of road ahead. "Oh no," she whispered. "It must have happened while he was driving me home."

"Uh, yes, I suppose it must."

"Well, don't you see? He'll blame me for it!" She groaned. "He won't even want to know me now."

"Now, Melissa, I think you're being dramatic about this," reasoned Dennis. "It's hardly your fault, after all."

"The point is, if he hadn't had to drive me home, the villagers wouldn't have had the chance to get at it. It stands to reason, that's why he didn't turn up at the swimming pool today!"

"Oh, I see." Dennis did not have much experience of discussing this kind of thing with his daughter, and he felt distinctly uncomfortable. He gave what he thought was a reassuring smile. "He'll get over it," he murmured lamely.

Melissa looked far from convinced. "How long will that take? There's not much time left." She gazed silently out of the window.

What peculiar little plot is she hatching now? thought Dennis uneasily. It occurred to him, not for the first time, that he really knew very little about his daughter.

The route took them past some roadside fruit stalls at the side of a small kampong. A herdsman was driving a flock of goats across the road, and Dennis eased the car to a halt. Instantly the appalling stench of *durians* came flooding in through the open window. Despite his years in Malaya, Dennis had never managed to get used to that malodorous fruit. Furthermore, the goat herder, a bony old man in a grubby sarong, was evidently in no hurry to get his flock across. A couple of young boys from a fruit stall ran up and thrust some *durians* in through the car window, noisily inciting the tuan to buy them. The boys were laughing uproariously, well aware of the revulsion that the fruit generally instilled in white people. Dennis was obliged to hand them some coins simply to get them to take the wretched things away. But the smell was now well and truly in the car, and even Melissa was inconvenienced enough to stop whatever it was she was plotting and place a hand over her nose.

IT WAS MESS NIGHT, but Harry could not raise the enthusiasm to go. He sat alone in his sitting room, just one small reading lamp lit behind him. He had told Pawn to leave, that he would not be going out, and with great reluctance she had agreed. She had realized that something must be very wrong, for the tuan's visits to the mess were as much a part of his routine as his tea out on the veranda.

"I'm just tired," he had said. "I need to rest."

Harry knew that what he really felt was an acute sense of betrayal. Quite unexpectedly the two people he loved most in the world had turned against him. Not only that, both of them had gravitated towards a man who, according to Harry, had no moral code whatsoever.

Harry sighed, gazing about the room. What a grim, cheerless place it was: the heavy teak furniture looked oppressive and only emphasized the emptiness of the room. There had been paintings and some wood carvings once, but these had been due to Meg's influence and he got rid of them after her death, for they served as constant reminders of her.

Dead, thought Harry sadly. Even the room is dead. For the first time in his life he felt near to resigning himself to a similar fate. There seemed little to go on for. The community here was falling apart. In a short while Melissa would be gone, and it grieved him to think she might leave before their quarrel could be repaired. As for Ché—well, he was at an impressionable age. It was possible that he would simply forget about the old man who had once meant so much to him. Then what would be left for Harry? Would he go on haunting the mess until the last stragglers had moved away to their British homes?

A feeling of coldness settled over his mind. He stood up slowly and went over to the ornately carved writing desk against the far wall. He pulled out the single drawer and extracted a heavy .38 revolver that had not been fired in many years. Reaching further into the drawer, he located a box of ammunition. He put the two items down on the desk, gazing at the weapon thoughtfully.

The doorbell rang. Harry glanced up in surprise. The only person who might call on mess night was the old Chinese trishaw driver, but Harry had not seen the fellow since his illness. Harry stood where he was for several moments, trying to decide what to do. Then he picked up the revolver.

The doorbell rang again, shrill, insistent. With a curse Harry slammed the gun down on the desk. He strode towards the door, unlatched it, and peered out into the night. All he could see was the silhouette of a small boy, and his first impulse was one of joy, for he thought this was Ché. He swung the door open and the boy stepped into the light, but it was a Chinese youth he had never seen before.

"Yes?" Harry inquired, puzzled.

The boy was clad in just a pair of khaki shorts and worn flip-flops. He was older than Ché, perhaps fourteen or fifteen, and he had that wide-eyed, undernourished look that many of the kampong children possessed. When he spoke, it was haltingly. "I come take tuan sol'ymess."

Harry gazed at the boy for a moment. "What?" he asked simply.

The boy smiled self-consciously. He repeated the phrase, then pointed up the path into the darkness. "Trishaw," he added.

"Ah. I see. Where's the other fellow?"

The boy's large brown eyes glanced regretfully at his feet. "My grandfather, tuan," he said glumly. "He dead two days now."

To Harry, the news was like a blow. He had to lean against the door frame for support. "Oh," he murmured. "Oh, I'm sorry." So they were all leaving him, one by one. Even the ones who really belonged here.

"Grandfather leave trishaw to me," explained the boy. "He also leave . . ." He struggled for a word he did not know, then brightened and pulled a piece of paper from his pocket and handed it to Harry. It had been scrawled on in pencil, but the characters were Mandarin Chinese. Harry could only shrug helplessly.

"Is *times*, tuan. Times you allus go sol'ymess. Grandfather make me promise to come for you those nights. Also, not take money till pay back what you give him. You unnerstan'?"

Harry nodded, sighed. "I understand. But I won't be going tonight, son. Too tired. Here, let me . . ."

He fished in his pocket for change, but the boy shook his head adamantly. "I not take money, tuan! Is promise I make." He gazed at Harry imploringly. "Why you not go, tuan? You think I not look after you? Don't worry, I small but strong!" He indicated his skinny little legs. "Go many mile awready. . . ."

"Yes. Yes, of course, it's not that I don't trust you."

"If you not go, how I pay back what Grandfather owe? I allus come for you. You see!"

Harry was suddenly struck by the boy's determination to fill his grandfather's shoes, to do a man's job. Harry felt ashamed, realizing how easily he himself had given up. He thought of the old Chinese driver who had not even let death prevent him from repaying a debt of honour. He could learn much from people like these.

"I'll get my coat," he said, and he strolled back inside, pausing only to replace the revolver in the drawer.

422

Minutes later the trishaw was whizzing smoothly along the coast road. The night was humid and rich with the scent of wild orchids. As they turned a bend, Harry could see the ocean far below, half masked by thick foliage. The sea air wafting over the treetops was a cooling respite before they plunged back between flanks of screening jungle, but the vision of glittering moonlight on restless waves stayed with Harry as they journeyed on.

Once again, he was at peace with the world.

Haji moved slowly through the screen of bushes that flanked the jungle road. He never took his eyes off the old Upright woman for a single moment. She seemed totally unaware that she was being followed and that she had had several lucky escapes. Every time Haji tensed himself for the short dash, something happened to disrupt the plan: a cart passed along, or a group of Uprights would call noisy greetings to her from the roadside. Now, the woman was dangerously close to Kampong Panjang.

It was getting increasingly difficult to secure an Upright. His presence was now so feared that people did not wander about after dark, and Haji had been forced to operate in broad daylight. He still hunted his usual prey whenever the chance arose, but his right foreleg was now almost completely useless, and it slowed him down terribly.

Haji was having to keep his wits about him. It seemed impossible to return to a kill without finding it disturbed in some way, and with an Upright lying in wait for him with the inevitable black stick. He had been shot at on two occasions, the roaring fire coming dangerously close, and he rarely returned to a kill any more without first patrolling the whole area and assuring himself that the coast was clear. Usually it was not. Most suspicious of all were the live cattle that Haji sometimes encountered, tethered in the very midst of the jungle. They made no attempt to run when they saw Haji, they simply tugged ineffectually at the ropes that held them and bawled pitifully. There was something so wrong about this that Haji steered clear of the creatures, even when he was very hungry. He had once encountered Timah, who was now heavy with cubs to be born in a few weeks' time, and saw that she was stalking one

423

of these strange cattle. Haji had intimated his fear to her, and she too had abandoned the scheme.

Haji kept his gaze on the old Upright woman. Now she was turning in at a short lane to the houses of the village, no more than twenty yards away. Haji cut through the intervening cover at a steady trot, hoping to surprise the Upright in the lane, but when he reached it, she was emerging into the area beyond and was passing into the shadow of the first house. The kampong seemed quiet in the heat of the day, but Haji was loth to follow her in there; then he noticed that she had come to a halt beside the second house, near the edge of the village. Haji came round the far side of the house she had passed, instinctively keeping to the shadow. Then he crept cautiously round the corner of it. The old Upright had begun to climb the ladder to an open door. She was calling out to someone within.

Inside, the woman's daughter was sitting cross-legged on the floor, attending to some sewing. She lifted her head at the sound of her mother's voice and was slightly puzzled by an abrupt bump that followed it. She stood up and strolled to the doorway with a smile on her face. The smile faded when she saw nobody there. The woman thought she saw a brief flutter of fabric behind the house and leaned forward a little, calling her mother's name. But outside all was silent save for the distant song of a bird. She began to think that she must have imagined her mother's arrival and was about to turn back. But she noticed something on the ladder below her, something wedged between the slats of wood. The woman recognized one of a pair of elaborate embroidered slippers that she had given to her mother some years before. It dawned on her slowly, horribly, that her mother's foot was still inside it, torn raggedly away at the ankle.

The woman screamed until she fainted.

BOB BERESFORD sat in the bare cheerlessness of his sitting room, cleaning his rifle with an oily rag and taking swigs from a can of Tiger beer. The last two and a half months had been a frustrating time. He had redoubled his efforts to catch the man-eating tiger, but the beast was very lucky, very cunning, or both. The closest Bob had got were a couple of fleeting glimpses as the tiger took off into cover.

The greatest blow to Bob's pride had been the realization

that Harry Sullivan was right about the mistaken shooting of the first tiger. As time went on and more lives were claimed, the Malayan Game Department had dispatched one of their own men to take care of the man-eater. His name was Mike Kirby, and he was an affable enough fellow. There was little competition between him and Bob. The fact that Bob lived locally and had already organized a good "jungle telegraph" for himself meant that the Australian tended to be onto the scene of a kill first, whereas Kirby seemed content to work from staked-out baits. He had a good knowledge of tigers, but he surprised Bob by explaining that in his estimation there was nobody who knew more about them than old Harry Sullivan. Bob had simply gritted his teeth and said nothing. And now the hunt had developed into a race against time: in a few weeks Bob's assignment here would come to an end. He had sworn to himself that he would not quit Malaya without taking the beast's head with him.

Lim now bustled into the room from the kitchen. "Food ready soon," she announced brightly. She came across to the table where Bob was working and began to tidy up his gun-cleaning apparatus.

"Leave that be!" he snapped, and she moved away as though he had slapped her, her pretty face collapsed into misery. She attempted to hide the fact that she was crying by turning her back.

"What's the matter now?" he shouted. For the last few days Lim had been acting strangely, crying at the least little thing, and Bob was beginning to lose patience with her. She ran back into the kitchen, slamming the door, and after a few moments he could hear her frenzied sobbing. He sighed. He was aware that his inability to bag the tiger was making him irritable, but he did think she was overdoing it. But then, he reflected, Lim was aware that soon the tuan would be heading home and that she had absolutely no chance of going with him.

He felt suddenly ashamed of his snappiness. He went to the kitchen door and peered in. Lim was standing by the sink, directing her sorrows into a large white handkerchief.

"Hey, Lim, I'm sorry." He slipped an arm protectively round her, a rare gesture of affection on his part. She hugged him gratefully, putting her head on his chest, and he stroked her dark hair. "Now, what's it all about, eh?" he asked her gruffly.

She sniffed softly. "I . . . I just wish you could kill that tiger, tuan. Then perhaps you not be so angry."

"I'm angry with myself, that's all," he assured her. "You wait and see, I'll get him before long. Anyway, how come you aren't afraid to say tiger? Most people up at the kampong wouldn't say it for a hundred dollars."

"I am not like them, Bob tuan. I think like Western woman. I know better." She dabbed her eyes with the handkerchief, then glanced at him slyly. "Soon Bob tuan go home, yes?"

"Er, yeah." Bob turned away from her. "I haven't heard anything definite about that yet, Lim." He changed the subject quickly. "Hey, how about a nice cup of coffee? I could use that! And look, no more tears now, OK?" He tousled her hair and went back into the sitting room, closing the door after him. He realized that perhaps he should have thought twice before getting involved with the girl, but it was far too late.

"Tuan!" A distant but familiar voice roused him from his thoughts. He stood up and hurried to the veranda. A battered-looking bicycle was clattering towards him, and seated on the perilous vehicle was the *penghulu* from Kampong Panjang. His little face was shining with sweat, and he shouted, "Another one, tuan! Kampong Panjang again!"

By now this had become a well-drilled operation. While the *penghulu* loaded his bicycle into the back of the Land-Rover, Bob rushed into the house to grab the bits of equipment that were not stored permanently in his vehicle. A few moments later he dashed to the Land-Rover and scrambled into the driver's seat. "How long ago?" he asked as the *penghulu* climbed in.

"Maybe half hour at most. I come soon as I hear."

"Good. Let's go!" Bob started the engine and the Land-Rover accelerated away.

The house was silent again, except for the clinking of crockery in the kitchen. Lim was feeling better now, and she hummed as she poured two large cups of coffee. Placing them carefully on a small tray, she went to the sitting-room door and opened it.

"Coffee ready, Bob," she called out. She stood in the doorway a moment, gazing round. She noticed that his rifle was no longer on the table. She set down the tray and walked slowly to the open door, her hands hanging limply by her side, her face impassive. The Land-Rover was gone, and the streets beyond the gate were empty.

Lim went back into the empty sitting room, sat down at Bob's worktable, and began to drink her coffee, sipping at it mechanically. Time was running out, and there was something she had to tell the tuan before he left her for ever. And meanwhile, that tiger was ruining the last few weeks that she might ever share with him.

If all the tigers in Malaya were to vanish overnight, it would make her dance with joy. Perhaps then the tuan could stay in one place long enough for Lim to tell him all the things she felt in her heart. With a sigh, she set her cup down on the tray, picked it up, and went back into the kitchen.

MELISSA ROLLED SLOWLY onto her back to allow the sun to scorch the front of her swimsuited body. With just a few weeks left before her return to England, she was doing what everybody else was occupied with: deepening a tan to make those back home suitably envious. For her too the last couple of months had been frustrating, to say the least. She had encountered Bob Beresford on only three occasions, all of them by chance. He had been polite, and quite indifferent to her charms. It was painfully clear to Melissa that Bob attributed the loss of his tigerskin to her. Now she was faced with the prospect of eating humble pie and presenting Victoria with her twenty dollars. The mere thought of it made her blood boil.

Melissa sighed. She stared up at the vast expanse of lapis-blue sky; a couple of fishing eagles were performing lazy gliding patterns at an incredible height, and she watched intently for some time. The day was absolutely still, with not a breath of wind. The ball of flame suspended in the sky above Melissa seemed to sap every ounce of energy from her body and it was an effort simply to turn her head.

If only he'd shoot that wretched tiger, she found herself thinking. Then maybe he'd be approachable. She understood that men are easier to get when they're feeling good.

THE MOOD IN THE KAMPONG had changed considerably. As they strolled past the first few houses Bob was aware of the heavy, all-pervading atmosphere of terror. This was the third killing in Kampong Panjang in as many months, and neighbouring villages had suffered too. People saw the gun-wielding Australian as their only hope of salvation.

"It is very bad, tuan," murmured the *penghulu* as he led Bob towards the scene of the killing. "Everyone is afraid."

428

"Did anybody see anything this time?" Bob asked.

"The woman's daughter saw a flutter of cloth. She heard her mother call, and when she went to the door, her mother was gone. So quick, tuan! He is no ordinary beast. He is a werecat. Perhaps the old *bomoh* who lives by Kampong Machis. Why, only last week two villagers came across him in the jungle; he was on all fours and growling, having just changed back from his animal state."

"It's not a monster we're looking for!" snapped Bob. "Just a plain, four-legged tiger. Have you found which way it went?"

"Alas, tuan, the ground here is very hard. Hardly a mark shows! There is another thing. What ordinary cat would come into a kampong this way?"

"I didn't say he was ordinary. Oh, he's smart, never doubt it. But forget all this nonsense about weretigers and *bomohs*. When I finally get a shot at him, he'll fall like all the rest." Bob turned abruptly. "Wasted enough time already. I'd better try to find some pugs. Maybe if you look over there."

"Oh, I am sorry, tuan, I must go now. My wife, she is afraid to be alone. She gets very cross if I leave her. Farewell, tuan, and good luck." He wandered away, and the Australian gazed after him contemptuously. As the number of killings steadily rose, so did the Malays' desire not to get involved in something that might take them nearer to the tiger's jaws.

Bob paused to gaze around at the area into which the cat had ventured. In front of the victim's house was a large, open space. For the tiger to have crossed an area where there was not the slightest bit of cover suggested that he was becoming either reckless or hungry to the point of near-madness. He must have taken the corpse across the road into deep jungle, but to find the point of entry would not prove easy. Bob stooped to examine the ground. Any disturbance of its surface had long disappeared, and he found nothing but a tiny patch of dried blood.

Shouldering his rifle, he moved forward to the corner of the building that flanked the jungle. Gazing round it, he was surprised to see a young Malay boy crouching on the ground, examining something. "Hello, what have you got there?" Bob asked.

The boy glanced up. He was perhaps twelve or thirteen, a lively-looking boy with large dark eyes and a thick mop of straight black hair. He was wearing khaki shorts and some worn flip-flops. He pointed solemnly at the ground and said, "Tiger pass this way."

429

Bob smiled at the certainty with which the boy said this, and he moved nearer. All he could see was a stretch of seemingly unmarked earth. "I don't see anything," he murmured.

"The stone, tuan!" The boy picked up a tiny pebble and held it out. "It has been moved. This side clean and smooth where rain and wind polish it. But it was lying the other way up." He displayed the other surface, which was coated with dry earth.

Bob frowned, rubbed his chin. "Well, maybe." Then he moved away, dismissing the boy from his mind, and began to cast left and right, but again the ground seemed devoid of clues. He was unaware that the boy was following close on his heels until the child gave a small cry of triumph and, rushing forward, snatched up a tiny brown fragment caught on a sharp rock. Similar in colour to its background, it had evaded Bob's eyes completely.

The boy handed his prize to Bob proudly. "From woman's slipper," he announced.

He turned away and continued ahead, bent low, his gaze fixed steadfastly downwards.

Bob examined the fragment. It did look like a sliver of soft leather. He gazed after the boy with a little more respect.

"Tuan, see! A scratch mark in the dirt. This is where tiger stopped to change his hold."

"Really?" Bob hurried over. Sure enough, there was blood and a faint, almost imperceptible mark. "What's your name?" he asked the boy. "And where have you been all my life?"

The boy grinned. "My name is Ché. I live here in Kampong Panjang! One day, hope to be best tracker in Malaya!"

"You're not doing too badly so far." Bob was delighted. He mopped his clammy forehead. "Well, look, uh, Ché, is it? How about showing me what else you can do?"

The boy's grin widened joyfully. "OK, boss!" He began to run ahead in a semi-crouch, stopping every now and then to inspect some new evidence. Bob followed, and it quickly became apparent that the boy knew exactly what he was doing. He kept pausing for Bob to approach and then he would explain some detail before bounding away again. Here, tuan, was where sarong fabric had snagged on a bush! Here was where the tiger's injured paw dragged crossways in the dirt! Here the woman's heel had carved a shallow furrow! Bob was vividly reminded of the time Harry Sullivan had tracked the pugs beneath the *machan*; there was the same wealth of information, the same quick, confident assessment of what had happened.

The trail continued for several hundred yards parallel to the secondary jungle, then plunged abruptly into it. The boy bounded in without hesitation, Bob struggling along behind him. The drag marks were easy to follow, but it got more difficult when the trail veered left and followed a narrow dirt lane for some distance. At last Bob and Ché emerged onto the main road, and Ché pointed out a few scattered bits of twig and grass.

"Tiger cross here." Ché made as if to bound across the road, but Bob grabbed his arm.

"Let me get my breath back," he gasped. "Where did you learn to track like that?"

Ché shrugged. "My friend Majid and I, we decided we would become great trackers! He soon got fed up, but I . . ." The boy tapped his chest proudly. "I practised every day. I went into the jungle and followed every track I found. And I read every page of the tuan's books."

"The tuan?" echoed Bob suspiciously.

"Yes, Tuan Sullivan. He gave me the books a long time ago, but before I only looked at the pictures. This time I read every word."

Bob snapped his fingers. So the old man was involved! "Well, well. You know Harry Sullivan, do you?"

"Oh yes, everybody knows him; just as everybody knows you and how you shot one great tiger and how you are hunting the demon that hunts the people of the kampongs."

"Hmm. Aren't you afraid of the tiger, Ché? Most people round here won't even say the word."

Ché sighed. "Alas, it is too late for me, tuan. When I thought that you had shot the man-eater, I began to take his name in vain. His curse is already on me; but I do not fear, for soon you will kill him and then I shall be safe from his jaws. Besides . . ." He pulled something from his pocket, a small object wrapped in leather. He untied the bundle and held out a tiger's claw. "My grandmother bought me this, from a man in Kampong Machis. It was very expensive, and it keeps me safe when I go into the jungle."

Bob nodded slowly. And I bet I know where that came from, he thought drily. A vivid image of the tiger's lacerated body, stark in the lantern light, came briefly back to him. But the boy probably knew nothing about the theft. He felt a sudden flash of guilt when

431

he realized that he had been quite unreasonable in transferring his resentment to Melissa Tremayne. She too was innocent of blame, yet he had let his anger linger on for several months. He remembered her kisses in the Land-Rover. . . . But he had to force his mind back to more immediate problems.

"Well, let's move on," he suggested.

Ché was across the road like a greyhound let off the leash. Bob followed at a more cautious pace, unslinging his rifle in case of trouble. "Don't get too far ahead," he warned.

They moved into thicker jungle. The drag marks became evident, a wide trail of flattened leaves and disturbed grass over rough terrain. The trail led onwards for about half a mile, and at last they came to a broad stream where they found the corpse of the woman lying. It was not covered with foliage in any way.

"He must have heard us coming," whispered Bob, gazing round. "I'll bet he's not far away."

He reached out an arm protectively to draw the boy back from the dismembered body. Then he turned to take a long, slow look at his surroundings. It was terribly quiet, not the sound of a single bird broke the silence. And there were any number of places where the cat might be lying up. That long stretch of grass there. Behind that vine-covered fallen tree. The thick bamboo over to the right. Bob sighed. His desperation had not reached the point where he was prepared to go after the tiger on foot.

"All right, Ché, let's go back for the *machan*. We . . ."

Bob broke off in alarm as there was an abrupt rustle to his left. He swung the gun round to bear on the movement, which was progressing quickly towards him.

A large magpie flapped into the open, then took off at a steep angle with a few strokes of his powerful wings. Bob swore beneath his breath and lowered the rifle. He felt jittery today. The thought of another night spent on a hard *machan* made his spirits sag. But chances were that if he gave in, along would come Mike Kirby to put the beast down with one lucky shot.

He mopped his sticky brow with his sleeve. He still could not rid himself of the powerful notion that the cat was watching him, somewhere close by. He turned back to Ché and saw the boy gazing at him curiously.

"Look kid, you did a good job here. How would you like to track for me again?"

432

Ché nodded eagerly. "I would like that very much, tuan!"

"Good boy." Bob reached into his pocket and produced a couple of crumpled dollar bills. "You get that each time you track for me. And a special bonus when we finally put an end to old stripey. You just hold yourself ready to go whenever I call."

"Maybe you'll get him tonight," suggested Ché encouragingly.

"Tonight. Yeah, maybe." But Bob was dismayed to realize that he doubted this. Too many failures were leading him to believe that the tiger would never be shot from a *machan*. Maybe the time would come when he'd have to follow him up through the long grass with just his wits and his gun to aid him.

But for the time being he'd give the *machan* another try. He retraced his steps back into the jungle, Ché close on his heels. Soon their figures were lost in the dark shadows of the trees. Several minutes passed in silence. Then there was a slow, swishing motion in the edge of the grass, and a lean striped shape emerged to continue the interrupted meal.

HARRY STROLLED in through the doorway of the mess. It was Wednesday afternoon, and although Dennis would not be able to keep their usual appointment, Harry had decided to come anyway. He was shocked to see that for the first time he could remember, he and Trimani were the sole occupants of this hallowed place. He approached the bar, and the little barman shook his head as if to say, Ah yes, tuan, how sad that it has come to this.

Harry accepted a glass of Tiger beer and drained it, indicated that he would like another. He took out his cigar case, handed a smoke to Trimani, and took one himself. He lit the cigars, and there was a long moment of silence as the two men inhaled and exhaled, lost in their own memories. At last Harry asked, "How much longer do you stay open, Trimani?"

"Until the very end, tuan. Two, maybe three week."

"And what will happen to you then?"

"Oh, it is not too bad! I am old now, ready to step down. I have a good family, who will take care of me."

"You will be getting a pension from the British government?"

"There has been no mention of it, tuan."

"And how long have you been working here?"

"Fourteen years."

Harry nodded slowly. He felt ashamed that such ingratitude

could be dealt to a man as loyal and trustworthy as this one. "Have a drink with me, Trimani," he suggested suddenly.

The barman shook his head. "Thank you, tuan, but you know it is not allowed. The rules—"

"Oh, hang the rules! Fourteen years you've stood behind this bar, and not once have you been able to have a drink with me. What difference can it make now, for heaven's sake? Pour yourself a beer. I'll have another one too."

Trimani still did not much like the idea. But after a glance around, he poured two cans of beer into glasses. He handed one to Harry.

"That's the spirit, Trimani! Now. What shall we drink to?"

Trimani turned and indicated a large framed photograph hanging above the bar. "Let us drink to this fine lady," he suggested.

Harry smiled and raised his glass to the photograph. "To Queen Elizabeth the Second!" he announced.

"One fine lady!" added Trimani. The two men drank deeply. Trimani banged down his empty glass on the counter. "Ah, very nice!" he exclaimed.

"Pour yourself another one," suggested Harry.

"Oh, but I should not, tuan."

Harry gazed around at the empty bar. "Do you see anybody here who's likely to complain?"

Trimani grinned. "No, tuan, I don't!" And he took another two beers out of the refrigerator.

"What shall we drink to now?" asked Harry. His mood was improving by the minute, and he was beginning to feel slightly tipsy. He usually made it a rule not to drink more than two Tiger beers during the heat of the day, when its effect seemed most powerful, but now he cast caution to the winds.

"Let us drink to our friend Captain Tremayne," suggested Trimani brightly. "He has always been most kind to me."

"Dennis it is!" agreed Harry gleefully. "Nobody more deserving of being drunken to. To Dennis!" he cried.

"Captain Tremayne!" The two men drank their beers.

"Ah, that's better," observed Harry. He mopped his brow. "Whew, it's hot in here." He slipped off his jacket, laid it across the bar, and rolled up his shirtsleeves, a rare break with decorum on his part. "Now, come along, Trimani, another two beers."

"Oh, tuan, I'm not sure I should."

"Nonsense! Do you want me to have to drink alone?"

Trimani sighed, shook his head. He took two more beers out of the refrigerator.

An hour passed. Nobody else came in, and Harry and Trimani steadily drank their way past the point of no return. They proposed toasts to an increasingly obscure series of subjects.

"Whash next?" inquired Harry blankly, as Trimani was, with great difficulty, pouring another round.

"Oh, tuan," he groaned. "The room is going around my head."

"Nonsense!" Harry grabbed the next glass of beer and stood swaying dangerously. "Whash next?" he demanded again.

"Ah, tuan, I know!" Trimani pointed excitedly to the tiger's head over the doorway. "Your old enemy. You always drink to him, but today when we are toasting, you have not!"

"You're a genius!" Harry gazed up at the snarling face. "Trimani, did I ever tell you how I came to shoot that fellow?"

"No, tuan. I ask many times, but you would never speak of it."

"I wouldn't?" Harry looked puzzled. "I'll tell you now," he announced grandly. He set down his drink. "It was . . . 1958. A big tiger was taking cattle from the kampong stockades. He wasn't a man-eater, he'd just wandered out of the jungle, looking for food . . . but everybody got on to me to go and have a crack at him. 'Course, in those days I was always ready to have a go. So I tied out a cow, built myself a *machan*. That night the tiger came to eat, and I put a bullet through him; but it was a bad shot, he ran off into the jungle. Naturally the *sporting* thing was to follow him up and put him out of hish misery." Harry laughed bitterly. "Well, he went into a patch of long grass and I waded in after him, like the arrogant fool I was. Then . . . thish is hard to explain. . . ." Harry reeled away from the bar, stumbled over to the corner of the room, and snatched up Trimani's broom, which he wielded as though it were a rifle. "Now, I crept through the long grass," he narrated, and began to move stealthily forward, the broom held ready to fire. "I couldn't see much, but from time to time I heard the tiger'sh roar. And the tiger, hearing movement below him, began to creep across the rock until he was directly above me. I could sense that he was about to come down, so I looked upwards. I could just make out the glint of his eyes. I've never been more terrified than I was in that moment, Trimani. I thought I was going to die. But I twisted the rifle round, pointing upwards. Small rocks began to fall on me, and I could hear the noise of the tiger's body sliding off the rock and into space. It was coming down right on top of me. Right on top, mind you! I squeezed the trigger. *Bang!* I heard a squeal, and the tiger seemed to fly over my head. It landed hard, it lay there for a moment, and then it lifted its head and it looked at me. It looked at me! And its eyes seemed to be asking me Why, why had I done this thing? And then . . . then . . ." Harry broke off as a savage pain erupted in his chest. He gasped, clutched at his heart, and the broom clattered to the bar-room floor. Trimani looked at him in alarm.

"Tuan? What is wrong?"

"Trimani, I think I . . ." The sentence collapsed in a brief exclamation of pain. The colour drained from Harry's face. He tried to take a step but fell forward in a sprawl, bringing several chairs clattering around him. He slumped onto his face, and then Trimani was beside him, turning him over.

"Tuan, what is the matter?"

Harry's face was ashen. "Too much to drink," he hissed through teeth that were gritted in pain.

"I get help!" cried Trimani desperately. He leaped up and raced out of the bar, his footsteps pounding on the wooden floor.

Harry groaned softly. He tried to sit up, but another spasm shook his body. From where he lay, he could see the stuffed head of the tiger snarling down at him. He gazed back calmly, unafraid. The head seemed to grow slowly in size, and it lost definition, dissolved into a huge orange blob that sizzled in front of Harry's eyes like a great ball of flame. Then the clouds of sleep that were tugging at his brain took over and floated him downwards into a dreamless world. A vague thought wheedled its way up from his subconscious mind. Death. That's one thing we forgot to drink to.

10

The night was calm and humid. Haji lay some twenty yards away from the female Upright he had killed earlier that day. He was concealed by the stout limb of a fallen tree, and he lay on his side, occasionally dozing or lapping at the festering wound on his foreleg. From time to time a slight breeze carried the smell of decaying meat in his direction, and his stomach churned at such torture; but the young Upright was on the scene as usual, perched in a tall *kapok* tree near the kill. Still Haji lingered, hoping that the Upright would fall asleep or return to his own lair.

The silvery orb of a full moon cast an eerie illumination that touched the bushes and swaying grasses with restless, dappled light. Haji was incapable of sleeping for more than a few moments at a time, for there was in him this night a nagging, fretful mood.

He got to his feet and began to pace up and down behind the log. His useless paw hampered him even in such aimless movement, and the insecurity in him turned quickly to an all-encompassing anger that he was unable to direct at anything. A long rumbling roar escaped from his throat, and echoed in the night.

There was a brief silence. Then Haji's sharp ears detected a rustle of movement in the *kapok* tree as the Upright shifted position. Haji stopped pacing and fixed the tree with an intense glare. He could see it clearly in the moonlight, could discern the low fork where the Upright had fixed his wooden seat. Haji's rage continued to grow. Soon even his healthy fear of the black stick was forgotten, for now the Upright was a focus for all his bitterness. Pressing his body low against the ground and keeping his gaze fixed on the tree, Haji began to circle to his right, slipping silently through the undergrowth. He could see that the Upright was looking in the opposite direction, unaware of his approach.

Now Haji could see the hated black stick, and this, more than anything else, drove him mad. He raced directly at the tree, covering the few yards in seconds. With a bellow of rage, he launched himself at the *machan*.

Then all was chaos. At the last instant Bob turned and found himself looking full into the face of death. Haji's forepaws struck the broad fork of the tree, and the cat hung suspended by his claws while he tried to lever himself forward to tear at the creature that had long tormented him. Bob screamed in pure terror and made a clumsy attempt to bring his rifle round; but the barrel hit a stout branch and the gun went off, firing harmlessly into the treetops. The rifle's shattering roar assailed the night, and the tiger's eyes were momentarily lit with fire. Bob felt the hot gusting breath of the cat mere inches from his face. A roar spilled from the open jaws, seeming to shake the entire tree to its roots. Desperately Bob struck out with the butt of the rifle. The cat snatched it in his foaming jaws and sent it spinning away like a useless toy. Bob scrambled further up the tree, but Haji, pulling himself into the lap of the fork, came after him. Somebody had told Bob that tigers had limited climbing ability, and he could only pray that this was the case as he made his way out along a network of thinner branches, with the demonic jaws slavering at his heels. He edged on, terrified that a mishap might send him down to the jungle floor where the tiger would make short work of him. He felt the branch beneath his feet bow dramatically, and glancing back, he saw to his horror that the tiger was inching his way along the same limb. With an oath, he scrambled higher, lost his footing, dangled for several moments by his hands while his flailing feet searched for a new hold. Haji reared up and swung at the feet, but this caused the branch on which the cat was crouching to give a long, agonized splitting sound and he moved quickly back to the fork with a snarl of rage. There he turned to watch the struggles of the Upright.

Bob's feet could find no hold, and his hands, slippery with sweat, were failing to grasp the smooth bark of the limb above him. He glanced desperately at the jungle floor. He could see his rifle lying there, but doubted that he could drop to the ground, reload and fire before the tiger dropped onto him from above. He clenched his teeth, and digging his fingers as much as he could into their precarious hold, he began to raise himself tenaciously towards the branch from which he was hanging.

Suddenly Haji's rage dispersed, to be replaced by a sense of curiosity. He turned away, jumped down to the forest floor and padded out beneath the Upright, gazing up at the man's frantic struggles.

Bob was horribly aware that his shaking fingers were losing their grip, and he considered falling to earth and snatching his rifle; but glancing downwards, he saw the tiger's amber eyes gazing patiently at him. The shock galvanized him into making one last desperate heave and he swung his legs up and wrapped them round the branch. The limb bent but it held, and Bob was able to take a better hold with his hands. Hugging his perch tightly, he craned his head round to stare triumphantly down at the tiger.

"Beat you!" he screamed. "Let's see you get up here!"

But Haji was already strolling away. He paused to sniff at the kill, but it had been disturbed and he did not trust it. He glanced back at the Upright who was screaming and gesticulating like some agitated tree ape.

438

"You thought you had me, didn't you! Well, you won't get another chance! D'you hear me? I'm going to put a bullet through you if it's the last thing I do!"

Haji gave a low growl of irritation and continued slowly on his way. After a few moments he was lost amid the undergrowth.

Bob clung to the branch, trembling violently. In his mind there was a vivid image of the tiger's eyes, lit by the flare of the rifle. They had been full of hatred, those eyes, and they would haunt Bob's dreams for many nights to come. Glancing wildly about to assure himself that the cat was really gone, he inched clumsily back along the branch and half clambered, half fell down the tree. He ran to his rifle and rammed a cartridge in the chamber. The stock of the gun held several deep gouges where the tiger's teeth had sunk into it. Bob imagined those same teeth tearing into his flesh, and he felt nauseated. He loosed off three shots into the air and then moved back against the trunk of the tree, pressing against its reassuring hardness. He squatted there, cradling the gun in his arms and waited for the villagers to come.

It was some time before it occurred to him that he was crying.

THE TELEVISION SCREEN brightened gradually from greyness and flickered into life. Melissa stared at it for several moments. It was a Chinese melodrama with English subtitles, the kind of programme she detested. With a groan, she reached out and pressed the off button.

"I'm bored!" she announced dramatically.

Kate glanced up from a novel and gave her daughter a sympathetic smile. "Why don't you read? I could lend you a book."

"I hate reading," retorted Melissa wearily. This was not altogether true, but when she was in this kind of mood there was little that would distract her.

"Oh dear, dear. You're not happy at all, are you?" Kate closed the novel and put it aside. "We could go out later, when your father gets home. The mess, perhaps."

"No, thank you! Anyway, you loathe the place more than I do."

"True," admitted Kate. "But who knows, you might bump into Mr. Beresford there." This was intended as a casual tease, but it quickly became apparent from Melissa's face that something was wrong. "Well, don't tell me you're even bored with *him!*"

"It's not that I'm fed up with him," said Melissa. "More the other

way round really. Since that incident with his trophy he's had no time for me."

Kate sighed. "Perhaps it's just as well, dear. You'll be going back to England soon and the last thing you'd want is a romantic entanglement that would make it difficult for you to leave with a clear mind."

"Ah, good old Mummy! Always so practical." Melissa felt a surge of fondness run through her, and getting out of her seat she went to give her mother a fierce hug.

"Goodness!" exclaimed Kate in mock surprise. "Well, thank you for that, dear." Headlights played across the sitting-room window as a car pulled in through the gates. "There's your father now."

The front door opened and Dennis hurried into the room, a grave expression on his face. "Harry Sullivan's had another heart attack," he announced. "He was admitted to the hospital at Kuala Hitam but discharged himself this morning."

"Discharged himself?" echoed Kate. "Was that wise?"

"Not at all, but you know Harry. I just got the story from Trimani before I came home. Apparently Harry was horsing about in the mess, pretending to be shooting tigers or some such nonsense. Honestly, sometimes you'd think he was a six-year-old instead of sixty-seven. . . ."

"We'd better go up and visit him," suggested Kate. She and Dennis both directed their gaze in Melissa's direction.

"You've not been to see Harry since the two of you had that run-in," observed Dennis admonishingly. "You haven't even apologized to him. He was right about Beresford's tiger, after all."

Melissa nodded. "Of course I'll come," she said simply.

It was a fine, clear evening as they drove to Harry's. Far off to the right, richly forested hills plunged down to meet the tranquil waters of the ocean. Abruptly Melissa found herself reflecting that there were some things she would miss about this country. She knew that England had its own cold, rather austere beauty, but where would she ever find a scene so relatively untouched by civilization as the vista that she could glimpse now through the car window?

Dennis brought the car to a halt outside Harry's bungalow. They all got out and stood gazing apprehensively at the closed doors and darkened windows. Dennis rapped politely at the front door. The house seemed ominously silent. At last they were rewarded by a soft tread within. The door opened, and there was Harry, looking in the peak of health. He peered out into the night, and his tanned face broke into a cheerful grin.

"Hello there, Dennis, Kate! Well, you two are a sight for sore eyes, I must say! Come in, come in." He ushered them inside, and then he noticed that they had not come alone. Melissa stood on the doorstep, an expression of uncertainty on her face.

"Hello, Uncle Harry," she murmured.

He stared at her in silence for a moment, a little taken aback. "Hello, stranger," he said at last, and his voice was rather tremulous. "Well now. Come along in. It's good to see you again."

"It's good to see you too, Uncle Harry. But before I come in . . ." Melissa glanced self-consciously at her parents, and they obligingly moved into the house. "I rather think I owe you an apology."

"Indeed?" Harry raised his eyebrows. "And why is that?"

"The argument we had. About Bob's tiger. I was a little fool, Uncle Harry, shouting my mouth off about something I didn't know anything about. Then when you were proved right . . . well, I was just too proud to admit that I was wrong. Pride is terrible!"

"That's true enough," admitted Harry. "And I've got more than my fair share of it, I can assure you." He smiled, extended his hand. "Are you going to stand around on the doorstep all night?"

Melissa smiled, accepted his hand and squeezed it gently. She let Harry pull her inside.

BOB BROUGHT the Land-Rover to a halt in front of his house. He took his hands off the steering wheel and sat for a moment with his head slumped forward. It was afternoon, but only in the last hour or so had he felt capable of driving home from Kampong Panjang. He had spent the day wandering numbly around the kampong, trying to pull his frayed nerve endings together. Now he felt exhausted, grateful to be alive, and more resolved than ever to get the tiger. He shook his head and got out of the Land-Rover.

Lim came running from the house. "Bob tuan!" she cried. "I was so frightened. I thought the tiger had eaten you!"

Bob threw an arm round her. "Strewth, I need a drink . . ." He broke off in surprise. Standing on the veranda was a tall, gaunt Malay with piercing black eyes and a thin, pockmarked face. He was naked save for a sarong and the inevitable flip-flops. "Who's this?" demanded Bob irritably. He had had enough for one day.

"This man has come from the *bomoh* at Kampong Machis," Lim

442

told him. "He came this morning, asking to see you. He would not go."

The man stepped forward. "I am student of the *bomoh*," he explained. "I come fetch you. He needs talk with you."

"Oh yeah? I suppose he's going to tell me he's the tiger that's been doing all the killing, is he?"

The man looked horrified. "Oh, no, tuan! The *bomoh* is concerned many people say he is the man-eater. He want to give you advice, how to catch striped one."

"Very nice of him," sneered Bob. "Well, there's only one place I'm going right now, and that's to bed. So you tell the *bomoh* maybe I'll look him up later on, when I've had some rest."

But the man shook his head adamantly. "I wait here. You sleep." He crossed his arms and took up a resolute stance, his legs slightly apart, his dark eyes staring out towards the garden.

Bob felt too tired to attempt throwing the fellow off the veranda. "Well, suit yourself!" he snapped. "You'll soon get fed up!" And with that he turned and strode into the house.

In his bedroom, Bob stripped off his clothes and fell into bed. The moment his head touched the pillow he was asleep, but it was not a peaceful slumber. He sank quickly into a vivid and particularly disturbing dream.

He was in the jungle again and it was night, dank and humid. He could see a violent swishing in the long grass. Lifting his rifle, he grabbed the bolt, intending to punch a cartridge into the chamber. The gun fell apart in his hands. . . .

Bob woke, sobbing violently. He was sitting up in the darkness of his room, his arms wrapped protectively around his body. Above him the metal blades of the electric fan clicked rhythmically, disturbing the humid air. With a gasp, he groped for the bedside light and flicked it on, needing the reassurance of vision. He sat blinking in the glare for a moment, but the room seemed alien, unfamiliar. He fumbled for the cigarettes beside the bed and lit one with shaking fingers.

The bedroom door opened and Lim peered in. "Bob tuan all right?" she whispered.

"Fine. I'm fine. What time is it?"

" 'Bout six o'clock."

He took another drag on his cigarette. "I'd better get up," he announced. "Turn on the shower for me, will you?"

"All right." Lim smiled happily and hurried off.

The cold water of the shower brought Bob fully awake. He washed his hair, noting a line of itchy red bumps around his scalp where mosquitoes had laid into him the night before. "Little vermin," he murmured ruefully.

He dried himself, dressed in clean clothes and began to feel happier. He strolled into the sitting room, where he found Lim watching television. She reached out and switched it off as soon as she noticed Bob's presence.

"Bob tuan like drink?" she asked.

"Yeah, please. A straight whisky with a little ice." She ran to fetch it. When Lim returned with the drink, he drank half of it in one gulp. Lim stared at him thoughtfully and then she sat down.

"What happen last night?" she asked cautiously.

"The tiger came after me. Jumped into the tree where I was sitting. . . ." Recalling the events now, they seemed unreal, ridiculously farfetched. "He just went berserk all of a sudden, and then he lost interest and went away."

Lim stared at him open-mouthed. "Oh, Bob tuan!" she exclaimed. "You must leave this tiger alone now. That was a warning!"

"Nah. I don't believe that stuff. But I don't intend to give him another chance to get so close, I can tell you." Bob strolled towards the open front door. Out in the calm evening, crickets had begun to sing. "No, the next time, I'll . . ."

He broke off in surprise. From the darkness of the veranda, a pair of glowing eyes had fixed him with a stare that almost caused him to jump out of his skin.

"What the . . ?" For a moment Bob was literally rooted to the spot with fear; then, with an oath, he reached out and snapped on the veranda lights. The *bomoh*'s assistant was standing in exactly the same place Bob had left him. The man seemed not to have moved so much as a muscle in the several hours he had been waiting there.

"Tuan ready to come along now?" inquired the man hopefully. Bob stared in disbelief. "You don't give up easily, do you?"

"*Bomoh* help catch real man-eater, so people know the truth."

"Bob tuan," Lim gasped. "I think you should not go with that man! The *bomoh* is very wicked, very powerful. Many people in the kampongs are afraid to go near his hut."

Bob chuckled. "I thought you didn't go in for all this superstitious claptrap. I thought you prided yourself on being a modern girl."

Lim frowned. "You do not know what these people want of you."

"Lim, they just want to spout a bit of mumbo jumbo at me, that's all. Besides, I need all the help I can get with this tiger!" He went into his bedroom, took a khaki jacket out of the wardrobe, and slipped into it.

"You are always leaving me alone in the house," complained Lim bitterly.

"I won't be long." He went back to the front door, where the *bomoh*'s assistant was still waiting. "Come on then, Gunga Din, let's see what your boss has to say for himself."

He motioned the man to follow him, and the two of them got into the Land-Rover. As Bob started up the engine, he glanced back. Lim was standing in the doorway, looking out at him with a worried expression. He felt a wave of fondness pass through him. Lim was a good kid, she gave him everything she had and got precious little in return. He would have to make an effort to be nicer to her. He waved briefly and drove away.

THE *BOMOH*'S ASSISTANT directed Bob to a deserted stretch of dirt road a short distance beyond Kampong Machis and told him to stop the car. On either side of them lay thick jungle. Bob did not much fancy the prospect of wandering in there at this late hour.

He groped around in the back of the vehicle, found his rifle and torch. He slung the rifle over his shoulder and hurried after the *bomoh*'s assistant, who was already striding fearlessly through the long grass that bordered the road. "Hold on a bit. I've got a light here," called Bob.

"I know my way," replied the Malay. He ducked beneath a tangle of low branches and disappeared into the gloom. Cursing to himself, Bob followed, tripping and stumbling over the unfamiliar ground. At last he managed to catch up, and he directed a powerful beam of yellow light in front of them. In the stark glare, tree trunks and hanging creepers possessed a twisted, serpent-like look.

"How much further is it?" Bob demanded irritably of the man. "I wasn't expecting a bloody marathon."

"Not far now, tuan."

"Well, I hope not. Listen, if the *bomoh* was so anxious to talk, why didn't he come and see me himself?"

"The *bomoh* never leaves his hut. At least, not on *two* legs."

Bob gave a sneer of contempt. "Look, mate, don't try pulling the old mumbo jumbo on me, it won't wash!"

The man shrugged indifferently. He had come to an abrupt halt. "We are here," he announced tonelessly.

Bob stopped and stared in the direction in which the Malay was pointing. At first he could see nothing but an unrelieved backdrop of undergrowth. Then his light picked out a flimsy wooden shack surrounded on three sides by trees and bushes. It was a crudely constructed affair, not even raised off the ground in the local tradition. The tiny window apertures were glassless and covered with mouldy sacking, and the only element that suggested life within was a thin plume of smoke issuing from a hole in the corrugated-iron roof.

"The *bomoh* waits for you," murmured Bob's companion. "I leave now."

Bob hoped that he didn't look as apprehensive as he felt. Here goes, he thought to himself.

He approached the hut slowly, keeping one hand on the stock of his rifle so that he might snatch it from his shoulder if necessary. The low doorway was also covered with filthy sacking. He reached out to grip it, and a large black spider skittered down the material. Bob shuddered, and his skin began to crawl as he entered the hut.

A low wood fire was burning dully in the centre of the floor, and as well as the thick fragrance of woodsmoke there was a powerful atmosphere of incense, mingled with hashish. A small, half-naked man was sitting in front of the fire, his legs crossed beneath him. He was wiry, ape-like, with a completely bald head. Several diagonal scars ran across his cheeks, some kind of ceremonial markings, Bob supposed. The man's eyes were tightly shut, and he seemed to be in some sort of trance. Bob felt unsure of what to do, but then the man spoke, without opening his eyes.

"So you are here at last, Mr. Beresford. Come, sit opposite me. There is a place by the fire." The voice was surprisingly cultured, the command of English excellent.

Bob lowered himself awkwardly to the floor, half afraid that he would sit on a scorpion. It was oppressively hot in the cramped hut.

"Why are you afraid?" asked the *bomoh*. "There is nothing to fear here."

Bob was about to reply, but at that instant the *bomoh* opened his eyes, and the Australian was transfixed by the sight of them.

They were two pale orbs that caught the flickering glow of the firelight. In the very centre of each eye a tiny tar-black pupil rested like a pinprick of black emptiness. Despite the heat, a shiver coursed down Bob's spine.

He took a deep breath, but the thick cloying atmosphere only served to make him feel light-headed. "Let's get down to brass tacks, shall we? Why did you ask me to come out here?"

The *bomoh* chuckled, a low, guttural, unpleasant sound.

"We have similar aims, Mr. Beresford. We both wish to see the man-eater disposed of. I, because I fear that the wrath of the local people may turn against me. And you, because you are driven by a desire to prove yourself."

Bob was outraged. "I hunt that tiger because he's a menace, that's all. Somebody's got to put a stop to the killing."

"Well, whatever your reasons, I feel I can be of help to you. But the lateness of your arrival does not give us very long to talk. In a short while I must go out to hunt for my evening meal."

"Oh yeah," Bob muttered sarcastically. "You're the tiger man, right? Must make things very awkward for you."

"Indeed, it does, Mr. Beresford. The man-eating tiger must die if I am to enjoy the continued assistance of the kampong people."

"Assistance?"

"For years the local people have turned a blind eye to my preying upon their livestock, because they have respect for me, a respect born of fear; allow that fear to turn into anger and eventually they will fight back, you understand?"

Bob took another deep breath. The perfumed atmosphere was making him feel distinctly dizzy. And the *bomoh*'s fantastic conversation seemed to possess a vivid, hallucinatory quality.

"I can tell you for certain, Mr. Beresford, you will never catch the tiger by putting out baits, or by lying up in the treetops. He has lived too long and learned too much to allow himself to be trapped. It will be necessary to track him on foot, across his own terrain. It will require great courage and even greater skill, but only this way will he be laid to rest." The *bomoh* turned and picked up a small leather pouch that lay at his side. He untied a thong that bound the top of it. "Hold out your hand," he instructed.

"What for?"

"There is no trick involved. Trust me."

Hesitantly Bob held out one hand and the *bomoh* upended the bag, dropping several small brownish bones into Bob's open palm. "I want you to cast these onto the floor in one throw," explained the *bomoh*. "With them I can foretell your future."

"More mumbo jumbo," chuckled Bob. But he threw down the bones and watched as the *bomoh* began to talk in a low, toneless voice, hardly pausing to take breath.

"There are more deaths to come. One who dies has skin of white. The tiger will be found on a day when the sun is unobscured. There are *two* tigers. The first shall not die until the second has looked him in the eyes. The gun . . ." The *bomoh* paused, his fingers twitching on empty air. Then he leaned across the low fire, snatched Bob's rifle from his shoulder and held it against his own chest, his fingers moving slowly up and down the barrel. "*This* gun," he crooned. "Ah yes, *this* gun will bring the tiger low. But there will be a terrible price to pay, a terrible price." He glanced suddenly up at Bob. "You will fire this gun once more!" he cried. "Then never again. Never!"

Bob stared at the *bomoh*, shocked. He leaned across the fire and snatched the rifle back.

"Yeah, well, thanks, Doc! Is that all for now, or do I get a long-range weather forecast too?"

The *bomoh* said softly, "Is that not typical of the Western mentality? Always suspicious of that which they cannot readily explain. It is late now. You had better go. I wish to prepare myself for tonight's hunt."

"I'd really like to stick around and catch the act."

The *bomoh* nodded. "You are indeed a most obstinate man, Mr. Beresford. You may do as you think best."

A silence settled inside the hut, broken only by the crackling of twigs in the fire. The *bomoh* sat stock-still, but his chin sank gradually downwards to his chest. Only the slow rise and fall of his breathing indicated that he was alive. Bob was sweating uncomfortably in the claustrophobic atmosphere. He was fascinated that the *bomoh* was actually going to go ahead with the transformation. Well, I've got all night, he told himself.

Time passed. Gradually Bob became aware of a change in the atmosphere of the hut, as though the very air had become imbued with a powerful smell, a musky, animal odour. Now that *was* impressive! He felt like applauding, but as he turned his gaze back to the *bomoh*, he saw that he was breathing very heavily now, his chest rising and falling, his mouth gaping open to reveal sharply chiselled teeth. Bob felt the hairs on the back of his neck begin to rise and a terrible shiver convulsed his body. He tried to tell himself that this was just a device designed to play upon his imagination, but though his reason assured him that this was the case, his senses did not agree.

For now, the *bomoh*'s face was changing, dissolving upon itself, the features rearranging, horribly, inexplicably. The shape of the head became squat, rounded.

"No!" Bob screamed. "It's a trick!"

A deep, guttural boom of laughter exploded from the mouth of the old man.

Bob's nerve broke completely. He was on his feet in an instant, and he stumbled for the door, his head reeling. Out in the clear air, he was forced to rest for a few moments, with his back against the trunk of a tall tree.

Away from the incense and hashish of the hut he was able to gain control of his senses. Here the whole episode already seemed unlikely, a product of his overwrought imagination. He slung the rifle back over his shoulder and moved away in search of his vehicle.

He took the torch out of his shirt pocket and directed the powerful beam onto the narrow track ahead of him. He had taken no more than a dozen steps when he stood stock-still with an exclamation of surprise. For an instant, caught in the beam and framed amid a tangle of bushes, was the scowling face of a large tiger. But by the time Bob had unslung his gun again, the creature had slipped away into the undergrowth.

HAJI GAVE A LOW rumbling growl of discontent.

He had only followed the Upright for a short distance, attracted by the noisy headlong flight of him as he raced through the jungle. Haji had overtaken him and dropped down to lie in ambush at the far end of a narrow cattle trail. But then there had been the blinding, unnatural river of light, rushing straight into Haji's eyes. Then and there, the tiger had given up all thought of this troublesome prey. Now he was heading for the nearest kampong.

Off to the east an argus pheasant called, a lonely, haunting, *cuau-cuau* sound that faded gradually into the distance as Haji slipped like a scarred shadow through the trees.

11

The sound of a car horn intruded upon Harry's midday nap with all the delicacy of a brick thrown through a plate-glass window. He blinked owlishly, sat up in his rattan chair.

Paarp! Paarp! Paaaaarp!

"What the . . . " Harry got up and leaned over the rail of the veranda. There was a bright blue Volkswagen parked by the gate, a vehicle he had never seen before. The sun's reflection on the windscreen prevented him from seeing the driver. Muttering to himself, Harry strode down the pathway.

"Don't know what this place is coming to . . ." He broke off in surprise as the car door opened and the driver got out.

It was a middle-aged woman, rather stout but with fine, striking features. She was dressed in a shapeless green khaki shirt and a skirt of the same material. On her head she wore a crumpled, faded hat of the kind favoured by the Gurkhas for jungle warfare.

She fixed him with a glance from steely blue-grey eyes. "Lieutenant-Colonel Sullivan?" she inquired hopefully.

"Retired," he added. "Yes, that's me."

"Ah, excellent!" There was the faintest trace of a Scottish accent in her voice. She walked up to the gate and stretched out a hand. "The name's Burns. Marion Burns. I've had quite a time looking for you. Er, now, look here, I can't go on calling you Lieutenant-Colonel Retired, now can I? What's your first name?"

"Uh, it's Harry."

"Well then, Harry it will be!" She opened the gate and stepped onto the drive. "What a lovely little house! Perhaps we could sit on the veranda. It's awfully hot today."

"Yes. Of course." Harry was beginning to wonder if this was some mystifying dream.

"Forgive me for dropping out of the blue like this, Harry." She was already heading towards the veranda; he trailed along beside her. "I'm a feature writer for the *New Straits Times*, and I've been sent down to put together an article on the man-eating tiger. Goodness, what lovely chairs!" She settled into the seat where Harry had but lately been sleeping. "You see," she continued, "this is the first major man-eater the country's had since the mid-fifties. Oh, we've had them carry off the odd one or two, but they generally get caught before they can take matters further. This fellow has already reached seven!"

"I see. But—"

"There's a certain fascination in the subject. Of course, we all know the popular view of the man-eater as some rampaging, blood-lusting demon, but I want to get at the truth behind the myth, more or less present the tiger's side of it, you know?"

A coin dropped in Harry's memory. "You must be M. Burns!" he exclaimed. "Why, I've read many of your articles. But I always assumed you were a man!"

She smiled good-naturedly. "Sorry to disappoint you."

"Good heavens, not at all. I, er, Pawn! Are you in there?"

Pawn bustled to the door, wiping her hands on a tea towel. "Yes, tuan?"

"Some tea for the missy and myself, please."

Pawn gazed at Marion for a moment and grinned excitedly. "Oh, yes, tuan! Right away!" And she hurried away in the direction of the kitchen. Harry turned back to his guest.

"So, you intend to write an article on the man-eating tiger, eh? But what's all this got to do with me?"

"You may well ask! Well, naturally enough, when I got to Trengganu, the first place I headed for was the Game Department. I talked to a nice chap called Mike Kirby. And he told me that I would not find a more informed source of tiger knowledge than his old friend Harry Sullivan. So, here I am."

Harry smiled fondly. "Mike said that, did he? That's most kind of him, I must say."

"Then you'll help? Of course, you'll be mentioned in the article."

"Really? You know, I've always wanted to see my name in the *New Straits Times*. I was beginning to think I'd have to wait to see it in the obituary column."

Marion tilted back her head and laughed. She had a bright, infectious laugh, and Harry found himself chuckling too. He watched her for a moment as she stared out across the lush garden.

"I must say you have a delightful home here," she observed. "How long have you been a widower now?"

The frankness of the question shocked him momentarily.

"Seventeen years," he replied tonelessly. "But how did you . . ?"

"I always make a point of finding out about people," she replied.

"Part of my reporter's training. Actually, I'm widowed myself, so you see, we've got a bit in common."

There was a brief, uncomfortable silence; it was broken by the entry of Pawn, carrying a tray of tea and biscuits. She placed it reverently on the table, all the while grinning happily. And as Harry introduced her to Marion, Pawn grinned even more and bowed low, moving backwards into the house.

"Shall I pour?"

"Oh, please do." Harry watched as Marion picked up the silver teapot. She had small, dainty hands that belied her somewhat unfeminine appearance. Harry was usually rather formal and uncomfortable with strangers, but with Marion this was not the case. She struck him as being a very interesting character.

She sipped her tea. "Are you planning to head back to England when it all folds up here?" she asked.

"Oh no, I'll be staying on."

"Good. That's refreshing. I hardly seem to meet anyone these days who isn't looking forward to 'dear old Blighty'." She grimaced. "I've lived here most of my life, and the thought of returning to cold, blustery Scotland would be most unappealing." She switched the subject to a more immediate problem. "I expect it will take me two or three days to put the article together. Can you recommend a hotel in the area?"

"Well now, I really don't know any nearer than Kuala Trengganu, and to be honest I've no idea how good the amenities are."

"Hmm. Well, perhaps you've a spare room here that I might commandeer for a few days?"

"Well, there *is* a spare room. But . . ."

"Oh, of course, I could hardly impose. No doubt you'd be worried about what your neighbours might say."

"Not at all! It's just . . ."

"That's settled then! I must say, it's very hospitable of you."

"I . . . yes . . . right . . . " Harry was slightly dazed. But he couldn't honestly say that he wasn't looking forward to having a little company. "Well, I'd better tell Pawn to tidy the room a bit. It hasn't been used for a very long time."

"Now, don't go to any trouble." She gave that infectious laugh again, bright, bubbly, appealing. Harry felt the corners of his lips rising almost involuntarily.

"Perhaps you'd have some dinner with me later on?" He asked

the question cautiously, but she looked genuinely pleased at the prospect.

"Yes indeed, that would be lovely."

"Oh . . . right, then. If you'll excuse me, I'll just pop in and get things organized. Do help yourself to more tea."

He got up from his chair and hurried into the house, thinking wryly about this strange newcomer. Here only a few minutes and already she had wangled free accommodation. The odd thing was, Harry was actually looking forward to finding out more about his unexpected guest.

He found Pawn on her hands and knees, scrubbing the already sparkling tiles on the kitchen floor. "Ah, Pawn. The missy will be staying for a few days."

"Missy stay *here?*" cried Pawn delightedly. "With you?"

Harry cleared his throat. "The missy will be sleeping in the spare room, so would you please make sure that it's tidy?" Pawn grinned, nodded. "There's something else. Will you stay a little late tonight and prepare dinner for the missy and me?"

"Dinner? Oh, tuan!" Pawn clapped her hands to her face.

"You can take a taxi to the market and get whatever you need to make a special meal. Don't worry about the expense, get the best there is."

"Oh yes, tuan! I get very best!" He took out his wallet and handed her two fifty-dollar bills. She stood staring at them for several moments in disbelief. "And if there is any change, you might like to buy that grandson of yours a little something."

Pawn's grin faded, and she shook her head. "He not deserve anything from you, tuan. That boy promise me he come see you, but he not come. I am 'shamed of him. All he want do is talk about hunting, be like Tuan Beresford."

Harry frowned. "I expect it's just a phase," he said sadly. "You'd better run along to the taxi rank."

"Yes, tuan. I clean room when I get back." Pawn bustled away to collect her shopping bag, and Harry smiled at her eagerness to please. He wandered back to the veranda, humming to himself. Emerging into the glare of daylight, he saw to his surprise that both rattan chairs were empty. For a moment a dull sense of shock hit him, and irrational ideas flashed through his mind. Marion had panicked. Rather than go through the ordeal of dinner with a dry old stick like him, she had made an escape.

Then the gate clanged open, and to his relief he saw her coming along the drive, holding a small suitcase and a portable typewriter. He hurried down to relieve her of the luggage.

"Thank you kindly, sir! I thought I'd just get my things out of the car. Ah, don't look now, but I think your neighbours are having a good look at us."

Harry glanced up in time to see a curtain swish back into place in the front window next door. "Damned impudence!"

"Inevitable though." Marion smiled. "What are they like, your neighbours?"

Harry stepped up onto the veranda and put down the luggage. "I've no idea," he replied.

"Then you've not lived here long?"

"About eighteen years. I tend to keep myself to myself," he added, by way of explanation.

"That's no overstatement by the sound of it," said Marion. She settled down in the chair she had occupied earlier. "At our time of life, we have to be careful," she observed. "After all, no man—and no woman for that matter—is an island. A person could get terribly lonely out here, you know."

"I have a few good friends, but I've never been much for socializing. Too fond of my own company, that's the trouble."

Marion nodded. "I used to be that way, until after my husband died. When you're married, you're rather spoiled for company. But since then, the newspaper work has introduced me to any number of people. The older you get, the more important friends become."

"Well, that's your opinion."

"I think it's most people's opinion. But strangely enough, a lot of elderly people become frightened to admit how lonely they are. Perhaps it makes them feel too vulnerable."

Harry coughed nervously, somewhat taken aback by the accuracy of the observation. Marion noticed the discomfort she had caused him, and she quickly switched the subject. She took a small notebook from her jacket pocket.

"I suppose we could start right away," she suggested. "Can you tell me anything about our man-eater?"

Harry sat back in his chair. "Precious little in the way of facts. Of course, I could speculate until the cows come home. But to begin with what I know for sure, he's old. From what I've seen, I'd put his age at around fifteen."

454

"You said 'he'. What makes you so sure it might not be a lady?"

"I've seen the tracks. He's an old gentleman. And he's wounded in his right foreleg, makes him walk with a pronounced dragging motion. It must slow him down considerably, and that's no doubt one of the chief reasons he's become what he is."

"Does there have to be a reason?"

"Oh, absolutely. A healthy tiger would never attack a human being. Tigers have their natural range of prey, and they prefer to stick to it. Also, they have a perfectly understandable fear of mankind. Our man-eater has conquered that fear, and you can bet that the major factor involved was the prospect of starvation."

"So why hasn't he been caught yet?"

"Well, I imagine his great age hasn't dulled his wits; on the contrary, it will have made him cunning. The mistakes of youth were made long ago, and he survived them. He's not about to start making any more at this stage of the game."

Marion smiled. "It sounds very much as if you admire the tiger."

"Admire him? Yes, you could say that. He's survived a long time, in a world where survival for creatures like him is increasingly difficult." Harry sighed. "Tigers and dinosaurs. There's not much room for either in this new Malaya."

"Dinosaurs?" She looked puzzled. "I'm sorry, I don't follow."

"Oh, forgive me. Just something a friend and I were talking about. But you know, I remember this place when it was nothing but a few huts perched on the edge of the jungle. How quickly it grew, estates hacked out of the forest; but then the British troops needed homes, and who was going to tell them that the jungle should be preserved? So in went the bulldozers, and the trees came down like ninepins. Wrong, all wrong. I couldn't see it then, of course. You don't when you're a part of it all." He put up his hand to shield his eyes from the sun. "Now the British are leaving, but the Malays have learned from our glorious example. Every time I go out, it seems there's a new building under way, a road being constructed. Every day they cut a little deeper into the green, whittling away, destroying the habitat. Progress, they call it."

"You're a conservationist," observed Marion.

"No." Harry chuckled. "I'm a dinosaur. But tell me, do you think this article you're writing will make any difference to what's happening here?"

Marion shook her head. "I lost that kind of naivety years ago.

But somebody might stop to think about it for a few moments. That's worth something, surely?"

Harry did not reply. He sat silently gazing out across his garden, like a king surveying his domain. Marion stared at him for a few moments, but he had retreated to a world of his own making.

MELISSA STROLLED aimlessly along the road, her gaze fixed thoughtfully on its sunbaked surface. Her recent dip in the swimming pool had refreshed her briefly, but already she felt sticky and uncomfortable, her nagging worries returning to assail her.

She was glad she was no longer feuding with Uncle Harry. Looking back, she could scarcely believe she had treated him so abominably. He had been very kind to her the other night, so forgiving it had made her feel ashamed. And to think it had all happened because of that stupid obsession with Bob Beresford.

"Hey there! Want a lift?"

Melissa nearly jumped out of her skin. She'd been so lost in her thoughts that she hadn't even noticed the vehicle coming up behind her. She spun round and found herself staring into the tanned, smiling face of Bob Beresford.

"Sorry, I didn't mean to startle you. Climb aboard!"

This was such an unexpected turn of events that Melissa was literally stunned. She stood at the roadside for several moments, debating what to do. Then she said coolly, "No, thanks. I'd rather walk." She turned and continued on her way.

Bob started the Land-Rover and brought it gently up alongside her. "All right, I get the picture," he said. "You're still mad at me, eh?"

"Mad at you, Mr. Beresford? Why on earth should I be?"

"For not turning up at the pool that time."

Melissa smiled. "Oh, you mean you didn't turn up either? And to think all this time I've been worried about standing you up, when in fact neither of us bothered to go."

"Well, I . . . I was detained. I wanted to go. Here, why don't you get in? It'll make it much easier to talk."

Melissa paused again, feigning indecision. Then, just as Bob began to reach over to help her in, she recommenced walking.

The Land-Rover cruised alongside her again. Bob was beginning to look faintly harassed. "Look. It's all very well giving me the freeze-out treatment. But I seem to remember you were far from

456

cold the time we made that little appointment. In fact, you were very friendly indeed."

"You were rather friendly yourself," retorted Melissa sharply. "But of course that was before the people of Kampong Machis stole your tiger."

"What? You surely don't think that's why I . . ."

Melissa shrugged. "I did get that impression." She began to walk on. This time she managed to travel some distance before the Land-Rover pulled alongside.

"I guess I owe you an apology," he murmured uncomfortably. "The fact is, you're right about that tiger. It was just so important to me, that's all. And remember, at the time I thought it was *the tiger*, the man-eater. But of course old Sullivan was right." Bob sighed. He glanced at Melissa hopefully. "You sure you won't accept a lift? I'm going your way, you know."

Melissa could feel her resolve weakening by the moment. Really, wasn't it absolutely typical? Just when she had made up her mind to forget that the wretched man even existed. "All right," she conceded at last. "Just a lift. No strings attached."

"Whatever you say!" Bob reached out and helped her up into the passenger seat. "It's good to be friends again," he observed. Melissa stared at him, amazed. He thinks everything's fine and dandy after one simple apology. Honestly, the sheer impudence of the man! But his handsome face was smiling winningly at her, and an appealing notion formed in Melissa's mind. If Bob behaved himself on the journey homeward, she just *might* invite him to dinner on Saturday night.

THE DOCTOR TAPPED the end of his pencil rhythmically against the scarred wooden surface of his desk while he waited patiently for the young girl to stop crying. She was hunched in her chair, sobbing her despair into the large white handkerchief that he had lent her. Over the years he had grown more and more accustomed to this scene.

Her sobbing subsided and she gazed imploringly up at him, her eyes full of tears.

"I'm afraid there can be no mistake," murmured the doctor. "You're two months pregnant. I am sorry that my diagnosis brings you no joy."

Lim sniffed, dabbed at her eyes. She had known in her heart

that she was with child, but she had put off coming to the doctor for as long as possible. Now, the truth could be avoided no longer.

"It's not too late for the condition to be terminated," the doctor went on. "You understand my meaning?"

She nodded, unable to meet his gaze.

"It is a simple enough operation. Of course, it requires money." He glanced at her inquiringly. "Do you know who the father is?"

"Yes."

The doctor looked at the forms in front of him. There it was in the girl's own laboured scrawl. Occupation: *Amah*. How many times had he been obliged to ask this next question!

"Is it your employer?"

Lim nodded.

"Well, then you must tell him. I have not the slightest doubt that he will be only too eager to pay for—"

Lim shook her head. "But I want to have the child," she cried. "I want to be its mother!"

The doctor stared at her in despair. "What are you saying?" he snapped. "Foolish girl, do you think for one moment that your employer will be willing to marry you? No doubt this man will soon be returning to his homeland. Do you honestly believe that he will take a Chinese wife with him?"

Lim gazed helplessly at the surface of the desk. "I cannot say," she stammered.

"Of course you cannot. Now, go home and tell this man what he has done. Do not waste much more time, or it will be too late! And no more foolish talk of keeping the child. One day you will meet a handsome young Chinese boy who may marry you; but not if you have a baby tucked under your arm, do you see? Go along now."

Lim got up, giving her eyes a last wipe with the handkerchief. The doctor was sorting through his papers. He had already dismissed her from his mind. She moved slowly towards the door. She could picture Bob tuan's face contorted with disbelief, and she flinched involuntarily from his outrage. She knew that despite the doctor's advice she could never bring herself to tell Bob the truth. She would just have to pray that he would offer to marry her. But come what may, she was determined that nobody would take this new life away from her. Come what may, she intended to be its mother.

458

HARRY TAPPED POLITELY on the door of the spare room. "Mrs. Burns . . . Marion? Dinner's served."

The door opened and Marion emerged. Harry stared, not prepared for such a transformation. She was wearing a blue silk evening dress. She had carefully brushed her short grey hair and had applied the merest touch of make-up to her eyes, emphasizing their lovely blue-grey tone. She looked five years younger and several pounds lighter than the woman who had arrived that morning.

Harry hadn't realized how openly he was staring at her until she said, "Well, I don't wear khakis *all* the time, you know!"

He coughed self-consciously. "Er, no, of course not. You look very . . ." He waved his hands ineffectually, realizing that he had forgotten how to compliment a woman. He reddened slightly. "Shall we go in?" he suggested.

"Yes, let's! I'm absolutely ravenous."

They strolled along the hallway and into the dining room. Pawn had laid out a feast on the large teak table. In typical Malay fashion, there was a plethora of small dishes from which the diner might choose: various curries, thick and fragrant with coriander and wild lime, varying from a mild chicken mixture, pale and creamy with coconut milk, to a fiery green curry laced with chillies and peppercorns. There was the much milder *nasi goreng*, a concoction of rice and prawns lightly spiced, and flecked with beaten egg; there was *kari kapitan*, shreds of chicken cooked with onions, chillies, yellow ginger and lemon juice; *satay*, barbecued kebabs of beef in a rich peanut sauce; and *nasi kandar*, white rice with a piquant shellfish and vegetable sauce. For sweet there was an equally magical array: freshly sliced papaya and winter melon were a mouth-watering follow-up to the hot dishes. *Mangosteen*, a succulent white fruit, had been sliced into thin segments and sprinkled with wild lime juice. There were chilled lychees in custard, and the greatest delicacy of all, the magnificently malodorous *durian* in all its thick glory.

"Where do you start?" inquired Marion wonderingly.

"Start by sitting down." Harry pulled out a chair for her, and then he sat opposite.

Marion surveyed the multitude of offerings. "It looks absolutely delicious," she announced. "Pawn is obviously a treasure."

The amah chose just this moment to bustle into the room,

beaming all over her wizened face. "I go now, tuan. Hope you and missy like dinner."

"Pawn, this is the finest meal you've ever made," said Harry.

"Thank you, tuan! I come 'morrow morning, wash dishes." She bowed slightly, and backed slowly out of the room.

Harry poured Marion a glass of ice-cold beer. "Cheers," he said, and they both drank. He took up his fork and spoon, and for the first time in ages he had a keen appetite. For several minutes the two of them ate in silence, then, as the edge of their hunger diminished, they fell into conversation.

"And what does your average tiger eat for dinner?" inquired Marion, as she reached out for a second helping of *kari kapitan*.

Harry smiled. "Well, hereabouts it's mostly wild pig or sambar deer, if they're around. If not, perhaps a wild gaur calf, provided he can get it away from the parents without being trampled for his pains. After that, well, tigers are adaptable. Monkeys, crabs, fish, rats—if he's hungry enough, he'll eat them. But it's at about that stage that the local cattle start to look tempting. And where there are cattle, there are usually people. And the more they see of people, the more they are liable to realize that we're a rather vulnerable and puny species. Rubber tappers are likely victims. They work alone and they're often out at strange hours."

"Oh yes, I remember one of our men being scared by a prowling tiger many years ago. It was difficult getting anyone to go back to work after—"

"Your men?" Harry looked puzzled. "I'm sorry, I don't understand."

"My husband owned a big plantation near Ipoh. Michael Burns, his name was, a Scotsman. He came out here just after the first war to make his fortune, and he brought a young and very green wife with him." She shook her head and smiled sadly. "Honestly, I didn't have the first idea what to expect. I'd never been further than the next village up till then. But Michael was an undaunted adventurer. He thrived on difficulties, and we prospered because of it. We had a long and very happy marriage."

Harry nodded. "Uh, how long ago did . . ."

"Oh, there's no need to be uncomfortable. He died a little over six years ago. He was making a routine business trip to Kuala Lumpur. Shortly after takeoff his plane crashed into the jungle. At least it must have been quick."

460

"I see. I'm very sorry."

"I know you are." She reached out and squeezed his hand reassuringly. "Then, of course, I was desolate. I walked around inside my grief, never going out, never seeing friends. Grief is a strange companion, you know. There's a side of you that loves—really relishes—the awful tragedy of it all. It's not that the grief isn't real, it's just that there's such a need to be *seen* to be suffering. You understand what I'm saying?"

"Yes. Yes, I think so."

"Well, I let it ruin my life for quite some time; and then one morning it just occurred to me that Michael would have hated to see me like that. He used to say that I could always make him laugh." She smiled fondly, then shrugged. "So that morning I took a good long look around the big empty house and the big empty gardens and the big empty plantation. And I realized that if I was ever going to pick up the pieces of my life, I'd have to go away from that place and start afresh. Before I married I had worked as a reporter on a local newspaper. I sat myself down there and then and composed a letter to the *New Straits Times*, explaining that I was the greatest feature writer in Malaya and that they would be totally insane if they didn't employ me. I put together an article about the rubber industry, the *Times* people liked it and used it, and it wasn't long before I had an offer of permanent employment. I sold the estate, moved to a little bungalow in Kuala Lumpur, and never regretted it for one instant. And that, in a nutshell, is how I come to be sitting here with you, eating this delicious meal. Would you pass the *satay* please?"

"Uh, yes, of course." Harry had become quietly mesmerized by her conversation. He was getting to like and admire this lady more by the moment. "You'd . . . never go back to being a housewife, if the chance came up? I mean, now that you've proved yourself?"

She glanced at him slyly. "Why, Mr. Sullivan! Is this some kind of proposal?"

Harry reddened. "Good heavens, no! I mean . . . I didn't . . ."

"Relax," she chuckled, "I was pulling your leg. No, I wouldn't dream of leaving journalism. It's my life now and a very rewarding one; also, taking it on taught me a very important lesson, one that I wish a few more people would get into their heads."

"Indeed? And what's that?"

"Simply that a person isn't automatically finished once they pass

461

their fiftieth birthday. It's a widely held belief that such is the case, I'm afraid. And if others let you know it often enough, it's possible to get yourself to believe it also. Hence, you end up doing nothing. You vegetate. But I, for instance, have produced the best, most fulfilling work of my life in the last few years. I may have grey hair, a weight problem, and slight deafness in one ear, but it doesn't mean I'm ready for the scrap heap."

"Bravo! I'll drink to that," said Harry, raising his glass.

The conversation continued late into the night. Harry couldn't remember when he had last enjoyed female company so much—when Meg was still alive, he supposed. Ah, such a long, lonely eternity ago. Thinking of her made him lapse momentarily into a melancholic silence, and Marion took the opportunity to observe that it was high time she went to bed. Harry nodded, and getting up, he began his nightly routine of securing the doors and windows, switching off the fans.

Before locking the front door, he strolled onto the veranda for a few moments. The insects had long since fallen silent, and the night air was warm and fragrant with the smell of frangipani blossoms. Harry took a deep breath. He had needed someone like Marion to make him realize how desperately lonely his life had been for such a very long time. He shook his head and went back into the house, bolting the door behind him.

Harry moved on, through the dining room and along the hallway. The bathroom was empty and he went in. While he was washing, he noticed several unfamiliar objects by the basin; a green toothbrush, a bottle of skin lotion, and a smaller one of perfume. He glanced critically at his reflection in the mirror. His hair needed cutting before too long, he decided. He went out of the bathroom, switching off the light. He was surprised to see that a light was on in his bedroom.

Marion was standing by the dressing table, gazing thoughtfully at the framed photograph of Meg. She glanced up as Harry entered. "Your wife?" she inquired softly. Harry nodded.

"She was a beauty," observed Marion. Then she put the photograph down and turned to look searchingly at him. "Harry," she murmured, "the way I see it, there are two things we can do. We can be terribly British and pretend that the interest we have in each other doesn't exist. But that would be a lie. I am attracted to you, Harry Sullivan, and from observing you this evening I know that you are attracted to me. On the other hand, we could, the two of us, have this night together. After all, we are two unattached, responsible, and fairly mature people." She smiled wickedly. "And it could be great fun," she concluded.

Harry scratched his head. "But," he began, "I'm sixty-seven years old."

"And I'm fifty-nine; does it really matter? You see, you've let yourself get brainwashed, Harry. You look just fine to me."

Harry felt the corners of his mouth lifting into a grin. He shook his head in undisguised admiration. "You make everything seem so easy, so right," he said.

"I try to," she replied. "Anyway, what do you think?"

Harry thought for a moment. Then reaching out, he killed the lights with a stroke of his hand.

12

Harry woke abruptly from a deep, dreamless sleep. He lay for several moments, gazing up at the ceiling. Then recollections of the previous night filtered into his mind, and he smiled. He turned his head, but Marion had already risen. It had been so good, the soft, reassuring warmth of another person. It was plain that Marion Burns was to be a special influence on his life. He could scarcely believe that he had met her only a day ago.

He climbed out of bed, slipped into his bathrobe, and went into the hall. Pawn's face popped out from the kitchen doorway. "Good morning, tuan!" she called, with a knowing grin.

Harry coughed uncomfortably. "Good morning, Pawn," he replied stiffly. "Good meal last night. Excellent." He slipped into the bathroom, where he showered and shaved, humming tunelessly to himself. Again he examined his reflection critically in the mirror, and this morning he decided that he had the kind of face that a woman could possibly love. He went back to his room, dressed, and feeling ready to meet the world went out to the veranda

Marion had placed her battered-looking portable typewriter on the rattan table and was pounding away on it. She had reverted to a loose bush jacket and a pair of knee-length shorts. He gave a loud "ahem" to announce his presence, but she was too intent on her work to give him any attention. He strolled nearer and glanced over her shoulder. The title of the article was, "The Hunter and the Hunted".

"Which is which?" he inquired politely.

Marion glanced up. "Oh, good morning!" she exclaimed. "It was such a lovely day, I thought I'd get up early and make a start. As for the title, that's just the idea! From one point of view it's the tiger who is the hunter. But one could just as easily say that the big property developers and highway builders are the real hunters and our old tiger was another victim. It's that kind of double-edged view I want to develop."

Harry nodded gravely. "Well, I shall certainly be interested to read it. Have you had breakfast yet?"

"No, I thought I'd wait for you. Besides, after last night's feast, a cup of tea is about all I can manage."

"Hmm. I'll second that. You carry on and I'll order some."

The morning passed pleasantly on the veranda; while Marion continued her typing Harry alternated between chatting, sipping tea, smoking cigars, and having forty winks. The day was imbued with the brilliant clarity that is so much a feature of the later months of the Malay year. High above jungle-clad hills, solitary fishing eagles drifted effortlessly on air currents that would carry them out over the glittering sea to where their dinner waited. Harry was nodding in the direction of sleep again, but was interrupted by the puttering of a car exhaust. Opening his eyes, he saw Dennis's car easing to a halt by the garden gate, but it was Melissa who got out and came strolling purposefully along the driveway. She hesitated when she noticed an unfamiliar figure on the porch, but then came on, no doubt intrigued.

"Good morning, Uncle Harry," she called. "I was hoping I'd catch you in. I didn't know you had company though."

"Ah yes, well, Melissa, let me introduce Mrs. Marion Burns. She's a journalist for the *New Straits Times*. She's going to be staying here for a few days. I'm, er, helping her with her research."

"Really? How exciting! And what exactly are you writing about, Mrs. Burns?"

"Tigers, my dear. Or more specifically, *the* tiger."

Melissa nodded. "I should have realized. Nobody knows more about tigers than Uncle Harry."

"So I've been told." Marion turned to Harry. "You didn't tell me that you had such a lovely niece."

"Oh, but I haven't! I mean, she's not really my niece."

"We're just good friends," chuckled Melissa, with a sly wink.

"Oh, I see," replied Marion, falling in with the joke. "Well, Harry, I must say, you've got excellent taste!"

Harry reddened somewhat. "Good heavens, Marion, you surely don't think . . ." he realized now that they were pulling his leg, and lapsed into silence, but not before Melissa had noticed his use of Marion's Christian name.

"We're having a little dinner party at our house tomorrow evening," Melissa said, "and of course it wouldn't be any kind of party without you, Uncle Harry. And since Mrs. Burns will be staying with you for a few days, she must come along too!"

Marion smiled. "Well, that's very kind of you."

"Not at all! It'll be a pleasure to have somebody new on the scene." Melissa grinned. "Also, Mrs. Burns, it could be very useful for you in a professional sense. You'll be able to chat with our *other* resident tiger expert."

"Oh no!" Harry's face fell dramatically. "Don't tell me Beresford is going to be there?"

Marion glanced at Harry, intrigued by his reaction. Receiving no elaboration from that quarter, she returned her gaze to Melissa.

"Bob Beresford, Mrs. Burns. The man who's doing his level best to shoot the man-eater. As you may have noticed from Uncle Harry's reaction, the two of them don't get on particularly well, so if the evening ends in squabbling, I apologize in advance."

"It sounds very interesting, I must say. I can hardly wait. That is, of course, if my host decides to go."

"He'd better," retorted Melissa, "or he'll never hear the last of it!" A car horn blared. "I'd better run along or they'll be leaving without me. Tomorrow evening then, eight o'clock. Lovely to meet you, Mrs. Burns." And then Melissa was racing off, anxious to tell her father about Uncle Harry's mysterious guest.

THE GAUR BULL was nervous. It kept raising its great horned head to glance this way and that, into the surrounding trees. Its flaring nostrils had caught no particular scent, but it was edgy and could not totally abandon itself to the pleasure of eating. Its mate did not share its caution. She kept her head low, swinging it in slow, rhythmic curves while she grazed in this lush and inviting jungle clearing.

But it was not the cow that Haji was watching, nor the heavily-muscled bull beside her. It was the leggy six-month-old calf accompanying the pair that demanded his attention. As luck would have it, Haji was downwind of the trio, and because of his lack of movement, he had not been spotted by any jungle sentries.

Still, the bull was alerted by some strange chemistry to the fact that all was not well. The great curved horns on its head were capable of ripping Haji open from end to end, so it was necessary that there be considerable distance between the bull and its more vulnerable offspring, if Haji were to bring off the attack. Luckily there seemed to be some chance of this happening. The calf was impatient to wander off. It kept moving across the clearing, its pink nose snuffling among roots and grasses. But each time it took more than half a dozen steps the bull would issue a low, guttural warning that would stop the calf in its tracks. However, after a few moments the calf would resume its course, one that was taking it nearer and nearer to the place where Haji was lying.

Haji licked his lips in anticipation. If the hunting had been better, he might not have considered so daring a raid; but the Uprights seemed to be very wary now. It was several days since anything more sustaining than marsh rats and frogs had entered his belly, and his hunger had grown intense. If he could get one good hold on the calf's throat, he could slip into the bushes through openings far too small to admit the vengeful parents. So Haji waited, absolutely still, his long body pressed tight against the ground.

The calf's life had recently undergone a major change. It had spent the first months of it as a member of a sizable herd, and because of this, it had received the best possible protection whenever danger was near. The adults would form themselves into a tightly packed circle with the youngsters in the middle, and, lowering their heads, they would present a near-impenetrable wall of bristling horns. But a month or so earlier a sudden, terrible sickness had come to the herd. In a matter of weeks the wild cattle had been decimated. Lacking a leader, since the dominant bull had fallen, the survivors had split up into small family groups and would remain that way until numbers increased sufficiently to form another herd. Life for the calf was now considerably more dangerous, but it had yet to realize it.

Glancing at its father from time to time, the calf gradually began to put distance between its parents and itself, and was well on the way to exploring the luxurious undergrowth that bordered the clearing. Haji tensed himself, muscles quivering. He raised his body just clear of the ground and focused his gaze on the calf. There would come a moment when everything was right, and then he would make his bid.

The bull raised its head and gave a loud snort of warning, aware at last of the considerable distance that separated the calf from them. Now the cow's head came up and she added her own, more plaintive voice to that of her mate. Haji waited, the calf's image trapped in the yellow orbs of his eyes. Silently he willed the animal to take a step closer.

The cow lowered her head, resumed her noisy ruminations, but her mate continued to stare challengingly at its disobedient offspring. The calf weakened a little, began to retrace its steps. Seeing this, the bull resumed its meal.

Now! The moment had to be now, or it was lost for ever! Haji's legs shot him out from cover like a bullet. His great front paws struck the ground, his back legs came in to power the leap that would carry him onto the calf, who had heard the slight noise of the tiger's approach and was half turning round in a clumsy panic. In the fraction of a second between leaps, Haji took careful aim and launched himself through the air.

It was the calf's panic that saved it. Its back legs gave way and it tipped sideways at the very instant Haji's outstretched paws touched it. It was too late to adjust the angle of flight; Haji's claws gouged deep furrows in the calf's tender hide, but impetus took the tiger across the body of his intended victim to tumble in a heap amid the undergrowth. With a roar of frustration, he thrashed to his feet. The calf was flopping helplessly on the ground, but a deafening bellow from the old bull's direction warned Haji that it was too late. There was a brief vision of a huge black shape bearing down on him, a pair of evil, curving horns. Instinctively Haji flipped his body sideways to avoid the full impact of the charge, but the thick part of one horn caught him with a crippling blow that drove the breath out of his body. The force of it rolled him over and over, blasting out his pain and humiliation. Wheeling round, the bull came back for another attempt. But this time, the cat threw himself into the bushes and vanished like a shadow.

The bull, maddened by the presence of the creature it hated most, flung itself at the spot where the tiger's rump had been a moment before, attacking the bushes in a brutal, senseless assault. By the time the bull realized that its adversary had escaped, Haji was over a mile away, lying up in a bamboo thicket and licking the spot where the bull's horn had carved a raw, stinging stripe.

IT BEING A SATURDAY, one of the nights that Harry habitually went to the mess, the young trishaw boy turned up at the accustomed time and was surprised to find that, as well as a different destination, he had two passengers instead of one. Accepting this with his usual resignation, he took a crumpled piece of paper from his pocket, the worn stub of a pencil from behind his ear, and placed another tick on his list.

"It ought to be two ticks tonight," Harry reminded him. "In fact, it should be *five*, because this is a longer trip."

The boy shook his head. "Grandfather would not like." But he did agree to putting down an extra tick for Marion.

"Poor little devil," whispered Marion as she eased her frame into the precarious seating. "For carrying someone of my build, he should have a hundred ticks."

Harry chuckled as the trishaw glided onto the road. It was mercifully cool, and a lively breeze, fragrant with jacaranda and frangipani, rippled through the fronds of the coconut palms. Off in the darkness, they could hear the restless sound of waves crashing onto the beaches far below. Nearer at hand, there was the weird rhythmic croaking of hundreds of tree frogs, the drone of unseen insects. Marion turned to look into the unfathomable green depths at the side of the road. "What do you imagine our tiger is doing now, Harry?"

"Oh, he's on the prowl, no doubt. They do most of their hunting at night."

The trishaw boy took a deep breath and increased his rate of pedalling dramatically. Marion had an abrupt mental image of a lean striped shape loping silently along behind them, and the idea was so horrible she put it out of her mind instantly. Both she and the trishaw boy were relieved to see the bright lights of their destination come into view.

Harry alighted and helped Marion out.

"The tuan at this house has promised to take us back in his motorcar," he told the trishaw boy. "You'd best get home to your family."

468

"OK, tuan. Have nice party. I go now!"

Harry led the way up to the Tremaynes' front door and rang the bell. After a few moments the door opened and there stood Kate, wearing a simple white cotton dress.

"Hello, Harry," she said. "For once, you're the last to arrive." She smiled at Marion. "And you must be M. Burns! I read your articles every week. I could hardly believe our luck when Melissa told us you were coming." She shook Marion's hand warmly.

"Thank you, Mrs. Tremayne. It was lovely of her to invite me."

Kate took them along the hallway to the sitting room, where they found Melissa and Bob Beresford deep in conversation, and Dennis nursing a drink. As the newcomers entered he leaped up and hurried over to them. "Harry, old man! Nice to see you." He was obliged to shout because of the loud rock music blaring out of the stereo. "And Miss Burns, isn't it?" He extended a hand awkwardly and Marion shook it.

"It's Mrs. Burns, actually, but Marion will do fine."

"Can I get you a drink? We have sherry, martini."

"Tiger beer, please, if you have any."

"Oh, yes indeed." Dennis glanced sideways at Melissa, who was evidently far too enraptured by the conversation of Bob Beresford to notice that the others had arrived. "Melissa," he snapped, "can't you turn that down a bit? I'm sure Mrs. Burns doesn't want to be pounded by that terrible din."

"This is at the top of the L.P. charts in Britain," protested Melissa. "Hello, Uncle Harry, Mrs. Burns. Besides, Daddy, if you knew the trouble I've had getting a copy—"

"That's not the point. Not everybody shares your questionable taste in music, you know."

Marion stepped gracefully in to pour oil on troubled waters.

"Don't turn it down on my account. I rather like Jimi Hendrix."

Melissa's mouth dropped open, as did Bob's beside her. "Golly, Mrs. Burns. How did . . ?"

"An old fogey like me know about Jimi Hendrix?" said Marion, completing the question.

"Oh, gosh, no, I didn't mean . . . It's just unusual, that's all." Now Melissa did reach out to turn down the volume control, a look of awe on her face.

"It's really simple," Marion said. "You see, Melissa, as well as writing weekly features for the *New Straits Times*, I also handle the music column. You may have read my article on Pink Floyd last week."

"You? But the music column is written by somebody called D. Rodgers."

Marion took a little bow. "That's me. Or rather, it's one of several names I use. Incidentally, I get lots of review copies. Perhaps I could send you some when I get back to Kuala Lumpur."

"Really? Wow! That would be fantastic!"

Harry just stood where he was in amazement. He learned new things about Marion every time she opened her mouth. Dennis took his arm and steered him towards the kitchen. "Come and give me a hand with the drinks."

"What? Oh, yes, of course."

They went out to the kitchen, leaving Melissa to introduce Bob to Marion.

"I say," murmured Dennis, "she's marvellous, isn't she? How on earth did you come to be mixed up with her?"

Harry poured beer into a glass. "Simple, really. She's writing about the tiger and she needed an expert. That's me. Cheers!"

"Yes, but how did she come to be staying with you? You know, there's going to be all kinds of gossip flying around."

"Hmmm, yes." Harry smiled drily. "I shouldn't wonder. Anyway, it's all quite aboveboard. There were no hotels in the area, so Marion suggested that she stay at my place."

"*She* suggested?" Dennis smiled, rubbing his chin thoughtfully.

"Well, Marion is a . . . very interesting woman," Harry said.

"What's that supposed to mean?"

"Make of it what you will, my friend."

"No, come on, don't be so cryptic. What's going on here?"

Kate bustled into the kitchen. "Come along, you two, people are dying of thirst out there! Dennis, Marion's waiting for that drink."

"Yes, dear." With a sigh of resignation, Dennis picked up the tray and went back into the sitting room.

Later, when dinner was under way, the conversation centred mainly on the food—roast beef and Yorkshire pudding. Then Marion changed the subject.

"Mr. Beresford, are you having much luck in your attempts to shoot the tiger?"

"Evidently not," muttered Harry in a voice just loud enough to be audible to everyone present.

470

Bob shook his head. "He's a clever devil and no mistake. The nearest I've come to him is a couple of wild potshots in the dark. The fact is, *he's* come closer to getting me. Chased me up a tree the other night. He came sneaking up behind me. The first clue I had of his being there was when I turned and saw him staring me in the face."

"Fantastic," Marion gasped. "Is it common for that to happen?"

"I couldn't tell you, Mrs. Burns. I'm a beginner in the tiger stakes. But I'm sure Mr. Sullivan there knows."

Marion turned to Harry. "Well?"

Harry chewed methodically for a few minutes before replying. "No, not common. But then, man-eating itself is comparatively rare. I've said before, this is a wily old brute. It's going to take a fair deal of wit—and a large slice of luck—to bring him down."

"One way or another, I intend to do it," replied Bob without hesitation, and Marion was slightly disturbed by his tone.

"What I can't understand," she continued, "is why you and Mr. Sullivan have never got together over this tiger business. Surely with his experience and your prowess as a marksman . . ." It went very quiet at the table. The clatter of cutlery and the sound of munching seemed painfully loud, but Marion pursued the point with calm determination. "I mean, when people are being killed, surely any personal differences you have should go by the board."

"It's not a matter of personal differences, Marion," said Harry softly. "As I've told Mr. Beresford before, I'm far too old to go gallivanting about after this tiger. It's as simple as that."

"Too old?" murmured Marion. "That's not my impression."

Harry reddened. Melissa clasped a napkin to her mouth to conceal a smirk. "Anybody like another drink?" asked Dennis uncomfortably, but he got no reply. Only Bob seemed to have missed the implication of Marion's remark.

"Mrs. Burns, there's nothing I'd like better than to have Mr. Sullivan along. I've tried, but he seems reluctant to get involved."

"Not at all!" snapped Harry. "But it's been *years* since—"

"Surely tigers haven't changed that much," reasoned Marion.

Now Melissa joined the fray. "I honestly think, Uncle Harry, you should give it a try. We'll all be pulling out soon. What will happen if the man-eater is still at large?"

"Well, good heavens, girl, there are people up at the Game Department."

471

"They haven't been much use so far, have they?"

Harry sighed. He toyed with the food on his plate for a few moments. "I suppose . . . if it was just in an advisory capacity, as a tracker perhaps. I suppose I could give it *one* try."

"Now you're talkin', Mr. Sullivan! The next time that tiger makes a kill, I'll be calling. You just keep your gun oiled and polished."

"I always have," Harry retorted.

The atmosphere lifted dramatically with Harry's decision, and the party was able to progress much more smoothly. For Marion it was a minor victory: her bullying him into action was another step along the path to the reforming of Harry Sullivan. As far as she was concerned, he was capable of a great deal more than he gave himself credit for.

13

Haji hardly dared to move. The Upright was not aware of him, he was sure of that. But the hunger was now so terrible, so all-consuming, that the fear of missing yet another kill made the cat uncharacteristically timid. The fact that the Upright carried a black stick was a worry, and there was the knowledge that this was not a stranger, but a tall, pale Upright who often appeared at the scene of Haji's kill. Haji knew his scent and it was this, more than the other two factors, that had kept him lying in concealment for over an hour, watching and waiting.

Perhaps the Upright had learned that this was the place where Haji had made his unsuccessful attack on the gaur calf the previous day. Now a sleek white goat was tethered in the centre of the clearing, grazing calmly. The Upright was barking instructions at two smaller companions, who were up in a large *kapok* tree, roping some wooden contraption into place. The Upright's black stick hung across his shoulder. He was no more than ten feet away from the place where Haji was lying.

The ball of emptiness in Haji's guts contracted spasmodically, and he ran his tongue around the inside of his mouth. Already his strength was depleted. If another day were to pass without sustenance, he would surely die. He fixed his gaze intently on a dark sweat stain that ran down the back of the Upright; he let the image burn into his vision until he saw nothing but the tall, straight back of his next victim. And he let a terrible rage burn up within him, push aside the fear that had so far held him back. He came out of cover in a swift run, an engine of destruction.

One of the smaller Uprights screamed an alarm from the shelter of the tree. The pale Upright whipped round, and for an instant Haji registered the round face frozen in shock and terror. Then the face swooped nearer as Haji's legs propelled him upwards; the face was a great moon that tumbled earthwards as Haji's jaws closed around the throat beneath it. The black stick went clattering uselessly away. The Upright shuddered violently for a few moments, his arms hitting out ineffectually. Then he went limp, flopped back onto the ground, and was still.

The Upright's two companions gibbered and shrieked in the tree fork, and Haji let go of the carcass to direct a great shattering roar in their direction. With gasps of terror, they launched themselves higher into the tree as they realized they were still within reach of a leap. In the confusion one of the Uprights lost his footing, slipped, and came plummeting earthwards, to land with a heavy thud six feet from Haji's side. The tiger took an involuntary step back, then roared again, sending a blast of power full into the face of the Upright, who promptly fainted.

Haji gazed at the fallen creature for a moment, then padded over to him and gave an exploratory sniff. There was no blood on the man, and Haji simply did not associate him with the idea of food. Instead, he moved back to the meat he had already slain, gripped it firmly, and began to drag it away. Hanging from a precariously slender branch, the remaining Upright gazed down, wide-eyed, scarcely believing the scene he had just witnessed. The tiger vanished into the bushes, taking the body of the tuan with him; nevertheless, the man allowed several minutes to elapse before he climbed down to revive his uninjured and incredibly lucky comrade. This accomplished, the two men headed for their kampong, screaming at the top of their lungs.

HARRY PUT DOWN the manuscript with an air of finality. "It's good," he said simply. "Very good."

"It's only the rough draft," Marion reminded him.

"Even so, I think you've stated all the angles very effectively. You've managed to evoke sympathy for the tiger, while at the same time admitting that he must be killed."

Marion smiled. "I'm glad you saw that in it. It was one of the points I was worried about." She took the manuscript back, patted it softly. "This must be in to my editor by tomorrow afternoon. That means I'll have to be moving on tomorrow morning."

"Oh." Harry gazed thoughtfully at the rattan table. He had of course expected this, but had forced himself not to think about it. "Must you go quite so soon? I thought tomorrow, we might—"

She stilled him with a wave of her hand. "Harry, it's my job. I have to."

"Yes. But look here, surely one more day couldn't make that much . . ." He broke off as a familiar vehicle came lurching dangerously up the street and slewed to a dusty halt at Harry's garden gate. An equally familiar figure leaped from the driver's seat, and in his haste to enter the garden vaulted the gate and came running breathlessly up the path.

"Beresford! What is the meaning of this?"

"No time, Mr. Sullivan, no time! Get your gear quickly, there's been another killing over by Kampong Wau. Happened a couple of hours ago, I just got the news."

Harry was not in the mood to go racing off into the jungle, and he silently cursed the agreement he'd made the night before. Perhaps if he could stall for time, the impatient Aussie might give up and be on his way. "Now look here, Beresford. I haven't got my kit sorted out yet and besides—"

Bob waved him to silence. "I think you'll *want* to come along, Mr. Sullivan," he said. "See, it wasn't some stranger who got killed this time. It was Mike Kirby."

"Mike!" Harry's eyes widened in disbelief. "There must be some mistake. Mike wouldn't be that careless. He's been hunting those jungles for years."

"I've talked to the boys who were with him. He was setting up a *machan*, and the cat came right up behind him. Mike didn't have a chance. Now, are you coming?"

Harry glanced at his feet. "I'll get my things together," he said, and he strode into the house. Bob sat down impatiently to wait.

"Mike Kirby," mused Marion sadly. "I've only met him once, but he struck me as such a *capable* man."

Bob shrugged. "It only takes one mistake, Mrs. Burns. Besides, he had no reason to suppose the cat would sneak up like that. It might just as easily have been me."

474

A sense of profound unease took Marion, and she remembered that it was her own interference that had got Harry involved in this venture. She gazed across the hot, silent garden, wishing she could explain the sudden terrible fear that had settled in her heart.

IT WAS CRAMPED and uncomfortably hot up on the *machan*. Harry and Bob sat side by side, sweating profusely in the dank heat of the night. They were both in a foul temper, though the older man had managed to suffer in silence, sitting as rigid as a dummy behind the thick screens of foliage he had so painstakingly erected, his rifle resting across one knee. Bob sneaked a glance at him and wondered how he could keep so still. Ever since calling at Harry's house, the Australian had regretted the whole idea. First, after nearly an hour's delay, the old man had emerged from the bungalow looking like the Great White Sahib himself, in two layers of clothing, a waterproof jacket over a thick khaki shirt, puttees and long drill trousers. Then he had spent an eternity packing odds and ends into a light haversack and even longer saying goodbye to the ubiquitous Mrs. Burns. By the time they were ready to drive away, Bob was positively screaming with impatience.

But hunting up the kill was a relatively smooth affair. The old man had followed the pugmarks with commendable efficiency to the hideous remains of Mike Kirby's body. At this point Harry insisted on saying a few prayers over the body, a gesture that Bob found a waste of valuable time. Next, Harry organized the two accompanying Malays into setting up the *machan*. The exact positioning of the platform seemed of great importance to him, and he was continually ordering the builders to shift it an inch or so to the left or right. When at long last the *machan* was erected to Harry's satisfaction it was nearly dusk, and the Malays scrambled off towards their kampong, casting nervous glances over their shoulders.

With a sigh of relief Bob clambered up into position. Once beside him, Harry issued a terse order. "Don't forget, not a sound nor a movement." Since then, the old man had not spoken a word. Three hours had crept leadenly by, with not the slightest interruption by any creature larger than the inevitable mosquitoes, of which there seemed to be thousands. Bob was being eaten alive and had begun to realize that shorts and bare arms were not the best outfit for night hunting; now the maddening itch on every bit of exposed flesh was making him wriggle on the hard wooden seat like an agitated monkey. At last Harry fumbled in his haversack and passed a small bottle to Bob. The Australian lifted the cap and sniffed.

"Strewth!" he gasped. "What's this?"

"Sssh!" hissed Harry. "Insect repellent. Put it on and shut up."

So that explained why the old man was able to keep so still. Bob was hardly surprised that the stuff was so effective, it smelled so bad it was liable to repel anything that came within range. He began to daub the vile stuff over his arms and legs.

Harry looked away, across the moonlit clearing below. Through a tiny slit in the foliage, he could see the corpse of his friend. It made Harry feel cheap and degraded to sit up like this, using Mike as the bait in a trap. Indeed, his first impulse upon finding the body had been to give it a decent burial, but the necessity of killing the tiger before it struck again had outweighed the demands of decency. Mike had no family; at least that was a blessing. Harry wondered glumly if it would be like that for him too. With the Tremaynes gone to England, there would only be old Pawn, perhaps Ché . . . and Marion, he supposed. He felt abruptly annoyed that he should be forced to spend the last night of her stay sitting up a tree in the middle of the jungle with a boorish Australian at his side. Life could be very unjust.

He started violently as a brilliant light flared up beside him. "What the . . ?" He stared at Bob in disbelief. The confounded man had just lit a cigarette.

"Sorry, Mr. Sullivan, but I was . . ."

"You . . ! *Gaahhh!* Don't you realize, you must have alerted every animal for miles around?"

"Hey, calm down a bit. It was only for a moment!"

"You oaf! It's quite plain to me why you've not managed to kill this tiger, if that's any sample of your bushcraft. Well, I've had enough of this fiasco. I'm going home!"

"Hold on, you can't give up that easily."

"Oh, can't I? Well, we'll just see about that." Flicking on the flashlight on his gun barrel, he climbed down at a dignified pace, his gun held ready to fire at anything that might come lunging out of the darkness. He could hear his reckless companion thrashing down the tree and hurrying after the bobbing glow of Harry's torch.

"Well, there's one thing for sure," said Bob. "After tonight I'm giving up on the *machan*. The next kill that happens, I'm going after that stripey on foot."

"Don't be a fool," replied Harry scornfully. "You do that and you'll wind up as dead as Mike Kirby. He was a more experienced man than you, my friend, and look how it ended up for him."

Bob fell silent and did not speak again through the long, gloomy trek back to Kampong Machis.

MARION'S FEW BELONGINGS were packed into the blue Volkswagen. The sun was well up on the horizon, and it was time for her to go. She walked slowly along the driveway with Harry beside her. They had both been dreading this moment.

"It's another beautiful morning," observed Marion lamely.

Harry nodded. "I wish you didn't have to go so soon," he murmured. "Things will seem quiet here without you."

She squeezed his arm affectionately. "Oh, come along, you old sourpuss! You've got an expression on your face like a mourner at an English funeral. We'll see each other again."

"Will we?" He sounded unconvinced.

"Here." She produced an envelope and handed it to him.

"What's this?"

"My address and phone number in Kuala Lumpur. Any time you care to look me up, there's where I'll be. There'll always be a place for you to stay, Harry." She looked at him suspiciously. "Not that I believe for one moment that you'll actually make the effort to get out there and see me."

"I haven't been up to Kuala Lumpur for years," he muttered.

"All the more reason why you should! And of course when work permits me to get up here, I'll be more than glad to return the favour. Remember, you've got a lot more free time than me."

"You'll be due for retirement soon, won't you?"

She chuckled, shook her head. "When my newspaper decides they want to be rid of me, they'll have a fight on their hands." She glanced at her wristwatch. "I really must go if I'm to submit this copy on time."

He reached out his hand to bid her a formal farewell, but she brushed his hand aside and moved forward to put her lips against the roughness of his suntanned cheek.

"Till next we meet," she whispered. "Remember now. Come and stay." And she stepped back to the Volkswagen, opened the door, and climbed in. She slammed the door shut, and wound the window down. "Goodbye, Harry. Thanks for everything!" Then the car was pulling away, kicking up a thin haze of dust. Harry stood staring glumly after it, shielding his eyes from the glare with one hand. The car rounded the curve of the road and Marion waved briefly before vanishing from sight. After a few moments the rumble of the engine faded into the distance.

Somewhere in the treetops at the end of the garden, a brain-fever bird was singing its maddening phrase over and over, its shrillness an insolent intrusion into the silent morning. Harry climbed the steps to the veranda and went on into the house.

It had never seemed so big and so empty before.

BOB GLANCED AROUND the deserted confines of the mess. Besides Melissa and himself, there were two other people, drinking at the far end of the bar. "Why did we come here?" he said. "It's dead. Why don't we go into Kuala Trengganu? There's a few nightclubs there, we could do it in style."

Melissa shook her head. "I've got a better idea. We could get a few cans of beer and just drive out somewhere. The beach would be nice. Might be a bit cooler."

Bob's face lit up at the notion. "Sounds great to me." He glanced at his watch. "You have to be home any particular time?"

"Not me. I'm a big girl now." Melissa looked directly into Bob's eyes for a minute and then glanced quickly away.

"Right," he murmured. "That's what we'll do then. Cheers!" He raised his glass, and they both drank. "I'll get Trimani to organize us some booze. Don't go away now!" And he was gone, hurrying off in the direction of the bar.

Melissa smiled triumphantly. She'd hooked him this time, sure enough. She could almost visualize the look of frustrated defeat on Victoria Plumly's face as the silver bullet was submitted for inspection. It would all be so very rewarding! With a grin, she drained the last of her gin fizz.

A peculiar warmth was spreading through her, and she felt pleasantly woozy. She stared up at the snarling tiger's head above the door and she growled, curving her fingers into mock claws. The tiger seemed momentarily to register surprise, and she stifled a giggle with her hand.

A hand squeezed her shoulder. It was Bob, with a paper bag tucked under his arm. "Hey, what's up with you?" he inquired.

"Nothing at all! Come on, let's go! This place is the pits!"

The pair of them made a noisy and rather undignified exit, watched by the silent and melancholy Trimani, who was polishing the already sparkling bar top with a spotless white duster.

"Come on, I'll race you to the car!" cried Bob, and he loped down the steps, Melissa following.

Once in the car park they climbed into the Land-Rover and roared out onto the coast road. Bob pushed the pedal down to the floorboards. A rush of fragrant, humid air blasted into Melissa's face, blowing her hair back in a tangled flurry. She rummaged around for the cans of beer and opened two of them, chilled froth spattering in their wake. She passed a drink to Bob and took a long swallow herself. "Where are we going exactly?" she yelled, the wind snatching her breath away.

"Wait and see," he retorted, with a mischievous grin. He leaned the car into a tight bend and powered into the straight. Melissa winced but kept a brave face for Bob's benefit. "Not going too fast, am I?" he yelled.

"I like going fast," she replied, and instantly regretted it as he took this as an excuse to drive even more recklessly.

Happily the journey was not a long one. A few miles along the road Bob turned off onto a deserted track and took the vehicle bumping and lurching through ranks of scrub jungle. Unexpectedly the ground dropped away to a long silvery stretch of beach and an endless vista of dark blue ocean lapping at the shore. The sea air smelled fresh and cool after the humid dankness.

"It's beautiful," sighed Melissa. "How come I've never been here?"

"It's not that well-known. Apparently the leathery turtles come to lay their eggs here at a certain time of the year. The locals know about it, and it's the only time you're liable to see people here."

"With our luck, it'll be tonight," giggled Melissa. She turned to him inquiringly. "Who told about this place, Bob? Was it your amah, perhaps?"

"My . . ." He glanced at her in surprise, then looked away again, reddening slightly. "What makes you say that?"

"I heard you had a thing for your little Chinese maid, that's all. It's nothing to be ashamed about, you know. Lots of men . . ."

"You don't want to believe everything you hear, my girl." He edged closer to her, slipped an arm across her shoulder. But she leaped from the vehicle and fled giggling along the beach. "Come back here," he shouted impatiently.

"No!" she shrieked defiantly. "You'll have to catch me first! I'm the tiger and you, you're the great white hunter. When you catch me, I'm all yours!"

Bob swore, his frustration rapidly getting the better of him; but he went racing after her, his long legs rapidly eating up the distance between them. Melissa veered right towards the surf, and then they were crashing through the shallows, their feet exploding the surface of the water into shattered mirrors of flying foam. Steadying himself, Bob lunged forward, grasped Melissa round the waist and dragged her out of the water, onto the firm sand higher up. She was laughing uncontrollably as he pulled her roughly against him and gazed at her face for a moment. In the moonlight it looked oddly white, almost doll-like. Desire coursed through him.

"I've caught you now," he said hoarsely. "You're mine. I can do anything I want with you."

Melissa stopped laughing. As Bob's mouth closed on hers she was both fearful and exhilarated. She lay gazing up at the vastness of the night sky, only dimly aware of Bob's impatient hands as he fumbled with her clothing. After what seemed an eternity, his handsome face moved into the range of her vision. She was momentarily perturbed by the expression in his eyes, a cold, ruthless aggression she'd never seen before, but she dismissed the idea. Nothing would spoil the perfection of this moment. Nothing.

She held her breath, savouring the warm perfumed air, the restless pounding of surf on sand. In the darkness she could see the glint of moonlight on the bullet-shaped pendant that hung around his tanned neck. She reached up to finger it inquisitively. Afterwards, she would ask him for it. It would be a keepsake, a love token.

And then suddenly, inexplicably, a sharp, wrenching pain tore through her, making her gasp.

"Bob!" she cried. "Bob, no, stop!"

"Don't be silly! Just relax."

But Melissa began to struggle. Without her even knowing it, her hand clenched tightly around the silver neck chain and snapped it, pulling it free.

"Bob, please, *no!*" The horror of the situation overcame her now, driving away the last numbing traces of the alcohol in her system. All she could see was his face above her, the expression on it that of a wild beast. It occurred to Melissa in one horrible flash that the man who was supposed to be making love with her was barely even aware of her presence. He was making love to himself. And she . . . she could only lie there miserably, praying for it to be finished.

THE SOUND OF THE CRASHING WAVES intruded into Melissa's confusion as the last of her tears subsided. Dimly she realized that Bob was sitting on the beach some distance away, his back turned to her.

"What was all that fuss about?" he asked at last.

She sat up, glared at him. "You beast!" she sobbed. "You filthy, horrible . . ." Words failed her. She was not schooled enough in the language of curses to articulate her real feelings.

"Hey, hey, steady on! What's the matter?"

"I want to go home," she announced flatly. She stood up, collected her clothes from the sand, and began to walk back towards the Land-Rover. She felt soiled, cheapened by the sordid encounter. Shame brought fresh tears to her eyes. She lifted a hand to wipe them away and became aware that she was holding something in her clenched fist. She opened her hand and gazed at the object blankly. It was the bullet-shaped pendant.

"Look, what's the hurry?" demanded Bob, stumbling after her. "It's early yet. Let's have a few drinks."

Melissa's eyes narrowed, and she closed her fist around the pendant. She whirled back to face him. "You're disgusting."

"Well, that's charming, isn't it?" The two of them were nearing the Land-Rover now. "I take you out, give you a good time—"

"Give yourself a good time, more like!" She shook her head. Wooziness had given way to a harsher, more disagreeable sensation in her stomach. She took a deep breath. "I want to go home."

"Don't you think you're laying it on a bit strong, Melissa?"

She looked at him for a moment. It was as though she were seeing him for the first time and it was not a particularly agreeable sight. "I knew you were arrogant," she murmured. "But I didn't realize how deep it went. You are a nasty piece of work."

"Oh, I see. Well, that's absolutely typical! A girl gives you the old come-on—and let's get it straight, it was you that was asking for the business all the way along—then you find you don't like it so much, and you start acting all high and mighty. Well, it won't wash, Melissa."

Melissa nodded sadly. "You're right about one thing, Bob. I certainly got what I was asking for, didn't I? Believe me, I won't make the same mistake in a hurry. Because, Mr. Lady-killer Beresford, I'm the sort of girl who learns by her mistakes. So the next time I bump into a stupid, insufferable pig disguised as a human being, I'll know better than to give him the time of day." She reeled aside and stumbled over to the Land-Rover, rested her weight against it. The turbulence in her stomach was rapidly worsening. "Take me home," she wailed miserably.

There was a long uncomfortable silence. The pounding of waves seemed to rise to a crashing crescendo. When Bob spoke again, his voice was quieter, more considerate. "Look, maybe I was a bit hard on you. But it's crazy to fight like this. The two of us, we've only got a week left. Surely we can work it out. If we could just . . ."

The rest of the words seemed to fade as a terrible queasiness filled Melissa's stomach. She gasped for air a couple of times and then dropped to her knees, her eyes blurring with tears, and was sick. She was dimly aware of his voice talking soothingly somewhere behind her, and there was a brief touch on her shoulder.

"Leave me alone," she groaned. And the hand and the voice were gone. She had the presence of mind to keep her own hand grasped tightly around the bullet-shaped charm, telling herself that it was better to come through the ordeal with something to show for it, rather than nothing at all.

14

Melissa moved slowly along the street. Behind sunglasses her eyes flitted restlessly left and right, as though she were afraid that somebody might be observing her—worse still, that somebody might know the dark secret of the silver pendant in the pocket of her shorts. She felt sure that Bob must have missed it by now, and she had spent a sleepless night anticipating a knock at the door of her parents' house and Bob's angry voice demanding the return of his good-luck charm. But now it was early morning, and Melissa was heading for a long-arranged assignation.

Her parting with Bob the previous night had been swift and terrible. He had leaned over and attempted to plant a kiss on her cheek. She had brought her hand across his face with all the strength she could muster and then stalked grimly into the house. This morning she had been up and about uncharacteristically early.

The old saying about things looking better in the daylight could not be applied in this instance. She still felt desolate about her own stupidity, and the conviction that she had been cheapened and soiled would not go away.

She came to a halt outside a parched stretch of lawn where Victoria Plumly lay sunning herself in a ridiculously skimpy red bikini. In the chaise longue beside her Alison Weathers did likewise. Melissa stood watching them for a moment. Her initial impression was of a basking hippopotamus sharing its favourite grazing spot with a huge stick insect.

The girls glanced up in surprise as the gate creaked open. They too were wearing sunglasses, and the three sets of secretive eyes gazed impassively at one another. "Oh," said Victoria, "it's you, Melissa." Her voice was flat. "Haven't seen you for ages."

"No, I've been busy." Melissa glanced off towards the house, where the shadowy figure of Mrs. Plumly waved briefly from the kitchen. "Getting your panic tan in, I see," she observed coolly. She was referring to the blotchy red freckles that covered Victoria's body. "Who knows, if you lie there long enough, you just might manage to mass them all in together."

Victoria didn't bat an eyelid. "That's always the problem for those of us with more *sensitive* skin," she mused sweetly. Beside her, Alison gave a brief giggle.

Melissa slid her hand into her pocket and let her fingers caress the cool shape of the pendant. "When are you two shipping out?"

"I'm leaving the day after tomorrow," announced Alison. "Victoria's got another three weeks."

"My goodness. What will you do without each other?" wondered Melissa. "Why, it'll be like Bogart without Bacall. Peaches without cream. Mutt without Jeff—"

Victoria interrupted irritably. "I hope you realize there's not much time left for paying that money you owe me," she snapped. "Let's face it, Melissa, anybody who doesn't keep their part of a bet isn't worth knowing."

"I agree with you," said Melissa calmly. "That's why I know that you'll be ready to do the decent thing." And she pulled the pendant from her pocket with a flourish and let it dangle in front of Victoria's shaded eyes.

There was a brief, terrible silence. Then Alison wailed, "She's got it, Vicky! She's won the bet!"

"I can see that!" growled Victoria. She snatched the pendant from Melissa and peered at it. "But how are we to know this is the real one? She could have bought this in Kuala Trengganu."

Melissa gave a derisive laugh. "I must say, Victoria, your faith in me is touching! Anyway, there's some inscription on it that you can barely make out. For goodness' sake, you can see how old it is. So when you're ready, I'll have that money, please."

"I don't have it right this minute," murmured Victoria. "You'll have to give me a day or so." She handed the pendant back to Melissa and then gazed at her thoughtfully. "So. You finally got Bob Beresford, did you?" She paused for a moment to allow Alison's inevitable bout of giggling to subside. "His pretty little amah would be a bit upset about it, especially with things the way they are now." She laughed, and Alison joined her.

"What are you two on about?" Melissa demanded.

"Us?" Victoria feigned wide-eyed innocence. "Oh, nothing at all." But the girls continued to smile smugly. "You know, Alison," continued Victoria, "the last time I saw Melissa, I offered to tell her all about it, but she just didn't want to know. Oh, Melissa, I do hope you won't end up like poor Lim, holding the baby."

"What? What was that?"

"Oh, now I've gone and let the cat out of the bag!" Victoria settled herself back on the chaise longue. "Well, after all, you must have known he was the reckless type."

"Are you saying that Bob's amah is pregnant?" demanded Melissa.

"So the grapevine says. The funny thing is that everybody knows about it. Everybody but Bob, that is." She laughed briefly. "It's an ugly fact, I'm afraid. Lim made the mistake of confiding in Mrs. Hoskin's amah and she told Mrs. Blair's amah, then . . ."

An all-encompassing rage erupted in Melissa's head, so sudden and so powerful that she was barely aware of her own actions. One moment she was standing gazing impassively down at Victoria's reclining body; the next, she was leaning forward over the chaise, slapping the girl's face. Victoria gave a loud, indignant squeal of protest and twisted away from Melissa's unexpected attack, upsetting the chaise and sending her heavy body sprawling onto the dry grass. "Alison! She's gone berserk!"

Her howl of pain was enough to bring Mrs. Plumly out of the house. "I say, what's going on out there?"

And then, as suddenly as it had begun, Melissa's anger subsided. She stooped, picked up the pendant, and crammed it back in the pocket of her shorts. She glanced at Alison, who gulped warily.

"You'd better clear off," warned Victoria. "And if you think I'm giving you that money now, you've got another think coming."

"Keep your money," growled Melissa as she turned to walk away.

She slammed out through the garden gate, ignoring Mrs. Plumly's demands that she stay where she was and be tongue-lashed. She set off down the street, one clenched fist still holding the bullet-shaped pendant. Head down, she kept walking in the direction of home.

LIM GLANCED UP from the dining-room table as the familiar sound of Bob's Land Rover ruptured the silence. She got up from the chair in which she had been sitting for nearly an hour, and she resolved that this time she would tell him. Through the open door she saw the Land-Rover screech to a halt, throwing up a thick cloud of dust over the garden. A moment later there was the creak of the gate, and Bob came hurrying along the path, an expression of intense preoccupation on his face.

Lim's hands came up to stroke her dark hair into position. She cleared her throat. He would be angry, of course, and though she hated to be subjected to his displeasure, she must bear it and speak her words slowly and simply so that he would understand.

He burst into the room, his face a mask of irritability. He did not even acknowledge Lim's presence.

"Bob tuan," she began, but he pushed by her and strode in the direction of his bedroom. She followed meekly, awaiting her opportunity to speak. But she saw that he was stripping the sheet off the bed that she had so carefully made up that morning. He searched through the bedclothes, then dumped them unceremoniously on the floor. He searched under the pillows, stooped to examine the floor around and under the bed.

"Bob tuan has lost something?" inquired Lim politely.

He nodded, scowled. "My luck," he replied tonelessly. He shifted his attention to the chest of drawers, scattering its contents onto the disrupted bed. Lim stepped forward.

"Let me look," she offered hopefully. "What have you lost?"

"My good-luck charm. You know, the bullet-shaped thing on a chain. You haven't seen it, have you?"

"No, Bob tuan, I no see. But please, may I speak about something that I—"

"Well, it's got to be somewhere. Things can't just vanish." He emptied out the last of the drawers, and turned to the wardrobe. "Could be in a jacket pocket." He began to desecrate that shrine of order. Meanwhile, Lim began to remake the bed.

"Please, Bob tuan, if I could just . . ."

"Nah . . . nah . . . this is crazy. It can only be somewhere where it might have fallen."

". . . tell you of a thing that causes much unhappiness . . ."

"The bathroom!" Bob snapped his fingers. "It could be in the shower basin, I suppose. Too large to go down the drain." He hurried out of the room. Lim gazed after him sadly for a moment, aware that he had not heard a word she had said. She followed him with dogged determination and found him crouched in the shower enclosure, examining the tiled floor.

"Please, tuan, can I speak of something?"

"Aw, Lim, don't bother me now, all right? This is important. See, that pendant is my good luck, I can't go hunting without it, it's like a superstitious thing I have going. Now, I've got to think." He moved past her again, rubbing his chin. "It's nowhere at work, I've checked. The mess, I'll have to wait till tonight to look."

"Please, Bob tuan, this too is important, like you speak."

Bob sighed, glanced at her. "Yeah, go ahead, I'm listening."

She paused, unsure of herself now that she had his attention. She began again, halting and self-conscious. "Bob tuan, I must speak of something that is very hard for me to say. You know I care very much for tuan, but I would not have you think I say this because I want to go to Australia."

"Now, Lim, you know I've told you before that there's absolutely no chance of—"

"Maybe you think different when you hear what I must say."

Bob shook his head. "Lim, frankly, I'm surprised at you talking this way. I thought more of you than that. It's been a fine relationship, but when the time comes to go, that's the way it has to be."

"Yes, but tuan, now I am . . . I am—"

"The beach!" exclaimed Bob, and he swore curtly beneath his breath. He turned and headed towards the door. "Listen, Lim, we'll talk about this another time, right? Only now I have to go find my luck, savvy?"

486

"Tuan, you have not listened! I try to tell you—"

"That's enough, Lim! I'll be back later on. Why don't you get working on a nice curry for dinner, eh? See you later." And he was gone, striding across the porch in his heavy work boots. Lim stared after him helplessly.

She shook her head. She had tried, but in her heart she knew that even if she had been allowed to say everything that was troubling her, still he would not have heard her. She returned to her seat by the table. Staring down at her reflection in the cheerless brown Formica, she wondered desperately what she would do.

WHEN THE PAPERBOY brought the copy of the *New Straits Times* that morning, Harry was waiting eagerly. He slipped the boy a silver coin and opened the paper, ignoring the lead items of world news that usually received his attention. On page six he found the article, under the resplendent title of "The Hunter and the Hunted". It seemed the same basic article that he had read on the veranda only a couple of days earlier, but fleshed out here and there in the final draft. Harry thought it was the best piece he had ever read on the Malay tiger, and he felt a glow of pride at his involvement in the project. What pleased him even more was a dedication that preceded the article:

> The author would like to thank the people of Trengganu whose hospitality was so generous and heartwarming; also, a special thankyou to Lieutenant Colonel Harry Sullivan (Retired), whose insights into the life patterns of the tiger proved invaluable and without whose help this article would not have been possible.

Harry sighed and folded the newspaper. He settled back in his chair, staring thoughtfully off across the garden. The papaya trees seemed to shimmer in the heat haze.

I'm missing her already, he thought, and he wondered if he might not soon travel up to Kuala Lumpur for a visit. No doubt she had been correct in her assessment of him. A stubborn old creature of habit, forever patrolling those areas that he had designated as his territory: the house and the garden, the mess. Soon the latter would no longer be open to him. He had the choice of slinking back into his house for the remainder of his life, or changing his habits, finding new ranges to patrol. Perhaps he might even ask Marion to be his wife. At the very worst she could only say no.

He closed his eyes, and the heat of the morning settled round him in a heavy, all-enveloping shroud. He slept, and dreamed that he was young again.

MELISSA APPROACHED Bob's house cautiously and was relieved to see that the Land-Rover was not parked by the gates. In her pocket her hand was clammy round the small metal object. She advanced along the garden path. The front door was wide open, and a radio was playing a Chinese pop song, the voice of the girl vocalist harsh and discordant to Western ears. Melissa stood in the porch for several moments before stepping forward to knock. A pretty young Chinese amah stepped into view and the two girls appraised each other in silence.

Despite herself, Melissa felt a twinge of envy run through her, because the girl *was* extraordinarily attractive. But then, as she looked closer, she experienced a sense of despair: it was quite apparent that Lim was pregnant, as any woman could tell at a glance. The baggy shirt she was wearing did little to hide the fact that she was beginning to lose her slender shape. And her eyes possessed the weak, washed-out quality that suggested she had shed many tears over the last few weeks. Melissa wondered how Bob could be so blind as to be unaware of the girl's condition. Too preoccupied with himself, as usual, she thought.

"Yes, missy?" Lim inquired meekly.

"I'm a friend of Bob's. Mr. Beresford's," began Melissa, and was saddened to see anxiety flare up in Lim's lovely eyes as she recognized a possible rival. Melissa felt burdened with an unspeakable guilt. "I have something that belongs to Mr. Beresford, perhaps you might return it for me." She took her hand from her pocket and held it out, palm upward, to reveal its contents.

"Oh, missy, thank you! Bob tuan will be so pleased. He has been looking everywhere for this." Her voice trailed away and her eyes narrowed slightly. "Please, missy, where did you . . ?"

"Mr. Beresford came to dinner at my house the other night. We found it on the floor." The reply was too quick, too forced. There was an uncomfortable silence.

"The missy would like to wait?" inquired Lim at last, and the reluctance in her voice was barely disguised.

"No, no, that's quite all right. Just give him the lucky charm. I'm sure he'll be glad to get it back." Melissa stood hesitantly on the porch, her arms hanging awkwardly by her sides. She was torn between the desire to get away before Bob appeared and the compulsion to help Lim in some way. She felt desperately sorry for the girl.

"When will you have your baby?" she blurted out abruptly.

Lim's eyes widened in shock. "How did you know?" she whispered fearfully.

"I have eyes," replied Melissa simply, not wanting to mention that the pregnancy was widely rumoured. "Soon even Tuan Beresford will notice. Then he'll be angry that you didn't tell him."

Lim shook her head sadly. "I have tried to tell him, missy. He will not hear me."

"Then you must *make* him hear you!"

"What is the use? He will not marry me!" Lim's voice dissolved into an incoherent flurry of weeping. Melissa could only stand and stare helplessly, unsure of what to do.

"Here now, that won't help at all."

Lim nodded, sniffed, stepped back into the sanctuary of the house. "I am sorry, missy. I will go now. Thank you for bringing the charm. Bob tuan will be very pleased."

"Lim, you must tell him everything, just as soon as he gets home. Promise me."

But Lim was gone, bustling into the interior, alone with her tears and her sorrow. Melissa called her name a couple of times but received no reply. After a short while she shrugged and walked away along the garden path. Abruptly her own worries seemed small and insignificant compared to the problems that assailed the young amah.

What had happened to Melissa was something transient, the memory of it would fade in time; but Lim would be for ever burdened by the shame and sorrow of her affair with Bob, by the very real and demanding presence of a child. The irony was that the girl so obviously worshipped the man who had brought about her ruin. One thing was certain. Once Bob Beresford found out the way things were, he would be off like a shot, perhaps leaving a little money to salve his conscience.

Her hatred for the man was now total, yet she headed for home with a lighter step than before. Getting rid of the silver bullet had served to convince her that the Australian was out of her life for good.

15

In the strange hazy light just after dawn, Bob Beresford was woken by a child's voice shouting his name. He came awake in an instant, grabbed his clothes, and began dressing quickly. After a few moments Ché burst into the room.

"Oh, tuan! The man-eater! He killed an old man in Kampong Panjang, just by the stream there. Maybe half hour ago. I borrowed a bike to get here."

"Good boy! OK Ché, you'd better come along with me." Bob snapped one hand up to trace the cool metal of his charm. "I feel lucky today. Wait for me in the Land-Rover."

Ché grinned and raced out of the room. Bob put on his jungle boots, then fumbled in the drawer of a nearby cabinet and began to fill his pockets with bullets. He became suddenly aware that Lim was watching him from the doorway, a look of apprehension on her face.

"Don't worry, I'll be all right."

"Yes. But last night, you said we could talk this morning."

Bob sighed. "I know that, darling, but I couldn't have any idea that this would happen, could I?" He gazed at her. "What's all this about, anyway? You're always wanting to have a talk these days." He buttoned up his pockets, picked up his hat from a chair.

"You make it so hard to speak," murmured Lim sadly.

"Lim, what's wrong with you?" he snapped.

"Can you not guess?" she asked him.

He shook his head in exasperation. "Look, I haven't got time for games. I've got a tiger to hunt. We'll talk about it later." He pushed past her towards the door.

"I'm pregnant," she said forcefully. "I'm going to have baby."

Bob froze in his tracks. He turned back very slowly. "What did you say?" he asked weakly.

"I am pregnant. You are the father."

He stared at her, as though unable to comprehend her words. "Pregnant?" he echoed at last. "But you can't be."

"I am. I have seen a doctor."

A few seconds of silence passed, then Bob said simply, "Good Lord." He scratched his head, glanced over to the open front door. "Well, look, I have to go now, Lim. We'll talk about this again, all right? Don't worry, we'll sort something out." He headed for the door at top speed.

"Bob tuan, it is too late to . . ." But he was gone, hurrying into the bright glare of morning.

Ché was waiting in the Land-Rover. Bob climbed in and sat for a moment, gazing blankly at the empty street ahead.

"Something is wrong, tuan?" inquired Ché, impatient to be off.

Bob shook his head. "Nah. Come on, kid, let's get after this stripey." He revved the engine and accelerated wildly away.

His driving was even more reckless than usual, and Ché was obliged to hold on tightly every time they bucketed over a rise in the road. It took a little more than ten minutes to reach Kampong Panjang, where a crowd of very excited villagers had gathered to await the tuan's arrival. Snatching up his rifle, Bob followed Ché in the direction of the stream, while the rowdy entourage trooped along in his wake. After a few minutes' walk they had reached the water, and the scene of the kill. A clear set of drag marks led away from the muddy ground and off into the undergrowth.

"Right. Let's go after him." Bob took a few steps forward, then realized that the villagers were still following him. "Tell this lot to stay where they are," he told Ché. "They'll scare the tiger away."

Ché translated the terse message, and the villagers quietened considerably. Bob and his young assistant were able to move off unattended, stooping to duck beneath a thick overhang of thorn-bushes. Beyond, everything was clammy green silence. Ché peered in apprehensively and gave a nervous cough. "Maybe tiger will be gone when we find the body," he reasoned.

"Maybe." Bob wished he could rid his mind of what Lim had just told him. She'd chosen a wonderful time! He frowned, shrugged, moved cautiously from sunlight into shadow. He turned to Ché for a moment, held one finger to his lips, and gave the boy a sly wink. They moved onwards, walking as silently as possible, and the bushes closed around them.

IT WAS UNUSUAL for Pawn to be late, and Harry was annoyed. It was not that he was particularly hungry and required his breakfast; it was simply that she was over an hour late, and Harry was suffering from irritation and anxiety. Supposing she was ill? Supposing she had suffered an accident on her way to the house? It was a break from routine, and at Harry's age there was nothing more upsetting.

He gave a sigh of relief when he heard the iron gate creak. He quickly settled into his favourite chair on the veranda, opening his copy of the *New Straits Times* and pretending to be absorbed in it.

Pawn came hurrying along the driveway, quite out of breath. "So sorry, tuan, so sorry I am late. It is unforgivable."

He glanced up nonchalantly, then looked at his wristwatch. "Well, so you are! Do you know, I'd quite lost track of the time."

"The man-eater, tuan, it killed an old man from the kampong this morning. Everywhere there was such a fuss, such a noise."

"Another one, eh?" Harry shook his head.

"Tuan Beresford was very quick coming this time. The people say there is good chance he shoot the striped one today. And with Ché tracking for him, he—"

Suddenly Harry was up out of his chair, the newspaper forgotten. "What was that?" he demanded. "Ché tracking?"

"For Tuan Beresford, yes. He has helped before, you see."

"Yes, I know. But are they going right after the tiger?"

Pawn seemed confused. "I cannot say, tuan. What do I know of hunting the *tok belang*?" She saw the look of intense worry on his face. "The tuan is troubled?"

"No, no, I'm fine. You can get about your business now, Pawn." She padded into the house.

It was ominously quiet in the garden. Harry felt a strong premonition of disaster settling around him. He thought of Ché, trailing through the jungle with that irresponsible idiot Beresford, and the image made his blood run cold.

"It's not done," he muttered grimly. "You just *don't* track a cat through his own territory." He got up again and walked out into the garden, where he paced restlessly for several minutes, muttering to himself. He squinted up at the sky. The sun was a relentless ball of flame, searing, oppressive. He could almost smell the humid jungle undergrowth; he could picture the great striped cat, crouched in shadow, awaiting the approach of the hunters. Harry turned to stare back at the house; then he was hurrying towards it, his mind made up. He went inside and to his bedroom, where he began to rummage frantically in drawers and cupboards. Moments later he appeared in the kitchen and handed a surprised Pawn his haversack and a water bottle.

"Put some food in here, will you, and fill this from the tap."

"The tuan is going somewhere?"

But he vanished back in the direction of his room without replying. Now it was Pawn's turn to mumble as she filled the haversack with whatever leftovers happened to be in the refrigerator. Had the tuan taken leave of his senses? What on earth was wrong with him? A short while later he rushed into the kitchen dressed in khaki-green jungle clothing and a broad-brimmed bush hat. He had his rifle slung over one shoulder, and he paused only to throw the haversack and water bottle across the other shoulder before heading for the front door.

"Where is the tuan going?" inquired Pawn meekly.

"Out!" was the simple reply. He was down the drive and out of sight in moments.

Once on the coast road, Harry strode along waving frantically at every vehicle heading in the direction of Kampong Panjang. Soon a battered pick-up truck drew to a halt and the driver was urging Harry to hop up on the back, along with a pair of tethered goats. He climbed aboard and sat straight-backed and resolute as the old jalopy sped to his destination.

Once at Kampong Panjang, it was simple to discover where the killing had taken place. A noisy crowd eagerly led him to the spot, and he stooped to examine the ground.

"Hunter man already go after him," an older boy observed.

Harry nodded. He looked calmly at the deep set of drag marks where they vanished into the undergrowth. Then he stooped to pass beneath an overhang of spiky thornbushes and set off in pursuit of the man-eater.

SHE NEEDN'T THINK I'm going to marry her, thought Bob, as he moved resolutely forward. The tiger had dragged his food an incredible distance, and the hunters had spent several hours creeping fruitlessly along behind him. The kill had to be close now, but Bob could not keep his mind on the matter in hand. After all, he thought, she's got no real hold on me. I can be well away before the baby's even born. Of course, I'll leave her some money to help make ends meet.

Ché was tugging at his sleeve, indicating that they should veer to the left. Bob wondered vaguely how the kid could know that. The ground here was hard and rocky. Unless that sudden birdcall had meant something.

He paused to mop his brow with his already sodden shirtsleeve.

Ché had edged ahead and was peering cautiously through the tangle of greenery. The silence was unbearable.

I'll have to tell her when I get home, thought Bob with conviction. I'll have to show her she can't trap me. You can't let one mistake ruin the rest of your life.

Ché was tugging at his sleeve again. He glanced down in irritation, then saw that the boy was pointing directly ahead, his dark eyes flashing with excitement. Bob stared intently at the place Ché was indicating.

And there was the tiger! He was stretched out in a small clearing beside a meandering stream, still feeding on the carcass. Gently, hardly daring to breathe, Bob inched his rifle up. He blinked the sweat out of his eyes and lined up a bead on the great cat's black-striped hide.

Sunlight dappled the tiger's fur, giving a false impression of movement. But the cat was sprawled like a domestic fireside tabby, tearing contentedly at the feast held in his vast front paws.

A neck shot, thought Bob calmly. Always the best chance that way. Take my time, no need to hurry. He glanced down at the boy beside him. Ché was staring at the target, absolutely still. The moment was almost at hand. The bullet would burst through the tiger's hide and smash that great old heart to pieces. Bob aligned the barrel fractionally, allowing the front sight to become as one with the tiny notch set in the back sight. A smile of triumph curved over his lips, and he squeezed the trigger.

The butt jumped against his shoulder, and there seemed to elapse an eternity of waiting before the bullet found its target. Then, abruptly, the tiger's long flank shook with the impact of a terrible blow that sent the heavy body lurching upwards through the air. It happened in eerie silence. There was no roar from the cat. The striped body simply twisted sideways and crashed through the undergrowth, rolling over and over and vanishing from sight in the greenery beyond.

The screams of exultation that erupted from the throats of both hunters seemed to echo through the jungle. They burst into motion, leaping up, flinging their hands skywards as they yelled their triumph to the winds.

"Tuan, you have killed him!"

"Did you see it, Ché? One shot, one brilliant shot! He went down like a stuck pig!"

"The man-eater is dead, tuan! Dead, dead!" And Ché was running forward, eager to examine the corpse, to see the size of his teeth, the curve of his great claws. Bob came strolling after him at a more leisurely pace, the rifle slung carelessly over his shoulder.

And then suddenly, horribly, everything was nightmare. The undergrowth burst aside and the tiger came charging out straight at Ché. Bob screamed something, he didn't know what. He tried to fumble the rifle to his shoulder, tried to work the heavy bolt, but his strength had evaporated and he could only look in horror at the awful slow-motion sequence playing out before his eyes—the huge bristling form of the tiger leaping now at the boy, the pain-maddened eyes blazing fire while the great open jaws roared thunder and vengeance. Bob fell to his knees, struggling with the bolt. The gun was jammed, he could not make it work. And then the teeth were around Ché's neck, and the child's frail body was being shaken like a rag doll, left and right.

The great scream of anguish from Bob's throat shattered the silence, drove the tiger back into cover, but it was too late. Ché was dead, his broken body discarded in the undergrowth. The victory had gone horribly, horribly awry. Sobbing, confused, Bob stumbled back in the direction from which he had come, the gun trailing uselessly from his hand. He ran blindly, banged headlong into a low branch, fell with a groan, and lay weeping like a child. And there, some minutes later, Harry Sullivan found him.

Harry had made good time through the jungle. The drag marks were well defined and needed little more than cursory glances. But it was the blast of the rifle that had brought him up with Beresford. What he saw confirmed his worst fears. He stood by the sprawled hunter and prodded the man's quivering shoulder with his boot.

Bob looked up, his tear-filled eyes not seeing. "Where's Ché?" demanded Harry.

Bob pointed back along the track and gestured helplessly. His voice when it emerged was a dry croak of despair. "The tiger . . . I put him down. A good clean neck shot, I was sure he was done for." He shook his head slowly. "The boy . . . ran forward. He thought . . . we both thought . . . and, oh God, the cat got back up, he came right out at the boy and . . ." His voice collapsed in wheezing misery. Harry reached down, grabbed a handful of his shirt and yanked him to his feet.

"Show me," Harry snapped. "Take me there!"

Bob's eyes widened in a stare. "No." The voice was now a whisper of dread. "I can't. The tiger, he's still there. It's too late to do anything for the boy, you see, it's too—"

He broke off as the flat of Harry's hand lashed across his face with a loud crack, knocking him back a step. Harry's expression was one of barely controlled rage.

"Damn you," he said through gritted teeth. "Damn you to hell, you insolent dog. There's a lot we can do for the boy. We can take him home to his family and tell them that the Great White Hunter didn't even bother to check that the tiger was dead before he let somebody approach it. Haven't you ever heard of throwing stones at a tiger, to check that he's not shamming? Didn't you have that written down in any of your books?" Harry was shaking with anger, and it was all he could do to refrain from striking the younger man again. "Now, you listen to me, Beresford. You're going to take me back to the place where it happened or I swear I'll put a bullet through your stupid head myself. Now move!" He prodded the Australian sharply with the tip of his rifle barrel, and Bob began to stumble along, his head bowed, his spirit completely broken. It did not take long to reach the place where Ché's body lay. Bob hung back, unable to look, but Harry went straight up to the corpse and stood staring at it in silence.

The boy's face was surprisingly calm in death. Harry knelt reverently, and reaching out a hand he closed the eyes with his fingertips. He had dearly loved those eyes. He thought of another time, when he had held out a shiny watch and the black, intelligent eyes had glittered with excitement. And Harry had made the boy say the word tiger to prove to him that it was superstitious nonsense to believe that he could bring down the beast's wrath. A glint of sunlight on silver made him look down, and there was the watch, dangling from its fob at the child's waist. Harry could see that the second hand was still ticking urgently round.

His eyes blurred with hot tears. He sobbed out his grief and wondered if it was possible for him to go on living with such sorrow, such horrible injustice.

He glanced up at Bob once and said coldly, "It should have been you."

The Australian looked away, not meeting the accusing gaze.

After a little while Harry wiped his eyes with his sleeve and then, reaching down, he lifted the body in his arms. He moved over to pass the burden to Bob. The Australian recoiled in horror. "I can't!" he gasped.

"You will," retorted Harry. He thrust Ché's body against Bob's chest so that the man had to accept it. "Take him back to the village, you hear me? Take him to his family and tell them what you've done."

"And you?"

"I'll go and finish the job," he said quietly. He stooped and snatched up his rifle.

Bob tried to speak, but Harry simply lifted the gun in a gesture of warning. Bob slowly turned and found a path through the undergrowth. Harry watched until the man was hidden from view. Then he picked up his haversack, slung it over his shoulder, and approached the thick tangle of bushes into which the tiger had vanished. He stood for a moment, staring straight ahead.

It's madness, he murmured to himself. You don't follow a tiger across his own ground. You simply don't. But it was a personal matter now. And the old beast would be in terrible pain.

Slowly, with infinite precision, Harry took his first step into the bushes. The cat was out there somewhere, wounded, desperate. Harry would keep searching until their paths crossed.

THE TRAIL LED deeper and deeper into the heart of the jungle. Harry followed at a cautious pace, stooping down occasionally to examine a pugmark or an overturned stone. There were frequent splashes of fresh blood on either side of the track, which suggested that Beresford's bullet had gone clean through its target: but the blood did not have the frothy appearance of a lung wound. The tiger clearly possessed a charmed life.

The ground declined gradually into a deep marshy valley overrun with tangles of swamp grass, bamboo thickets, and thick creepers covered with thorns that continually snagged the material of Harry's shirt. The Malays called the creepers *nanti sikit*, which literally meant wait awhile. It was midafternoon now, and Harry was tiring, finding it difficult to keep his breathing regular. But the tiger showed no sign of pausing. He was moving straight and true along well-worn cattle trails, as if heading instinctively for some refuge.

The trail led into a thigh-deep swamp, and Harry was obliged to wade through, an exhausting proposition as his boots kept slipping in the clinging mud beneath the stagnant water. He emerged on the other side, and after a brief respite he plodded on again, sweltering now in his thick khaki clothing. But he knew that if he had to spend a night in the jungle, he would be glad of it.

The ground began to incline towards a distant granite mountain, its slopes shrouded with coconut palms and thick stretches of rain forest. Directly ahead lay a wide, almost impenetrable bamboo thicket, and Harry hesitated. Some sixth sense warned him that the tiger was near. He thought he could feel the hot stare of a pair of yellow eyes peering at him. He began to move slowly towards the bamboo. Off to the east, a troop of monkeys chattered a nervous warning. Yes, he was in there! Lying up in cover, waiting for the hunter to come nearer. Harry licked his lips, the rasp of his tongue over the parched flesh incredibly loud in the silence. It would be impossible, to move into the thicket with his rifle held in firing position. He would have to walk with it pointing upright and hope that he could lower it sufficiently to fire when the opportunity presented itself. He went on, aware that the cat would hear every rustle of a leaf, every snap of a twig. Meanwhile, he willed the tiger to make a move.

HAJI CROUCHED on his belly behind the rotting stump of a fallen tree. The pain in his chest kept coming and going in jolting spasms, but he suffered the agony in silence. He kept his gaze fixed firmly on the old Upright moving gradually towards him. Haji did not know this Upright, but he could see the glint of a black stick, and he was afraid and wary and burning with the dark rage of the hunted. The old Upright was also wary, stopping every few moments to gaze intently around. It was clear that he suspected Haji's presence, but he had not spotted the hiding place. From the high treetops a magpie robin shrieked a warning, and the Upright swung about to stare straight in Haji's direction; then he came on again, the black stick held tight against him as he pushed through the narrow openings presented by the thick stems of bamboo. Soon he was near enough for Haji to see the thick film of sweat on his grizzled face. The magpie robin shrieked again, and the Upright stopped, resumed his careful scrutiny of the surroundings. Then he did an inexplicable thing. He sat down on the forest floor. He had clearly decided not to come any closer.

Haji growled, a low rumbling deep in his throat, too quiet to be audible to the Upright's hearing. It was to be a waiting game. Haji

498

inclined his head slightly to lap at the gaping wound above his right shoulder where the bullet had emerged. Blood was still flowing sluggishly, and the rasp of his tongue sent fresh spasms of pain ripping through his body.

Time passed. The magpie robin gave a last despairing cry and fluttered away above the treetops. Complete silence descended on the clearing. They settled down, the hunter and the hunted, each waiting for the other to make the next move.

HARRY SIGHED. His legs, crossed awkwardly beneath him in the confined space, were beginning to ache terribly. It seemed hours that he had been sitting here, but a glance at his watch informed him that it was a little over twenty minutes. The cat was here somewhere, that was for sure, but there were any number of places where he could be. Behind that tangle of scrub, perhaps. Or concealed in those great green ferns to his left; or stretched out behind that fallen tree trunk directly ahead.

Harry froze with shock. A head had slid up from behind the rotting wood—a great tawny-red, black-scarred face with blazing yellow eyes, and jaws wide open, bellowing hatred. The tiger crossed the decaying wood in one leap that made Harry's heart skip a beat, and then it began to power forward through the thicket, swift and terrible. To Harry the cat looked as big as a house, and the speed with which it was approaching left no time to think.

Harry attempted to struggle to his feet, but his legs were rubbery, so he settled into a kneeling position and fumbled the rifle up to his shoulder. The cat was dangerously close, it filled his vision with a blur of black and tawny movement. In the instant before his finger tightened on the trigger, the eyes of hunter and hunted locked together. Harry gave an involuntary cry. There was a feeling of recognition: it was like looking into the face of a long-lost friend, and the sensation was enough to stay his finger on the trigger. Then the tiger was leaping up and over him, its body blotting out the sun. Harry steeled himself for the impact of teeth and claws against his flesh. But the tiger continued up and over, to race madly away on Harry's other side, into the shelter of the thicket. Harry slumped down with a gasp of surprise and disbelief. The cat had altered its course at the last instant, to leap clear! It was as though that single exchanged glance had spooked the cat as much as it had Harry.

499

A slow, steady pain began to rise in his chest. He groaned, let his forehead sink down to bump against the soft ground. Jolting spasms thudded in his chest, and he gritted his teeth and lay still, waiting desperately for the pain to subside.

After a few minutes he reached weakly for his water bottle, unscrewed the top and swallowed a little of the precious contents. The pain was now dulled to a powerful ache that throbbed relentlessly.

Old fool, he muttered to himself. Coming out after a tiger in my condition. I ought to go home. But he located the pugs that the tiger had left and struck out in this new direction, massaging his chest with one hand as he went along.

WHEN TWILIGHT DESCENDED, Harry chose a clearing where there was little surrounding cover for any hungry predator. It was simple enough to collect dry branches and twigs, and he soon had a passable fire. He sat with his back against a tree, his rifle close at hand, and rummaged in his haversack for the provisions that Pawn had packed earlier that day: there were little pots of cold meat, slices of flatbread, fresh fruit. Using his jack knife as a utensil, he began to eat, staring into the fire. He felt exhausted after the long day's trek, and the rhythmic chirruping of the jungle insects soon lulled him into a shallow, restless sleep in which he was plagued by terrible nightmares about Ché's death.

He awoke abruptly, with the conviction that he was no longer

501

alone. The fire had dwindled to a red glow, and he was reaching forward to pick up another branch when a soft movement on the other side of the clearing made him freeze. He stared intently into the shadows and saw the fire reflected in two crimson sparks that seemed to hover in the darkness. He very slowly picked up the firewood and dropped it into place. The flames crackled, came alive, and there in the increased glow was the tiger, stretched out some fifteen feet away and staring across the campfire at Harry.

Harry took a long, deep breath. The cat looked to be in a bad way. His flanks were caked with dried blood and his jaws were open, his chest pumping spasmodically in a frantic effort to draw breath. Harry could see the creature's worn yellow teeth, the thick ruffs of grey hair that framed the noble face; and there in the foreleg was a swollen, suppurating wound. There was a pleading quality in the cat's eyes, a desperate, searching stare that was both saddening and terrifying.

Harry glanced sideways to where the loaded rifle lay, inches from his right hand. Beside it lay the pots of food that he had picked at earlier. Slowly, hardly daring to breathe, Harry began to move his fingers. The tiger gave a low growl of warning, but Harry continued the action. He felt both frightened and elated. The tiger had crept up as he slept and could have dispatched him easily, but it had chosen to wait, to lie and observe the hunter in the light of the fire. Perhaps it was simply not the right time to end the hunt.

Harry's hand closed, not around the stock of the rifle but around a pot of cold meat. He lifted the container slowly and threw the meat across the clearing, straight at the cat's feet. The tiger recoiled with a roar of warning, seemed on the point of running away; then the scent of meat reached his nostrils, and lowering his head, he sniffed. In an instant he had lapped the meagre contents up with his great rasping tongue. He glanced at Harry as though hoping for something else.

"That's all there is, old fellow," he murmured. "I'm sorry." He watched as the tiger sniffed at the empty container, lapped up a couple of crumbs from the ground. It would be such an easy task now to put the creature out of his misery. Harry's hand strayed in the direction of the rifle, but as if realizing the hunter's intention, the cat wheeled about and limped away into the darkness. Harry sighed.

Tomorrow then, he mused. We'll finish it tomorrow.

HAJI CREPT SILENTLY into the small cave. He paced restlessly around for a moment and then flopped down to lick his wounds. The pain was a constant torment.

He had gone to the fire of the old Upright earlier with the object of making a kill, but he had been unable to follow through. It was because the Upright had *looked* at him, gazed deeply into his eyes; no other of these creatures had ever done that to Haji. The same thing had happened when he had begun an attack in the bamboo thicket that day. At the last moment those eyes had looked into his, and the look had not been that of a stricken creature about to die. It had been the calm, peaceful gaze that one tiger gives another upon meeting. The shock had been so great that Haji had veered away. It was not that the Upright wasn't afraid; the lonely smell of terror had been on him. But that look, that calm, accepting, almost welcoming look, that was what Haji could not understand. And he feared the inexplicable.

He was exhausted, and despite his discomfort he soon drifted into a shallow, fitful doze. He woke just before dawn, with the firm conviction that the old Upright would come after him at first light. With a growl he settled down again. He could do nothing but lie, wide awake and racked with pain, till the first rays lit the sky.

SHIVERING IN THE LIGHT of dawn, Harry stamped the ashes of his campfire away and resumed the hunt, casting about until he picked up the trail that the cat had left the previous night. The tiger's wounds were slowing him up, and Harry felt sure that he could not have travelled far.

After a couple of miles he found a small cave where the cat had obviously rested for the night. There were dried bloodstains on the floor. From the cave mouth, the pugs led to higher, rockier ground, where tracking was difficult, but Harry climbed steadily, stopping occasionally to catch his breath. Soon he was able to look down into the lush valley, spread out some distance below. A little after eight o'clock his gaze was caught by a signal flare, soaring into the sky from the valley. Listening intently, he could make out the sounds of distant shouting. Clearly a search party had been mounted on his behalf. He felt rather flattered that anyone should take such trouble on his account, but he did not check his pace.

He moved into an area of deep granite gullies and strewn boulders, where there was scant vegetation but ample opportunity for a predator to take cover. Eventually he came to the site of a dried-up riverbed, where granite walls rose sheer on either side to obscured, boulder-littered ledges. Harry advanced cautiously. Everything was quiet as the grave here and he had, once again, the distinct impression that the tiger was not far away. It seemed likely that the cat had climbed one of the slopes to take up a position on a ledge. Harry decided to climb up to a ledge himself, hoping to get a better view of possible hiding places. He could only hope that he wasn't heading directly for the place where the tiger was concealed.

He began to move slowly upward, his boots slipping on the steep granite. It was hard going, and after a few minutes he was bathed in sweat. He was about three quarters of the way to the ledge when he abruptly realized that his luck was out. The tiger appeared from behind a large boulder directly ahead and came charging down the slope with a bellow of rage. Harry fumbled the rifle from his shoulder to swing it up into firing position, but he was badly out of balance on the steep ground. The tiger's great paws struck before he could fire a shot, knocking him to the ground and sending him sprawling over and over, back down to the riverbed. The tiger struck badly too, landing squarely on his injured leg some ten yards from Harry. For a moment neither of them moved.

Harry gave a slight groan. He had fallen awkwardly on one leg and was unable to move it. Glancing up, he saw the tiger was momentarily stunned. Harry began to look desperately round for his rifle, then spotted it on the slope ten yards above him. He started dragging himself towards it, gritting his teeth at the agony this induced in his left leg, which was obviously broken. Behind him, a low growl suggested that the tiger was recovering his senses quickly. Galvanized by fear, Harry lifted himself clear of the ground and literally threw himself across the slope. The shock of pain as he struck the ground nearly caused him to faint, but his hands closed round the stock of the rifle and he twisted over onto his back to stare down at the tiger.

The cat was hunched at the bottom of the gully, snarling ferociously and preparing to leap upwards. There was no time to aim. Harry simply pointed the barrel down between his feet and, as the tiger launched himself, squeezed the trigger. The tiger was in mid-leap as the bullet slammed right into his heart, killing him instantly. The leap fell short, but the tiger's great weight came crashing down on Harry's chest, pinning him to the rock. The beautiful yellow

504

eyes stared sightlessly into his own, and the great jaws were frozen in a grimace of death, mere inches from his face. `

Harry gave a groan of mingled pain and exhaustion. He put his hands beneath the tiger's carcass and attempted to lift it off, but it was a crushing weight that would not be moved. Harry dropped back, gasping. The terrible pain had returned to his chest.

He remembered the signal flare he had seen earlier, and with one last effort he pulled the rifle clear of the tiger's body. Pointing the gun into the air and working the bolt, he managed to loose off three shots before his strength finally gave out and unconsciousness overtook him.

16

Bob Beresford glanced apprehensively at the telephone booth. It was almost time. Early morning, and the long dusty street was completely deserted. He had not slept through the interminable night, plagued as he was by terrible guilt. He could do nothing to make amends for Ché's death. He recalled the faces of the boy's parents at the kampong, when he had brought the lifeless body to them. At first their expressions were just masks of inarticulate grief; as Bob had stammered his clumsy explanations, those expressions had turned to stares of hateful accusation. He had sobbed his apologies and escaped as quickly as possible, driving home at a dangerous speed, realizing that *there* was the only person in the world who could give him any consolation. Lim had stayed with him since then, attending to his every need, talking with him, insisting that he could not be expected to bear the full blame. She had not managed to convince him of it, but at least she had made the pain more possible to sustain.

She stood beside him now, a guardian angel that he did not deserve.

The telephone rang shrilly within the glass booth. Bob glanced nervously at Lim, then opened the door and picked up the receiver.

An operator's clipped tones reached his ears. "Mr. Beresford?"

"Speaking."

"Your call to Sydney, Australia. Will you put your money in now, please? I am trying to connect you."

"Thank you." He gorged the metal box with coins, pushing them into the slot. There was a long silence, during which he visualized mile upon mile of cable along which a tiny spark was speeding. Somewhere, a long way away, a telephone rang, a tiny, metallic insect buzzing for what seemed an eternity. Bob was on the point of replacing the receiver when someone answered.

"Hello?" The voice was painfully familiar, and the sound of it made Bob's eyes fill with moisture. "Hello, who's there?"

"Hello, Ma," he said simply.

"Bob? Is that you?" He could picture her astonishment. When she spoke again, her voice was tremulous. "Bob, where have you been? You never answered my letters."

"I've been very busy, Ma. But I'll be finishing up here in a week or so. I was thinking about coming home for a while."

"Home? Oh, that would be wonderful. You . . . you know that Frank will be here, don't you?" she added cautiously.

"Sure. Where else would your husband be?"

She sounded relieved. "He's a nice man, Bob. I'm sure you'll get on well if you just give him a chance. Oh, I can hardly believe I'm talking to you after all this time! It will be so good to see you, Bob. When can I expect you?"

"I don't know for sure yet, Ma. I've got to make all the arrangements. But I'm looking forward to being home. Things didn't really work out too well for me here." He glanced again at Lim through the glass. "One other thing, Ma," he added. "I won't be coming over by myself. I'm planning to bring a wife with me." There was a long, stunned silence on the other end of the line. "Ma? Are you still there?"

THE TAXI SCREECHED to a halt by the gates of the Kuala Hitam Army Hospital. Melissa thrust a note into the driver's hand and hurried out, not waiting for the change. As she rushed towards the hospital entrance, her father came out and escorted her inside.

"There's not much time," he told her tonelessly. "He's been asking for you." The grey corridors smelled of antiseptic.

"There's no hope?" asked Melissa in a small, anxious voice.

Dennis shook his head. "The doctors say it's a miracle he's hung on this long. If the Gurkha search party hadn't been so close behind him, he wouldn't have even survived the trip back. I've been with him all morning. He knows he's on his way out, but he's going with grace."

"But why me? Why does he want to see me?"

Dennis shrugged. "He didn't say. But listen, love, try to put a brave face on for him, eh?"

They came to Harry's door, and Melissa walked into the room and the door clicked quietly shut behind her. She stood where she was for a moment, staring sadly at the figure in the bed.

Her initial impression was of smallness. Harry's six-foot frame seemed to have dwindled to half its size, dwarfed by the great snowy immensity of the bed in which he was lying. Around him was the paraphernalia of science: bottles, tubes, electrical machines that clicked and buzzed, and all to no avail.

She took a step forward. "Uncle Harry?" she murmured. "It's me. Melissa."

His eyelids trembled, flickered open. He lay gazing up at her, and then the faintest trace of a smile curved his lips. "Melissa. So there you are."

Melissa moved forward to stand beside the bed. Instinctively she reached out to clutch his hand in hers, and she felt the gentle pressure as he tried to squeeze it in a gesture of affection.

"How . . . how do you feel?"

"Oh, restful. Very restful. I hope I didn't drag you away from anything important."

"Don't be silly. I'm glad to be here." She pulled up a chair and sat beside him, hardly knowing what to say.

"The tiger is dead now. Did they tell you? Ah, the poor old devil," sighed Harry. "In such pain, terrible pain. And did they tell you about Ché?"

"Yes, they did. They said it was Bob Beresford's fault. How I could ever have felt anything for that . . . that megalomaniac."

Harry shook his head. "We mustn't be too hard on him," he warned. "The poor bloke will always have it on his conscience. In a way, I wish that he'd been able to get that tiger. Then he would have been happy, and Ché . . ."

Melissa bowed her head. A terrible ache was filling her chest, and she could not prevent her eyes from filling with moisture.

"Now, now." Harry lifted an arm and tilted her chin up so he could study her face. "No crying. You'll spoil that pretty face."

"Oh, Uncle Harry!" She tried to say something else, but her words collapsed in misery. It was several minutes before she could control herself enough to hear what he had to say.

507

"You'll soon be off to a new life in England. I just wanted to tell you . . . forget about any mistakes you've made in the last few months. You're going to begin again and you're going to reach the potential I know you're capable of." He lifted his hand with a great effort and pointed to his bedside table. "Something for you."

Melissa turned to look where he was pointing. A silver chain lay on the table, with a tiny Saint Christopher medallion on it. Melissa thought of the bullet-shaped pendant she had contrived to possess, and she felt horribly ashamed.

"Uncle Harry," she whispered. "It's far too good for me."

"Nonsense, child. Please . . . keep it. Wear it . . . and think of me." His eyes widened a little and he seemed to be attempting to sit up. "Please . . . write to Marion for me. Tell her . . . tell her that I love . . ."

A shadow seemed to pass across his face. His eyes clouded, gentle in death, and his head moved slowly back onto the pillow. Melissa sat, his hand still clutched tightly round hers. She prized the gaunt fingers open, and clutching the Saint Christopher medal tightly she walked quietly to the door. As she went out, Dennis and a doctor came hurrying towards her. Melissa stared at them through a film of tears and shook her head blankly.

"I'll take you home," murmured Dennis.

"Please . . . no. Let me walk." And she hurried away along the corridor, wanting to be outside when the full grief hit her. She groped her way blindly out through the exit into the sunlight. She stood for a moment, gazing blankly around at the deserted barracks. This place too was dead now. Impulsively she ran across the parade ground, past a surprised sentry, and then she was out on the road, running between ranks of lush green vegetation, aware only of the aching void that was steadily rising within her. She had just witnessed the death of the finest man she had ever known. The misery in her chest welled into a great bitter balloon that burst abruptly, flooding her with sorrow. She slowed to a walk, her shoulders heaving with uncontrollable emotion, her eyes blurred with tears. Harry was dead. Nothing could ever make the loss seem easy to bear.

She walked on, her head bowed, and as she put distance behind her, bit by bit she gained control of herself. She wanted to be away from this place, away from the heat, the strange people and their ancient customs that she had never learned to understand. Harry had been a part of it all; he belonged somehow. But the day of the tuan was over now and Melissa wanted no part of it. What was it Harry had called himself that time? The last dinosaur in this patch of swamp. The edges of Melissa's mouth curved upwards the smallest amount, as she began to remember.

Melissa rounded a curve in the road. She wiped the last vestiges of moisture from her eyes with her sleeve, and then, lifting her head, she began to move in the direction of home. For the first time in many months she felt that she knew where she was going. She began to make plans for her return to England, and so occupied was she with her thoughts that she did not notice the approach of her father's car. She turned, looked in at Dennis.

"Better now?" he asked her cautiously.

She forced a smile. "Better," she replied. "Let's go, shall we?"

She opened the door and climbed in beside him. She could see from the redness of his eyes that he had been crying too. They sat in the car for a few moments, neither saying a word, both realizing that there was very little they *could* say. At last she reached out and squeezed his hand gently.

"It's over," she said simply.

"Yes." Dennis turned the ignition key. "I wonder . . ." he said, "who'll tell Marion?"

"*I* will," replied Melissa. "Harry asked me to."

Dennis glanced at her in surprise, noting the new look of determination in her eyes. She stared down at the small silver medallion in her hand. It had been clenched in her fist all this time, so tightly that it had left an angry red imprint on her palm. "He wanted me to have this," she murmured softly.

Dennis nodded. He let out the clutch and the car accelerated away down the road. They drove home in silence.

TIMAH APPROACHED the cave cautiously. Instinct had brought her to this place, just as instinct told her the time was near, that the movements deep in her belly could be contained no more. She hesitated, staring into the shadows. But there was no occupant. She slipped gratefully into the cool sanctuary and paced restlessly up and down in its narrow confines. Haji had been here recently: she could detect faint traces of his smell, and this comforted her, for it was her first litter and she was anxious.

After a while the head of the first cub emerged from her body.

509

She increased the pressure on her hindquarters and the cub slid smoothly out and dropped to the floor of the cave. Three more followed at ten-minute intervals. Only then did she set about freeing the cubs from their sacs. She licked them clean with her great rasping tongue, rejoicing at the wriggling motions they made in response. They all seemed healthy—blind, mewing little bundles that began to grope towards Timah's milk-filled teats the moment that she stretched herself out.

Outside, the light was failing fast as the brief twilight advanced. Tired from her exertions, Timah settled down in the shadowy sanctuary while the cubs moved warm and impatient against her belly, their toothless little jaws seeking nourishment. The anxiety of the last few hours had gone now, and a great contentment settled over her. She lowered her head to the cave floor and relaxed quickly into a deep, dreamless slumber. She woke once, some hours later, when one of the cubs moved restlessly in his sleep and tumbled away from his sisters. Timah raised her head and nudged him gently back to the reassuring warmth of her flank. She glanced calmly out to the mouth of the cave, but the unfathomable darkness there did not frighten her. It was an easy enough matter to find sleep again.

Philip Caveney

Philip Caveney is a remarkable young man. In conversation he is jaunty, almost offhand. But behind this is a streak of quiet thoughtfulness. He is thirty-two years old and lives in Manchester, where he owns a small bookshop. But for two years, when he was in his early teens, he lived with his parents in Malaya, where his father was serving in the RAF. *Tiger, Tiger* is his second novel, and here he tells us how it came to be written:

"I first got interested in this subject when I began recalling some of my own experiences in Malaya as a fourteen-year-old boy, at a time when British rule there was finally coming to an end. The image of a slowly crumbling Empire struck me as a decidedly powerful one, and though there is much about imperialism that I despise, I was aware that there were certain values in those times that I could identify with.

"I began doing some research about tigers and was immediately struck by the parallels between these rare and lovely creatures and people. Harry Sullivan, the hero of the book, describes himself as a dinosaur, a leftover from an earlier time. As the book progresses, his story and that of Haji, the old tiger, begin to interrelate, and the inference is that they are, both of them, endangered species, living on borrowed time. There is no room in the modern world for creatures such as these and, to my mind, that is the saddest admission of all.

"I suppose the theme of the book is a plea on behalf of the wild creatures of the world whose habitat is being destroyed at a terrifying rate. It's also a plea on behalf of the older members of society, people who are only too often considered to be of no use to anybody. This is a Western concept. In Eastern cultures old age is revered, and the grandparents are considered to be the wisest and most valuable members of a family unit."

Philip Caveney is now at work on his third novel, with yet another exotic setting—South America in the 1940s. When not writing books or looking after his shop, he presents weekly film reviews on a local radio programme. A remarkable young man indeed.

PICTURE CREDITS: OVERLORD: Page 4: US Army Photograph. Pages 6/7: US Army Photograph. Page 8: Popperfoto Ltd. Page 25: Map by Malcolm Porter. Page 39 (top): Popperfoto Ltd; (bottom): National Archives Collection of foreign records seized, 1941. Page 40 (top): US Coast Guard; (bottom left): US Naval Photographic Centre; (bottom right): Robert Hunt Library. Page 41 (top): US Office of War Information; (bottom): US Army Photograph. Pages 48/49: Map by Malcolm Porter. Page 56 (top): Imperial War Museum; (bottom): Imperial War Museum. Page 57 (top): US Army Photograph; (bottom): Imperial War Museum. Page 64 (top): US Army Photograph; (bottom left): Popperfoto Ltd; (bottom right): Popperfoto Ltd. Page 65 (top): Official US Navy Photograph; (bottom): Imperial War Museum. Page 72 (top): Robert Hunt Library; (bottom left & right): Robert Hunt Library. Page 73: BBC Hulton Picture Library. Page 80 (top): BBC Hulton Picture Library; (bottom): Popperfoto Ltd. Page 81 (top): Keystone; (bottom): Popperfoto Ltd. Page 88 (top): US Army Photograph; (bottom): Robert Hunt Library. Page 89 (top): Popperfoto Ltd; (bottom): US Office of War Information. Page 97: Map by Malcolm Porter. Page 104 (top): Ullstein-Bilderdienst; (bottom): BBC Hulton Picture Library. Page 105: ADN-Zentralbild, Berlin. Page 112 (top): Signal Corps Photograph; (bottom): Robert Hunt Library. Page 113 (top): Robert Hunt Library; (bottom): BBC Hulton Picture Library. THE CHILDREN'S GAME: Page 261: Christopher Wise. A KIND OF MAGIC: Pages 262/263: Victoria and Albert Museum. Page 265: Mollie Harris. Page 277: Central Library, Oxford. Page 281: Bodleian Library. Page 286: Mollie Harris. Page 289: Victoria and Albert Museum. Page 296: Oxford City and County Museum. Page 299: Central Library, Oxford. Page 305: Victoria and Albert Museum. Page 311: Victoria and Albert Museum. Page 313: Oxford City and County Museum. Page 321: Henley-on-Thames Town Council. Page 322: Mollie Harris. Page 329: Bodleian Library. Page 330: Mollie Harris. Page 335: Sue Chapman. TIGER, TIGER: Page 511: Peter Wilshaw.
